Peter James Dodd
1998

THE NUCLEAR INDEPENDENT
PARTICLE MODEL

The Shell and Optical Models

THE NUCLEAR INDEPENDENT PARTICLE MODEL

The Shell and Optical Models

A. E. S. GREEN
DEPARTMENT OF PHYSICS AND ASTRONOMY
UNIVERSITY OF FLORIDA
GAINESVILLE, FLORIDA

T. SAWADA
DEPARTMENT OF PHYSICS AND ASTRONOMY
UNIVERSITY OF FLORIDA
GAINESVILLE, FLORIDA

D. S. SAXON
DEPARTMENT OF PHYSICS
UNIVERSITY OF CALIFORNIA
LOS ANGELES, CALIFORNIA

1968

ACADEMIC PRESS   New York and London

ACADEMIC PRESS, INC.
111 Fifth Avenue, New York, New York 10003

United Kingdom Edition published by
ACADEMIC PRESS, INC. (LONDON) LTD.
Berkeley Square House, London W.1

LIBRARY OF CONGRESS CATALOG CARD NUMBER: 68-23483

PRINTED IN THE UNITED STATES OF AMERICA

Preface

In this work we describe the independent particle model (IPM) of the nucleus, i.e., the single particle shell model and the optical model. This simple description of bound and scattering states of nuclei is based upon the approximation that any one nucleon (N) [either a neutron (n) or a proton (p)] is influenced by all the other nucleons in a manner approximately represented by an average nucleon–nuclear (N–$\mathscr{N}$) potential. This IPM potential, which in large measure has been found by phenomenological analysis of experimental data presumably will, at some point yet in the future, be derived from fundamental principles by some procedure analagous to the Hartree–Fock method in atomic physics.

The work begins with a description of the early evolution of the IPM model. Then some of the basic aspects of quantum mechanics as required for shell and optical model calculations are presented. These are applied, in the remainder of the first chapter, to a description of primitive forms of the IPM model. The second and third chapters are devoted to realistic shell and optical models which were developed by mid-1959, when most of the active workers assembled for the *First International Conference on the Nuclear Optical Model* (Florida, 1959).

Rather than go into the justification of the model in Chapters I to III, we take a point of view which might be characterized by the Latin phrase: *res ipsa loquitur*—the thing speaks for itself. Thus we simply describe the model, the mathematical formalisms used, and show how the model works for protons and neutrons in organizing a tremendous body of diverse experimental data. Chapters IV and V discuss various limits of the optical model description and the use of velocity dependent, energy dependent, and nonlocal nucleon–nuclear potentials. Recent phenomenological studies of protons, neutrons, and composite particles scattered by nuclei are described in Chapter VI.

In the final chapter, we begin with a description of the elementary aspects of the nucleon–nucleon interaction which have been established by phenomenological studies. In the second section we discuss the foundations of the nuclear shell model concentrating on simple physical descriptions which are based upon simplified nucleon–nucleon forces. In Section 3, Chapter VII, we present the formal foundations of the optical model, concentrating on simplified limits. The final section is devoted to a detailed discussion of one boson exchange potentials which has recently emerged as a reasonably simple and accurate description of the N–N interaction, based on meson field theory. While this form of N–N interaction has not yet been applied extensively to the nuclear many body problem, it is clear from trends of the current literature that it will be used increasingly as the fundamental nuclear force. The final figure in Chapter VII portrays schematically various theoretical efforts now underway which are directed toward achieving a fundamental understanding of nuclear physics.

Our particular order of presentation has been chosen so that this work might serve not only for the individual reader but also as a monographic text for an introductory course in nuclear physics. It is assumed that the reader has been exposed previously to an elementary quantum mechanics but not necessarily to the Pauli spin formalism or to scattering theory.

While the independent particle model of the nucleus represents only one facet of nuclear physics, nevertheless its close relationship to a fundamental self-consistent field description, as well as the insights afforded by the tremendous body of experimental data which it so compactly summarizes, should be useful to the development of understanding in all aspects of nuclear physics.

A. E. S. GREEN
T. SAWADA
D. S. SAXON

September 1968

Acknowledgments

═══════════

This work was written in many places during the period 1960 to 1968. One of us (AESG) would like to acknowledge the secretarial support of General Dynamics, Convair, which provided assistance in the initial phases. Another of us (DSS) would like to express his thanks to the Fulbright Commission and to the John Simon Guggenheim Foundation, whose support during a year abroad was most helpful. In connection with its final integration and completion, the work benefitted greatly by research carried out at the University of Florida under a grant by the United States Air Force Office of Scientific Research.

We would like to express our thanks to our many colleagues for permission to use diagrams and tables drawn from their works. In addition, thanks are due to the McGraw-Hill Book Company for their copyright release on the book "Nuclear Physics" from which some elementary discussions have been drawn.

Finally we would like to express our thanks to Roger L. Bass for his excellent draftsmanship and to Marilyn Yeates, Julia McClure, Marylee Tennyson, Linda Easley, Rene Ebert, and Sharon Cohen for their assistance in the preparation of the final manuscript.

Contents

====

I. General Features of the Independent Particle Model (IPM)

II. Realistic Shell Models

III. Realistic Optical Models

THE NUCLEAR INDEPENDENT PARTICLE MODEL

PARTICLE MODEL

The Shell and Optical Models

I

General Features of the Independent Particle Model (IPM)

1.1   The Evolution of the Independent Particle Model

The year 1932 is frequently assigned as the birthdate of modern nuclear physics. The discovery by Chadwick (1932) of the neutron led immediately to Heisenberg's (1932) proton-neutron model of the nucleus. Simultaneously Cockroft and Walton and Lawrence established the usefulness of artificial accelerators for providing projectiles to probe the nucleus and stimulate nuclear processes.

It is rather interesting to note how quickly the independent particle model (IPM) concept of nucleons, moving independently in an average central potential established by all the other particles in a nucleus, was developed. Within two or three years, Bartlett (1932), Elsasser (1933, 1934), Guggenheimer (1934), Margenau (1934), and Heisenberg (1935) had explored simple nucleon-nucleus (N–$\mathcal{N}$) potentials. Indeed they had established some of the periodicity properties of nuclei, in particular what are now referred to as the "magic numbers" 2, 8, and 20. Calculations of average N–$\mathcal{N}$ potentials using Hartree and Fermi–Thomas approximations borrowed from atomic physics were attempted soon afterwards (Heisenberg, 1934, 1935; Weizsäcker, 1935; Wick, 1934). These early beginnings of the IPM are discussed thoroughly in the early review of Bethe and Bacher (1936).

The first direct application of the IPM to the problem of the scattering of neutrons by heavy nuclei was carried out by Fay (1936). Starting from an N–N interaction of an exchange type used by Van Vleck (1935) and Feenberg and Knipp (1935) in bound state calculations, Fay derived a potential for the incident neutron. He found a reasonable potential whose depth decreased slowly as the neutron velocity increased because of exchange

1

effects. Using the method of partial waves he calculated the cross sections and found marked variations with velocity and atomic number.

About the same time Breit *et al.* (1936), in a study of the yield of alpha particles in the bombardment of lithium with protons, used a phenomeno-logical complex potential well to characterize the interaction of the proton with the lithium nucleus. Assuming the reaction to be caused by S waves, they found agreement with experiment if the well were chosen with the radius 3.5 F (1 F $= 10^{-13}$ cm) and the depth 35 MeV. They introduced into the calculation a small imaginary part which was identified with the loss of flux from the incident channel.

These two early works on N–$\mathcal{N}$ scattering, in conjunction with the shell model studies already mentioned, contained the basic conceptual elements of modern approaches to the IPM in bound and scattering states.

Not long afterwards the roots of what appeared to be a diametrically opposite nuclear model, the strong interaction model (SIM), was brought forth in a number of studies. Here the underlying concept is that the nucleons in a nucleus interact strongly because of the strong and short range nature of the N–N interaction. The view of the nucleus as a liquid drop with nucleons playing the role of molecules came forth in an effort to explain the systematics of nuclear binding energies. The notion of alpha particles as stable subunits inside the nucleus also was considered early in the nuclear literature and also suggested that SIM is a predominant feature of nuclear physics. However, to a large extent the fact that low energy neutron cross sections for capture and other reactions displayed large and closely spaced narrow resonances, provided the strongest support for the strong interaction model. These data led N. Bohr (1936) to propose his compound nucleus model of a nuclear reaction and Breit and Wigner (1936) to propose their well-known dispersion formula for resonance cross sections. According to this approach the narrow resonances occur because the strong N–N interaction leads to a sharing of incident energy immediately by many particles. Correspondingly, the mean free path Λ is expected to be much smaller than the nuclear radius R. Thus, it takes time to concentrate enough energy on the outgoing particle in a nuclear reaction for it to escape, implying a long lifetime of the compound state.

To a large extent the two themes, the IPM and the SIM, have been rivals for nuclear popularity since the very beginning, and to some extent the issue has not yet been resolved. To demonstrate how much the SIM and IPM models were already embodied in the very early literature we refer the reader to the monumental work of Bethe and Bacher (1936) summarizing the status of nuclear physics in 1936.

The beginning of attempts to achieve a fundamental understanding of nuclear phenomena also was started in this same era with the proposal by Yukawa (1935) of the first form of meson theory. Yukawa's work on scalar meson theory was followed by Proca's (1936) study of vector meson theory. Then Kemmer (1938) developed the remaining tensoral fields, pseudoscalar, axial vector, and tensor, and introduced isotopic spin into meson theory. Thus within the first six years of the beginning of modern nuclear physics the foundation had been laid of our current fundamental understanding of nuclear forces.

Following these earlier efforts the predominant point of view, and without doubt the most considered point of view, of nuclear physicists was that we must first understand in detail the basic N–N interaction before we could hope to understand the properties of many nucleon systems. Unfortunately this basic tenet of faith, still held by many, was not borne out in the evolution of nuclear physics during the next quarter of a century. This was due largely to the fact that the fundamental N–N interaction has proven to be exceedingly complex and has resisted clarification until very recently. Thus the bulk of experimental and theoretical efforts in nuclear physics during this period has been devoted towards attempts to achieve an understanding of nuclear laws by studying the properties of complex nuclei directly.

In this monograph we shall, in the first six chapters, be concerned primarily with direct studies of the gross aspects of the many body problem. In the last chapter we shall describe recent developments on our understanding of the fundamental interaction from a meson theoretic viewpoint and consider how these developments will probably influence our understanding of the nuclear many body problem and, in particular, the IPM.

The discovery of fission by Hahn and Strassman (1939), followed shortly by Bohr and Wheeler's (1939) interpretation of fission in terms of the liquid drop model, along with developments in the statistical theory of nuclear reactions greatly advanced the SIM viewpoint. It is intriguing to note that the first serious development of the optical model of the nucleus, which is now viewed as an IPM type theory, was made in an effort to pursue the SIM theory of nuclear reactions. Thus in an attempt to develop a statistical theory of the compound nucleus model of nuclear reactions, Bethe (1940b) introduced a complex potential to calculate average N–$\mathcal{N}$ cross sections, by disregarding or rather averaging over the effects of the individual levels. He noted that such a continuum theory is related to dispersion theory (as the classical theory of a solid), describing it by phenomenological constants, as conductivity is related to a quantum theory which would take into account each electronic and vibrational quantum state of the crystal. Bethe accepted the basic idea underlying the theory of the compound nucleus (Bohr, 1936); that there is a strong interaction between a nucleus and any nuclear particle incident upon it which leads to an amalgamation of the two. However, he characterized the large absorption property of a nucleus for nuclear particles by an "absorption potential" $\sigma(r)$, which we will denote by $-W(r)$.

Thus in contrast with the potential used with Schroedinger's equation in bound state problems, Bethe, just as Breit *et al.* (1936) in their earlier work on reaction theory, used a complex function of space, which may be written

$$V(r) = U(r) + iW(r). \tag{1}$$

In essence the real part of the optical potential characterizes the refractive properties of the medium, and the imaginary term $W(r)$ characterizes the absorptive properties of the nuclear medium. Using the Schroedinger formulation of quantum mechanics, it is simple to establish the continuity equation,

$$\frac{\partial \rho}{\partial t} + \text{div } \mathbf{j} = 2W(r)\frac{\rho}{\hbar} \tag{2}$$

where $\mathbf{j}$ is the Schroedinger current density and ρ the particle density. If $W(r)$ is negative (i.e., $\sigma(r)$ positive), then the complex component of potential implies a loss of particle flux which represents particles lost through nuclear reactions and scattering via the compound nucleus.

From the mathematical point of view Bethe's formulation already had the main ingredients of the optical model of the nucleus as we know it today. However, Bethe concentrated his attention on the case $U = 0$ and $W \approx -30$ MeV (-20 to -40), and indicated that his results should not be changed appreciably for $U \neq 0$. In the light of current knowledge, Bethe was pursuing a parameter realm not physically relevant to the N–$\mathcal{N}$ problem at moderate energies $(E < 50 \text{ MeV})$. Thus the large imaginary term implied (see Section 1.4) $\Lambda \ll R$ and hence contradicted the notion of an IPM orbit.

The tide began to turn in favor of the IPM in 1948 when Maria Mayer (1948, 1950) and Haxel *et al.* (1949) extended the description by incorporating a strong spin orbit term in the nucleon–nuclear (N–$\mathcal{N}$) interaction. By also embodying schematically a pairing interaction so that pairs of outer nucleons couple to zero angular momentum, they could use the shell model to provide a very reasonable account of nuclear spins and magnetic moments (Nordheim, 1951). We shall not go into these aspects of the shell model since they have been treated rather thoroughly in a number of works (Mayer and Jensen, 1955; Feenberg, 1955; deShalit and Talmi, 1963). Instead we shall concentrate our discussions on the detailed nature of the IPM potential.

For the most part these early shell model studies were pursued with the aid of primitive and rather unrealistic N–$\mathcal{N}$ potentials such as the harmonic oscillator, the spherical box, or the square well. In this respect they simply provided a schematic means for ordering levels, rather than a quantitative way for fixing the positions of nuclear energy levels in specific nuclei.

Despite this ascendancy of the IPM shell model for bound states, the SIM still prevailed for scattering states at moderate energies $(<50 \text{ MeV})$. The IPM of scattering states of a single particle in a potential well would correspond to the hyperbolic orbits of the Kepler problem just as the bound states correspond to the elliptic orbits. However, the concept of a potential description implicitly assumes that a particle moving in this average potential has a mean free path which is long compared to a nuclear radius. As we noted, estimates of Λ based upon the statistical theory indicated that $\Lambda \ll R$ at moderate nuclear energies.

The fact that $\Lambda \gtrsim R$ at high energy (~ 100 MeV) was noted by Serber in 1947, who suggested that at high energies N–$\mathcal{N}$ collisions should proceed by way of collisions with individual target nucleons. Using the available N–N cross sections and a multiple scattering description, he estimated that the N–$\mathcal{N}$ cross section should correspond to a mean free path of the order of nuclear dimensions (~ 6 F at 90 MeV). Later Fernbach *et al.* (1949), and Pasternack and Snyder (1950) developed further these physical observations into a semiclassical optical description of a nucleon moving in a nucleus as a wave propagating in a medium having a complex refractive index. Then the scattering and absorption of the incident beam is completely described and all nonelastic processes, i.e., absorption, reactions, and inelastic scattering, are lumped together as absorption in so far as they effectively remove particles from the incident beam. Experimental measurements of N–$\mathcal{N}$ cross sections at 90 MeV by Cook *et al.* (1949) confirmed the predictions of this model.

These early indications of the meaningfulness of an optical model description at high energies occurred just when the shell model was gaining ascendancy for bound states. Nevertheless, since the N–$\mathcal{N}$ cross section increases rapidly at lower energies these studies did not dispel the prevailing view that at moderate energies Λ should be much less than R.

Indeed the considerations underlying SIM motivated the next major attempt at an "opaque" continuum theory of neutron reactions, known as the boundary condition model (BCM) (Feshbach *et al.*, 1947; Feshbach and Weisskopf, 1949). According to BCM, the neutron waves which penetrate into the nucleus are absorbed so rapidly that they do not return to interfere with incoming waves. Without going into details of the mathematical formalism (see Blatt and Weisskopf, 1952) we shall simply report that the major result of this continuum theory is that the total cross sections decrease monotonically with increasing energy and vary monotonically with radius according to

$$\sigma_t = \frac{4\pi}{k(k^2 + K_0^2)^{1/2}} \qquad (\lambdabar \gg R)$$

and

(3)

$$\sigma_t = 2\pi(R + \lambdabar)^2 \qquad (\lambdabar \ll R)$$

with $K_0 \sim 1$ F^{-1}, and with $\lambdabar = 1/k$.

The sequence of developments which led most nuclear scattering theorists to shift from the SIM to IPM viewpoint went approximately as follows. First Bohm and Ford (1950) noted that neutron scattering lengths which represent the neutron cross sections of the various nuclei at zero energy (these correspond to the parabolic orbits of the Kepler problem) show broad resonances (called size resonances) at about mass numbers 12, 55, and 155. Such resonances can be explained naturally, if the nuclear potentials established by mass numbers 12, 55, and 155 would bind a $2S$, $3S$, and $4S$ neutron respectively at zero energy. Then a broad resonance would be stimulated by a low energy incident neutron. Accordingly, the Bohm–Ford size resonance observations suggested that zero energy scattering phenomenon at least can be described by a potential or IPM description (with $W = 0$).

The next theoretical scattering study favoring the IPM description was the work of LeLevier and Saxon (1952) who obtained a rather good account of the angular distribution of 18 MeV protons scattered from aluminum using the complex N–$\mathcal{N}$ potential

$$V = - U_0 - iW_0 \quad (r < R) \qquad \text{and} \qquad V = 0 \quad (r > R). \qquad (4)$$

The *coup de grace* of the opaque view of the N–$\mathcal{N}$ potential was finally delivered by Barschall and his colleagues, who carried out experimental studies of neutron scattering. They (Barschall, 1952; Miller *et al.*, 1952) found that the averages over many individual resonances which are automatically obtained from low resolution studies displayed broad maxima whose positions vary in a systematic way with mass number and energy (Fig. 1). Later measurements of Walt and Barschall (1954), Snowden and Whitehead (1954), and others of angular distributions also showed broad resonance type variations of the differential cross section with mass number and with energy (Fig. 2). These experimental results with neutrons contradicted the monotonically varying cross sections predicted by the continuum theory of Feshbach, Peaslee, and Weisskopf (Blatt and Weisskopf, 1952).

In response to these decisive experiments Feshbach *et al.* (1953, 1954) discarded the boundary condition model and adopted the complex square well model. They initially (1953) chose $U_0 = 19$ MeV, but prompted by the observations of Adair (1954) they switched to $U_0 = 42$ MeV and the radius $R = 1.45A^{1/3}$ to preserve the Bohm–Ford size resonance picture. When they used $W_0 \sim 2$ MeV, they obtained variations of total cross sections and of angular distributions which agreed qualitatively with experimental results by Walt and Barschall (1954) and Snowden and Whitehead (1954) and others.

The mathematical techniques and physical substance of the early phase of the IPM or the shell and optical models will be the main subject of the remainder of Chapter I.

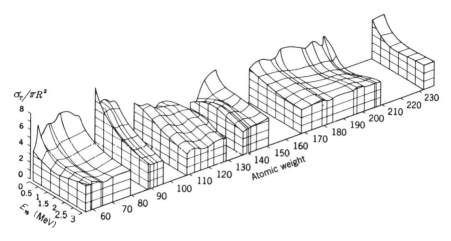

Fig. 1. Total neutron cross sections of elements heavier than Mn as a function of neutron energy. The surface is based on measurements for atomic weights at which straight vertical lines appear in the figure (Barschall, 1952).

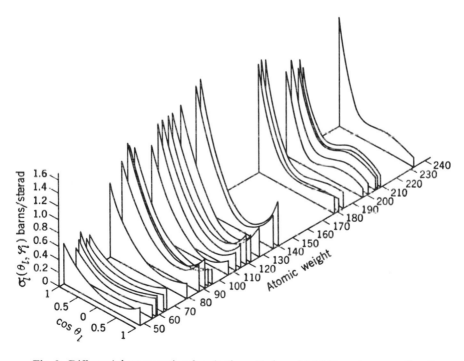

Fig. 2. Differential cross section for elastic scattering of 1 MeV neutrons as a function of the cosine of the scattering angle and of atomic weight (Walt and Barschall, 1954).

Once the weight of experimental evidence disposed of the rather sophisticated theoretical arguments against the model, the development of this conceptually simple model proceeded rapidly. The center of attention became that of finding realistic potentials which lead to results which are quantitatively consistent with experimental data. The fact that this search was started when computing machines were becoming available at many institutions helped greatly in the search for good N–$\mathcal{N}$ potentials. Furthermore, the fact that low resolution data were most easily amenable to interpretation was also a great boon since many machines had poor resolution. Possibly never before had so vast a body of experimental data come forth just at a time when a theoretical framework and numerical techniques became available for its organization. Those involved in the experimental, phenomenological, and theoretical work during this period were exhilarated by the fruitfulness of their efforts. The remarkable successes of the model in fitting vast bodies of diverse and highly structured experimental data made it no longer necessary to apologize for or justify these efforts. To borrow a legal principle concerning the burden of proof: *res ipsa loquitur*—the thing speaks for itself.

An opportunity for most of the active experimental and theoretical workers who participated in the 1953–1959 development of the shell and optical model to discuss and consolidate their advances was provided by the 1959 International Conference on the Nuclear Optical Model. These conference proceedings (Green *et al.*, 1959[1]) pointed to the main advances which had been made. These advances will largely be the subjects of Chapters II, III, and IV. It also brought forth many of the unsettled questions which are subjects of active research to this very day. Our discussions of the unsettled questions and active research areas will be concentrated in Chapters V, VI, and VII.

Let us go to the mathematical techniques and the physical substance of primitive shell and optical models.

1.2   Schroedinger's Equation and Pauli Spin Formalism

1.2a   The Central Field Problem

In a broader context the discovery of quantum mechanics in the 1924–1927 era by de Broglie, Heisenberg, Schroedinger, Dirac, Pauli, Born, Jordan, and others represents the true beginning of efforts towards a fundamental understanding of nuclear physics. The first indications that quantum mechanical laws apply to the nucleus were made by Gamow (1928) and Condon and Gurney (1928) in their wave mechanical description of alpha decay. They viewed the alpha particle as acted upon by a potential such as

---

[1] Further references to this work will be by place and date, i.e., Florida (1959).

illustrated in Fig. 1. Here the inner region represents schematically a potential which is a combination of a nuclear potential and the Coulomb potential. At longer range the interaction goes over entirely to the Coulomb potential energy

$$V_{\text{coul}} = ze\phi_c = zZe^2/r \tag{1}$$

Fig. 1. Schematic diagram indicating the energy relationships in alpha decay, and a hypothetical potential energy function for the alpha particle and the daughter nucleus.

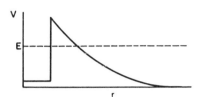

where z is the charge number of the alpha particle and Z the charge number of the daughter nucleus, and e the magnitude of the electronic charge.

In the interior the wave function for this alpha particle resembles very closely the bound state wave function of the IPM. In the exterior it is like the outgoing wave of the optical model. The calculation of the leakage of alpha particles through the intermediate barrier leads to a relationship between the alpha particle decay constant and the energy of the outgoing alpha particle and the charge of the parent nucleus. With the adjustment of two parameters, one of which could be interpreted as a nuclear radius, their relationship provides a very good account of the experimental data. Not only did these studies indicate that Schroedinger's equation applies to the nucleus, but at the same time they pioneered techniques which were later used extensively in the development of the shell and optical models.

To a large extent the development of the IPM has been a tremendous collective exercise in the application of wave mechanics. It will be assumed that the reader has already been introduced to the elementary aspects of this subject. However, for the sake of completeness we will begin with a review and summary of the Schroedinger equation and the real central potential. These features will serve as reference points when we later consider spin dependent, complex potentials, spheroidal potentials, velocity dependent and nonlocal potentials and, finally, multiparticle potentials.

As a starting point in our description of the IPM of the nucleus, we shall assume that a particle (a nucleon in most of this work), having mass m_1 is acted upon by the remaining nucleus of mass M via a potential

$$V(\mathbf{r}) = V(x, y, z) \tag{2}$$

where $x = x_1 - X$, $y = y_1 - Y$, and $z = z_1 - Z$, where x_1, y_1, z_1 refer to the particle coordinates and X, Y, Z to the coordinates of the nucleus. The fact that the force depends upon the relative coordinates introduces a great simplification in permitting us to reduce the two body problem to an equivalent one body with the reduced mass

$$m = \frac{m_1 M}{m_1 + M} \tag{3}$$

moving in a potential established by an infinitely heavy center.

Thus, after separating out the center of mass motion of the system, the Schroedinger time independent equation becomes

$$\{-(\hbar^2/2m)\nabla^2 + V(\mathbf{r})\}\psi(\mathbf{r}) = E\psi(\mathbf{r}). \tag{4}$$

Here ∇^2 denotes the Laplacian operator, $\psi(\mathbf{r})$ the wave function, and E the energy of the system in the center of mass system. Except in Sections 2.4 and 4.2, where we discuss the motion of a particle in a nonspherical potential, we assume that, unless otherwise stated, the potential function furthermore is of the central type, i.e., $V(\mathbf{r}) = V(r)$ where $r = (x^2 + y^2 + z^2)^{1/2}$. Then the fact that the orbital angular momentum is a constant of motion also greatly simplifies the quantum mechanical analysis just as it does the classical analysis. The fact that the potential is central insures that Schroedinger's equation can be separated in spherical coordinates. Expressing the Laplacian operator in spherical coordinates, Schroedinger's equation takes the form

$$\left\{ \frac{1}{r^2} \frac{\partial}{\partial r} \left(r^2 \frac{\partial}{\partial r} \right) + \frac{1}{r^2 \sin^2 \theta} \frac{\partial^2}{\partial \phi^2} + \frac{1}{r^2 \sin \theta} \frac{\partial}{\partial \theta} \left(\sin \theta \frac{\partial}{\partial \theta} \right) \right.$$

$$\left. + \frac{2m}{\hbar^2} [E - V(r)] \right\} \psi(r, \theta, \phi) = 0. \tag{5}$$

We separate variables by writing

$$\psi(r, \theta, \phi) = R(r)\Theta(\theta)\Phi(\phi).$$

By virtue of the independence of r, θ, and ϕ we can deduce from Eq. (5) three ordinary differential equations for $R(r)$, $\Theta(\theta)$, and $\Phi(\phi)$ involving two separation constants α and β. On the basis of the physical requirement $\Phi(\phi) = \Phi(\phi + 2\pi)$ it can be shown that $m_l = \alpha^{1/2} = 0, \pm 1, \pm 2$. The corresponding normalized Φ functions are

$$\Phi_{m_l} = \frac{1}{(2\pi)^{1/2}} \exp(im_l \phi). \tag{6}$$

It can also be shown that the requirement of finiteness at $z = \cos \theta = \pm 1$ imposes upon β the form

$$\beta = l(l + 1) \qquad l = 0, 1, 2, \ldots, |m_l|. \tag{7}$$

The normalized well-behaved solutions associated with each allowed l and m_l are the well-known associated Legendre functions

$$\Theta_l^{m_l}(z) = \left[\frac{(l - |m_l|)!}{(l + |m_l|)!} \frac{2l + 1}{2} \right]^{1/2} (1 - z^2)^{|m_l|/2} \frac{d^{|m_l|}}{dz^{|m_l|}} P_l(z) \tag{8}$$

where $P_l(z)$ are the familiar Legendre polynomials, the first three of which are

$$P_0 = 1 \qquad P_1 = z \qquad P_2 = \tfrac{1}{2}(3z^2 - 1).$$

It can be shown by constructing the Schroedinger operators associated with the square of the orbital angular momentum that the solution

$$Y_{l, m_l}(\theta, \phi) = \Theta_l^{m_l}(\cos \theta)\Phi_{m_l}(\phi) \tag{9}$$

is an eigenfunction belonging to the eigenvalue $\hbar^2 l(l + 1)$. Further, $\Phi_{m_l}(\phi)$ is an eigenvalue of the operator associated with the z component of orbital angular momentum belonging to the eigenvalue $m_l \hbar$ where $|m_l| \leqslant l$. The function Y_{l,m_l} is called the spherical harmonic.

Going now to the radial wave equation the substitutions $\beta = l(l + 1)$ and $R(r) = G(r)/r$ give

$$\frac{d^2 G}{dr^2} + \frac{2m}{\hbar^2} \left[E - V(r) - \frac{\hbar^2 l(l + 1)}{2mr^2} \right] G = 0. \tag{10}$$

If we define the effective potential

$$V_e = V(r) + \frac{\hbar^2 l(l + 1)}{2mr^2} \tag{11}$$

the radial wave equation with G as the wave function becomes identical in form with a one-dimensional wave equation. Since the quantity $\hbar^2 l(l + 1)$ is the square of the magnitude of the orbital angular momentum of the particle about the origin, we may interpret the term $\hbar^2 l(l + 1)/2mr^2$ as the quantum counterpart of the classical "centrifugal energy." This centrifugal energy is always positive; it corresponds to a repulsive force, the centrifugal force.

The well-behaved solutions of the Schroedinger wave equation may be divided into two general classes corresponding to negative E values and positive E values. The former corresponds to the states of binding analogous to the closed orbits of a planetary system, and the latter to the unbound states. Binding can occur only if the potential function corresponds to a strong enough attractive force (negative V). The normalization condition for the radial wave function is

$$\int_0^\infty R^*(r)R(r)r^2 \, dr = \int_0^\infty G^*G \, dr = 1. \tag{12}$$

Since $R = G(r)/r$ we impose the requirement $G(0) = 0$. Furthermore, to be normalizable $G(r)$ must vanish at $r \to \infty$, i.e.,

$$G(r) = 0 \qquad r \to \infty. \tag{13}$$

For the types of attractive potentials which arise in the N–$\mathcal{N}$ problems, well-behaved radial wave functions exist only when E is one of a finite discrete set of negative values. The order and magnitudes of the allowed negative energy values depend upon various detailed features of the potential function.

For nuclear problems, we take $V(r)$ to have a finite range (of nuclear dimensions), that is, we treat it as vanishing rather rapidly at sufficiently large separations. If the independent particle has electrical charge ze, then the IPM potential must be supplemented by the Coulomb potential, Eq. (1), which usually complicates the analysis because of its long range. For the optical model potential we choose $V(r) = U(r) + iW(r)$ which also complicates the analysis.

1.2b Pauli Spin Matrices and the IPM Potential

In the case of protons and neutrons a considerable body of experimental evidence suggests that the bound state and the optical model potential must contain a spin orbit term, i.e.,

$$V(r) = V_1 + \xi \mathbf{S} \cdot \mathbf{L} \tag{14}$$

where $\mathbf{S}$ is the spin angular momentum and $\mathbf{L}$ is the orbital angular momentum operator. The results for a spinless particle then follow as a special case in which $\xi = 0$. For scattering studies both V_1, the central part of the potential, and ξ, the spin orbit part, are to be regarded as complex operators, not necessarily local. In consequence the wave functions become combinations of Schroedinger operands and Pauli operands.

For the reader who has not had prior experience in dealing with Pauli spin operators and operands, we present a summary of their properties and the manner in which they may be used in conjunction with the Schroedinger formalism. The reader who is familiar with this formalism may skip directly to the next section.

In the Pauli formalism dynamical variables are represented by Hermitian operators which are two by two matrices. The unit matrix I and the Pauli spin matrices σ_1, σ_2, and σ_3 are the fundamental matrices in the algebra of two by two Hermitian matrices. These matrices are defined by

$$I = \begin{pmatrix} 1 & 0 \\ 0 & 1 \end{pmatrix} \qquad \sigma_1 = \begin{pmatrix} 0 & 1 \\ 1 & 0 \end{pmatrix} \qquad \sigma_2 = i\begin{pmatrix} 0 & -1 \\ 1 & 0 \end{pmatrix} \qquad \sigma_3 = \begin{pmatrix} 1 & 0 \\ 0 & -1 \end{pmatrix}. \tag{15}$$

These Pauli matrices have the properties:

(1) the eigenvalues of the Pauli matrices are $+1$ and -1,

(2)

$$\sigma_1{}^2 = I, \qquad \sigma_2{}^2 = I, \qquad \sigma_3{}^2 = I \tag{16}$$

and

$$\sigma_1{}^2 + \sigma_2{}^2 + \sigma_3{}^2 = 3I, \tag{17}$$

(3) they satisfy the commutation relations

$$\sigma_1\sigma_2 - \sigma_2\sigma_1 = 2i\sigma_3 \qquad \text{cyc}, \tag{18}$$

(4) they anticommute, i.e.,

$$\sigma_1\sigma_2 + \sigma_2\sigma_1 = 0 \qquad \text{cyc}, \tag{19}$$

(5) they are further related by the equations

$$\sigma_1\sigma_2 = i\sigma_3 \qquad \text{cyc} \tag{20}$$

and

$$\sigma_1\sigma_2\sigma_3 = iI \qquad \text{cyc} \tag{21}$$

(where cyc means " plus the additional equations obtained by cyclic permutation of the indices 1, 2, and 3").

Another basic property is that the most general Hermitian two by two matrix may be written as a linear combination of these Pauli matrices and the unit matrix with real coefficients. Thus

$$\begin{bmatrix} a & c + id \\ c - id & b \end{bmatrix} = \frac{a+b}{2} I + \frac{a-b}{2} \sigma_3 + c\sigma_1 - d\sigma_2, \tag{22}$$

All these algebraic relations and properties may be verified by straightforward applications of the matrix algebra.

It is interesting to note that if we accept Eq. (18) as the basic algebraic relations, then we may deduce the remaining equations by the methods of symbolic algebra (Messiah, 1958).

1.2c The Pauli "Functions" or Operands

The matrix "functions" or operands

$$U_+{}^3 = \begin{bmatrix} 1 \\ 0 \end{bmatrix} \qquad U_-{}^3 = \begin{bmatrix} 0 \\ 1 \end{bmatrix} \tag{23}$$

and their adjoints

$$U_+^{3*} = \begin{bmatrix} 1 & 0 \end{bmatrix} \qquad U_-^{3*} = \begin{bmatrix} 0 & 1 \end{bmatrix} \tag{24}$$

have a basic role in operand space. They possess the normalization property

$$U_+^{3*}U_+^{\ 3} = 1 \qquad U_-^{3*}U_-^{\ 3} = 1 \tag{25}$$

and satisfy the orthogonality conditions

$$U_+^{3*}U_-^{\ 3} = 0 \qquad U_-^{3*}U_+^{\ 3} = 0. \tag{26}$$

The most general one by two operands may be expressed as linear combination of $U_+^{\ 3}$ and $U_-^{\ 3}$. Thus

$$U = C_1 U_+^{\ 3} + C_2 U_-^{\ 3}. \tag{27}$$

The following relations between Pauli operators and Pauli operands may be readily verified by matrix algebra:

$$\begin{aligned} \sigma_1 U_+^{\ 3} = U_-^{\ 3} \qquad \sigma_2 U_+^{\ 3} = iU_-^{\ 3} \qquad \sigma_3 U_+^{\ 3} = U_+^{\ 3} \\ \sigma_1 U_-^{\ 3} = U_+^{\ 3} \qquad \sigma_2 U_-^{\ 3} = -iU_+^{\ 3} \qquad \sigma_3 U_-^{\ 3} = -U_-^{\ 3}, \end{aligned} \tag{28}$$

$$(\sigma_1^{\ 2} + \sigma_2^{\ 2} + \sigma_3^{\ 2})U_+^{\ 3} = 3U_+^{\ 3} \tag{29}$$

and

$$(\sigma_1^{\ 2} + \sigma_2^{\ 2} + \sigma_3^{\ 2})U_-^{\ 3} = 3U_-^{\ 3}. \tag{30}$$

The third and the last members of Eq. (28) and Eqs. (29) and (30) have the form of the eigenvalue equation in Schroedinger's quantum mechanics. According to basic interpretive postulates these equations, therefore, imply that when a system is in the state $U_+^{\ 3}(U_-^{\ 3})$ a measurement of the dynamical variable σ_3 will certainly yield the result $+1$ (-1) and a measurement of $\boldsymbol{\sigma} \cdot \boldsymbol{\sigma}$ will certainly yield the result 3 (3). We may interpret the first of Eq. (28) to imply that the operator σ_1 when applied to the state $U_+^{\ 3}$, will flip the spin to the state $U_-^{\ 3}$. Similar interpretations may be given to the other relations.

We readily devise operands which correspond to the eigenstate of σ_1 and σ_2. Thus let us assume that

$$\sigma_1 U_+^{\ 1} = 1U_+^{\ 1} = U_+^{\ 1} = C_1 U_+^{\ 3} + C_2 U_-^{\ 3}. \tag{31}$$

We note immediately that if $C = C_1 = C_2$, we have

$$\sigma_1 U_+^{\ 1} = \sigma_1(CU_+^{\ 3} + CU_-^{\ 3}) = C(\sigma_1 U_+^{\ 3} + \sigma_1 U_-^{\ 3}) = C(U_-^{\ 3} + U_+^{\ 3}) = U_+^{\ 1}. \tag{32}$$

Thus we may conclude that when the system is in the state characterized by the Pauli function $U_+^{\ 1} = C(U_+^{\ 3} + U_-^{\ 3})$, the value of σ_1 is certainly $+1$.

To normalize this function we let

$$\begin{aligned} U_+^{1*}U_+^{\ 1} &= C^*(U_+^{3*} + U_-^{3*})C(U_+^{\ 3} + U_-^{\ 3}) \\ &= C^*C(U_+^{3*}U_+^{\ 3} + U_+^{3*}U_-^{\ 3} + U_-^{3*}U_+^{\ 3} + U_-^{3*}U_-^{\ 3}) = 2C^*C \end{aligned} \tag{33}$$

where we have used Eqs. (25) and (26). Thus

$$C = (1/\sqrt{2})e^{i\gamma} \qquad C^* = (1/\sqrt{2})e^{-i\gamma} \tag{34}$$

where γ is an arbitrary real number.

In a similar way we can determine the eigenoperands of σ_1 belonging to the eigenvalue -1, and the eigenfunction of σ_2 belonging to the eigenvalues ± 1.

1.2d The Spin Operators and Functions

The algebraic properties of the Pauli matrix operators are closely related to the spin operators. Indeed, if we let

$$S_x = (\hbar/2)\sigma_x \qquad S_y = (\hbar/2)\sigma_y \qquad \text{and} \qquad S_z = (\hbar/2)\sigma_z \tag{35}$$

where σ_x, σ_y, and σ_z are formally identical with σ_1, σ_2, and σ_3, respectively, then it is obvious that the S's will satisfy the basic algebraic relations for angular momentum vectors, and further that each component of spin angular momentum has the eigenvalues $\pm\hbar/2$. For a system in an $\alpha(\beta)$ spin state, $S_z = \hbar/2(-\hbar/2)$, where $\alpha(\beta)$ are operands formally identical with $U_+{}^3(U_-{}^3)$. It is permissible to identify any of σ_1, σ_2, and σ_3 with σ_x, σ_y, and σ_z. The identification chosen above has certain conveniences when the spatial wave functions are treated in spherical polar coordinates. L_z then is a simple differential operator, and it turns out to be advantageous also to choose for σ_z the diagonal Pauli matrix. A particular direction in space, of course, has meaning only in relation to some external vector such as a magnetic field or, in the case of scattering, to the direction of the incident beam.

The spin operators are intimately related to the so-called Cayley–Klein parameters used to characterize the orientation of a rigid body in classical kinematics (Goldstein, 1950).

In the quantum mechanical treatment of a single particle when spin dependent forces exist, the Schroedinger formalism must be generalized to include this problem. We wish here to show how the spin degree of freedom may be introduced and treated.

Let us consider as an example the Hamiltonian of a single particle in a central field when the spin orbit force is present. We have

$$H = (p^2/2m)I + V(r)I + \xi(r)\mathbf{L}\cdot\mathbf{S}$$
$$= (\hbar^2/2m)\,\nabla^2 I + V(r)I + (\hbar/2)\xi(r)(L_x\sigma_x + L_y\sigma_y + L_z\sigma_z) \tag{36}$$

where each operator is now a product of a space operator and a spin operator.

The wave function must depend upon the spin orientation variables as well as the space vector $\mathbf{r}$. We shall use S_z for this purpose. Thus $\Psi = \Psi(\mathbf{r}, S_z)$.

To find a solution of the wave equation we generally attempt to use a wave function having the product form

$$\Psi(\mathbf{r}, S_z) = \psi(\mathbf{r})\psi(S_z) \qquad (37)$$

or else a sum of functions having this form. The most general spin space function can be written as a linear combination of the spin space function belonging to the α spin state and the spin space function belonging to the β spin state. Thus we have

$$\Psi(\mathbf{r}, S_z) = \alpha\psi_\alpha(\mathbf{r}) + \beta\psi_\beta(\mathbf{r}) \qquad (38)$$

where the normalization condition is now (using the orthogonality conditions)

$$\int \Psi^*(\mathbf{r}, S_z)\Psi(\mathbf{r}, S_z)\, d\tau = \int \psi_\alpha{}^*(\mathbf{r})\psi_\alpha(\mathbf{r})\, d\tau + \int \psi_\beta{}^*(\mathbf{r})\psi_\beta(\mathbf{r})\, d\tau = 1. \qquad (39)$$

The general Schroedinger–Pauli energy equation takes on the form

$$H\Psi(\mathbf{r}, S_z) = E\Psi(\mathbf{r}, S_z). \qquad (40)$$

We now allow the S_x, S_y, and S_z spin operators to work upon the operands α and β in accord with Eq. (28). We may commute the component operators in a spin space at will in relation to the operators in real space. However, within spin space and within real space we must obey the rules for matrix operators and for the Schroedinger differential operators. The spin and space functions also may be arranged in arbitrary order. Proceeding carefully, according to these rules we obtain

$$\left\{-\frac{\hbar^2}{2m}\Delta + V(r) - E\right\}[\alpha\psi_\alpha(r) + \beta\psi_\beta(r)] + \frac{\hbar}{2}\xi(r)L_x(\beta\psi_\alpha + \alpha\psi_\beta)$$

$$+ i\frac{\hbar}{2}\xi(r)L_y(\beta\psi_\alpha - \alpha\psi_\beta) + \frac{\hbar}{2}\xi(r)L_z(\alpha\psi_\alpha - \beta\psi_\beta) = 0. \qquad (41)$$

Let us now multiply through by α^* and then by β^*. The orthogonality and normality properties [Eqs. (25)–(26)] then lead immediately to the set of equations

$$\left\{-\frac{\hbar^2}{2m}\Delta + V(r) - E + \frac{\hbar}{2}\xi(r)L_z\right\}\psi_\alpha(r) + \left\{\frac{\hbar}{2}\xi(r)(L_x - iL_y)\right\}\psi_\beta = 0$$

and   (42)

$$\left\{-\frac{\hbar^2}{2m}\Delta + V(r) - E - \frac{\hbar}{2}\xi(r)L_z\right\}\psi_\beta(r) + \left\{\frac{\hbar}{2}\xi(r)(L_x + iL_y)\right\}\psi_\alpha = 0.$$

These equations contain only the space function ψ_α, ψ_β, and the differential and multiplicative Schroedinger operators. As we see, the differential equations are now mutually dependent. The spin dependent potential has "coupled" these two wave functions. If we attempt to find the well-behaved solutions of these two simultaneous wave equations, it will be found that two sets of solutions exist. It can be shown that one set corresponds to the total angular momentum

$$\mathbf{J} = \mathbf{L} + \mathbf{S} \qquad (43)$$

having the associative quantum number $j = l + \tfrac{1}{2}$ and the other set having the value $j = l - \tfrac{1}{2}$.

1.2e   Angular Momentum Eigenstates

The solution of the partial differential bound state or optical model Schroedinger's equation can also be reduced to the solution of a set of ordinary differential equations by introducing appropriate angular momentum eigenfunctions. Because of the presence of the spin orbit term, we must find simultaneous eigenfunctions of $\mathbf{L}^2$ and $\mathbf{S} \cdot \mathbf{L}$, or equivalently of $\mathbf{J}^2$, where $\mathbf{J} = \mathbf{L} + \mathbf{S}$ is the total angular momentum. This equivalence follows since, using $\mathbf{S}^2 = \tfrac{3}{4}\hbar^2$,

$$\mathbf{J}^2 = \mathbf{L}^2 + 2\mathbf{S} \cdot \mathbf{L} + \tfrac{3}{4}\hbar^2. \qquad (44)$$

A complete set of commuting operators is then seen to be $\mathbf{J}^2$, $\mathbf{L}^2$, and J_z and we label the states correspondingly by j, l, m_j. By the vector addition rule, j can only take on the values $l \pm \tfrac{1}{2}$ and hence, the eigenvalues of $\mathbf{S} \cdot \mathbf{L}$ are

$$\mathbf{L} \cdot \mathbf{S} = \tfrac{1}{2}(\mathbf{J}^2 - \mathbf{L}^2 - \tfrac{3}{4}\hbar^2) = \begin{cases} \tfrac{1}{2}l\hbar^2 & (j = l + \tfrac{1}{2}) \\ -\tfrac{1}{2}(l + 1)\hbar^2 & (j = l - \tfrac{1}{2}) \end{cases} \qquad (45)$$

It is possible to construct linear combinations of the form of Eq. (38) which are simultaneous eigenfunctions of $\mathbf{L}^2$, $\mathbf{S}^2$, $\mathbf{J}^2$, and J_z. The results (Rose, 1957) denoted by $\psi(l, \tfrac{1}{2}, j, m)$ or $\psi(j, m)$ are

$$\psi(l + \tfrac{1}{2}, m) = [C^+ \alpha Y_{l, m - \frac{1}{2}} + C^- \beta Y_{l, m + \frac{1}{2}}] R^+(r) \qquad (46)$$

and

$$\psi(l - \tfrac{1}{2}, m) = [-C^- \alpha Y_{l, m - \frac{1}{2}} + C^+ \beta Y_{l, m + \frac{1}{2}}] R^-(r) \qquad (47)$$

where

$$C^+ = [(j + m + \tfrac{1}{2})/(2j + 1)]^{1/2} \quad \text{and} \quad C^- = [(j - m + \tfrac{1}{2})/(2j + 1)]^{1/2} \qquad (48)$$

These numerical coefficients are special values of the more general coefficients called Clebsch–Gordan coefficients or vector addition coefficients. If we insert Eqs. (46) and (47) into Eq. (40) and use the orthonormality properties of the

α, β, and the $Y_{l,m}$'s we find that the radial equation for each value of j now takes on precisely the form of Eq. (10) with

$$V(r) \to V(r) + \tfrac{1}{2}\hbar^2 l\xi(r) \qquad \text{for} \qquad j = l + \tfrac{1}{2}$$

or   (49)

$$V(r) \to V(r) - \tfrac{1}{2}\hbar^2(l + 1)\xi(r) \qquad \text{for} \qquad j = l - \tfrac{1}{2}$$

Thus the problem is identical with the usual central field problem except that we must solve the radial equation twice for two slightly different potentials. We shall now apply these results to the nuclear shell model.

1.3   The Single Particle Shell Model

Much of the early work on the IPM shell model was carried out before electronic computers became commonplace, and theoreticians necessarily relied heavily upon the traditional analytic methods used for treating wave equations. Thus most of the earliest investigators chose form functions for their potentials in which physical reasonableness was sometimes compromised in favor of the mathematical tractability of the solutions of the wave equation associated with the potential. The infinite spherical well and the three-dimensional harmonic oscillator were the potentials most widely used in this context. Let us first consider the spherical box problem which is the simplest to cope with mathematically.

When solving Schroedinger's equation it is convenient to work with dimensionless quantities. To this end we refer lengths to some convenient base length a, such as one fermi (F) or the nuclear radius. Thus we define the dimensionless distance parameter and the corresponding energy parameters

$$\rho = r/a \qquad \text{and} \qquad E_0 = \hbar^2/2ma^2.$$ (1)

If we take $a = 1$ F and $m_1 = (m_n + m_p)/2$, then $E_0 = 20.73[(A + 1)/A]$ MeV. Alternatively, it is frequently convenient to take $a = R$, i.e., we let a nuclear radius serve as the unit of length. If, for example, we assume that this potential energy extends over a radius given by $R = r_0 A^{1/3}$, then

$$E_0 = \frac{\hbar^2}{2mR^2} = \frac{\hbar^2}{2m_1 r_0^2 A^{2/3}} \left(\frac{A + 1}{A}\right) \approx \frac{10}{A^{2/3}} \quad \text{MeV}$$ (2)

where in the last expression we have used $r_0 = 1.45$ F.

It is also convenient to define the dimensionless total energy parameter ε by

$$\varepsilon^2 = \mp \frac{E}{(\hbar^2/2ma^2)} = \mp \frac{E}{E_0}$$ (3)

where the upper sign is used for negative energy states and the lower sign for positive energy states. For *attractive* potentials of the form $V(r) = -V_0 \xi(r)$, we define the dimensionless potential energy parameter

$$\varepsilon_0{}^2 = V_0/E_0 = 2ma^2 V_0/\hbar^2. \tag{4}$$

When $a = R = r_0 A^{1/3}$, this well strength parameter also depends upon mass number and is given by $\varepsilon_0{}^2 \approx 4A^{2/3}$ when $V_0 \approx 45$ MeV. With these conventions the radial wave equation is

$$G'' + \left[\varepsilon_0{}^2 \xi(\rho) - \frac{l(l+1)}{\rho^2} \mp \varepsilon^2 \right] G = 0 \tag{5}$$

where a prime here denotes differentiation with respect to ρ, and the upper sign is for negative energy states and the lower sign for positive energy states.

Let us now assume that the particle is trapped in a spherical box defined by

$$V(r) = -V_0 \quad (r < a) \qquad V(r) = \infty \quad (r > a). \tag{6}$$

This corresponds to $\xi(\rho) = 1$, $\rho < 1$. On physical grounds the wave function must vanish identically for $r \geq a$ or $\rho \geq 1$. This attribute of the problem greatly simplifies the mathematics and provides us with a simple point of departure from which to examine more realistic problems. For S waves the wave equation for the interior region is

$$G_i'' + \varepsilon'^2 G_i = 0 \qquad \varepsilon' = (\varepsilon_0{}^2 - \varepsilon^2)^{1/2} \tag{7}$$

where the subscript i denotes the word interior. The solution which satisfies $G_i(0) = 0$ is

$$G_i = C_i \sin \varepsilon' \rho \tag{8}$$

where C_i is the normalization constant. In view of the properties of the sine function, G_i will vanish at $\rho = 1$, the box boundary, if

$$\varepsilon' = n\pi \tag{9}$$

where n is an integer. The quantity $v = n - 1$ specifies the number of intermediate nodes of the radial wave functions. We conclude that the allowed total energy parameters for S waves are given by

$$\varepsilon^2 = |\varepsilon_0{}^2 - n^2\pi^2| \qquad \text{or} \qquad E = -V_0 + n^2\pi^2 E_0. \tag{10}$$

This is precisely the form of the energy eigenvalue equation for a particle in a one-dimensional box. When consideration is given to the normalization condition, we find that the well-behaved radial functions for S waves are

$$G = (2/a)^{1/2} \sin(n\pi r/a) \tag{11}$$

It is interesting to examine also the P wave case. Here when we let $\varepsilon = 1$ and $l(l + 1) = 2$ in Eq. (5), we may verify by differentiation that a solution of this equation which vanishes at the origin is

$$G_{ip} = C_{ip}\{[(\sin \varepsilon'\rho)/\varepsilon'\rho] - \cos \varepsilon'\rho\}. \tag{12}$$

Assuming that this wave function must vanish at $\rho = 1$, we find the eigenvalue condition $\tan \varepsilon' = \varepsilon'$. This equation is satisfied by values of ε' which are a trifle smaller than $3\pi/2$, $5\pi/2$, $7\pi/2$, etc.

The solutions for D, F, ... states may each be investigated in turn and the corresponding eigenvalues determined by the analysis of the radial wave equation belonging to each case. However, a more systematic method is to find the well-behaved solutions of the general radial wave equation, Eq. (5) with $\xi = 1$.

The solutions of this equation, which vanishes at $\rho = 0$, are

$$G_{il} = (\varepsilon'\rho\pi/2)^{1/2}J_{l+\frac{1}{2}}(\varepsilon'\rho) \tag{13}$$

where $J_{l+\frac{1}{2}}$ are Bessel functions of half-integral order. To satisfy the condition that the wave functions vanish at $\rho = 1$, the values of ε must be such that $J_{l+\frac{1}{2}}(\varepsilon') = 0$. The roots ε_{nl} of the equation $J_{l+\frac{1}{2}}(\varepsilon') = 0$ may be found in tables of Bessel functions. For a fixed value of l the first and successively larger roots correspond to the lowest and successively higher energy states, and the corresponding wave functions have 0, 1, 2, etc., intermediate nodes. The energy eigenvalues may now be expressed by

$$E_{n,l} = -V_0 + (\hbar^2/2ma^2)\varepsilon_{nl}^2. \tag{14}$$

Thus we see the simple way in which the concept of particles in an infinite spherical well leads immediately to a quantization of energy levels. Figure 1 shows these energy levels relative to $V_0 = 0$. Also shown are the occupancy capabilities of each state, i.e., $2 \times (2l + 1)$. In view of the array of levels the magic numbers of the spherical box, i.e., the cumulative occupancy numbers, turn out to be 2, 8, 20, 34, 40, 58, 92, 132. In relationship to currently known magic numbers, the low numbers are good but the higher numbers are spurious.

Another analytically solvable potential which was used in many early discussions is the three-dimensional harmonic oscillator. Since the potential is used to this day for many studies in nuclear spectroscopy, let us consider its application to the problem at hand. We assume that a nucleon is bound by a potential of the form

$$V(r) = -V_0 + \tfrac{1}{2}kr^2 = -V_0 + \tfrac{1}{2}m\omega^2 r^2 \tag{15}$$

where $\omega = (k/m)^{1/2}$ is the harmonic oscillator frequency. It can be shown that the radial equation, with Eq. (15) as the potential, can be transformed to a differential equation obeyed by the associated Laguerre polynomials.

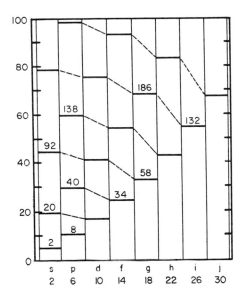

Fig. 1. Energy levels, degeneracy numbers, and magic numbers of an infinite well. The dotted lines join harmonic oscillator states.

Thus the well-behaved solutions are (Mayer and Jensen, 1955)

$$G(r) = \mathcal{N} r^{l+1} e^{-\frac{1}{2}z} L_{n-1}^{l+\frac{1}{2}}(z) \tag{16}$$

where $n - 1$ represents the number of intermediate nodes in the radial wave function, $L_{n-1}^{l+\frac{1}{2}}$ represents associated Laguerre polynomials, $\mathcal{N}$ is a normalization constant, and $z = m\omega r^2/\hbar = \alpha^2 r^2$.

The energy eigenvalues associated with these solutions are

$$E = -V_0 + \hbar\omega(N + \tfrac{3}{2}) \tag{17}$$

where N the so-called oscillator number is defined by $N = 2(n - 1) + l$. The normalized wave functions for the first two radial states for a given l are given by

$$R_{l,1} = \left[\frac{\alpha^3 2^{l+2}}{\pi(2l + 1)!!}\right]^{1/2} z^{l/2} e^{-z/2} \tag{18}$$

and

$$R_{l,2} = \left[\frac{2}{2l + 3}\right]^{1/2}\left[\frac{2l + 3}{2} - z\right] R_{l,1}. \tag{19}$$

The energy levels of the harmonic oscillator are shown in Fig. 2.

Thus we see how the harmonic oscillator model provides a simple sequence of states whose energies are characterized by the oscillator numbers. Figure 2 also illustrates these states and shows the degeneracy numbers associated with each orbital. Also shown are the total degeneracy of the oscillator

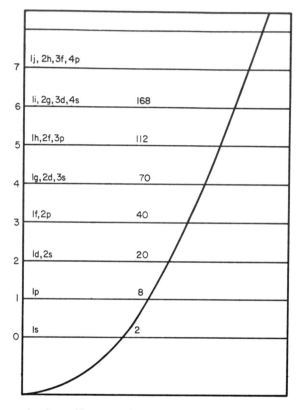

Fig. 2. Energy levels, oscillator numbers, degeneracy numbers, and magic numbers of a three dimensional harmonic oscillator.

shells as well as the cumulative occupancy numbers to a given shell. It should be clear that the harmonic oscillator readily accounts for the magic nature of the numbers 2, 8, 20. However, the oscillator model leads to the spurious magic numbers 40, 70, 112, and 168 which are not manifested in the experimental observations.

The harmonic oscillator potential, because of the analytical convenience of its wave functions, is still extensively used for many investigations, particularly in nuclear spectroscopy. For certain purposes we can correct for the unrealistic degeneracy of the harmonic oscillator states by introducing an artificial perturbation

$$H_l = -d\mathbf{L} \cdot \mathbf{L}/\hbar^2 = -dl(l+1). \qquad (20)$$

This term may be used to simulate the effect of the difference between a realistic potential which vanishes as $r \to \infty$ and the harmonic oscillator potential. Such a difference would be an intrinsically negative perturbation which cancels out the unrealistic positive potential generated by the $\frac{1}{2}kr^2$ term in the harmonic oscillator potential at large r. It acts more strongly on the states of higher angular momentum representing the fact that their wave functions are concentrated in the neighborhood of the surface. The effect of this perturbation is to break the harmonic oscillator degeneracies in a fashion suggested by the spherical box potential.

This type of effective splitting of the harmonic oscillator degeneracies has turned out to be an important guide to the accepted explanation of nuclear magic numbers.

As we have indicated previously the resolution of this problem came with the introduction of strong spin orbit coupling. The essential aspect of the work of Mayer (1948, 1950) and Haxel *et al.* (1950) is that the spin orbit effect introduces an additional splitting of comparable magnitude. Essentially they assumed the presence of a spin orbit force given by

$$V_{so} = -\beta \mathbf{L} \cdot \mathbf{S}/\hbar^2. \qquad (21)$$

Such a term, as indicated in the previous section, leads to energy shifts

$$\Delta E(j = l - \tfrac{1}{2}) = \tfrac{1}{2}\beta(l+1) \qquad \text{and} \qquad \Delta E(j = l + \tfrac{1}{2}) = -\tfrac{1}{2}\beta l \qquad (22)$$

where j is the quantum number which characterizes $\mathbf{J} = \mathbf{L} + \mathbf{S}$, the total angular momentum of the individual particle. Essentially it is assumed that the splitting of the nodeless states for each l builds up more and more strongly with l in such a way that the lower member of an oscillator number family becomes competitive with the states of one oscillator number lower. Figure 3 illustrates how the numbers 2, 8, 20, 28, 50, 82, and 126 immediately follow from such a simple sequencing of levels without any detail calculations. Furthermore, Mayer (1948) showed how this same level order may be used to provide a good account of the total spins of odd A nuclei.

We must call attention to the fact that we cannot draw a single set of energy levels appropriate to all nuclei, and to both neutron states and proton states. Even assuming a universal nuclear well depth constant V_0, the number and spacing of the energy levels vary with the radius, which, of course, depends upon A. Furthermore, the Coulomb interaction between protons shifts the proton levels upward relative to the neutron levels to an extent which depends upon Z. In addition, interactions between individual particles

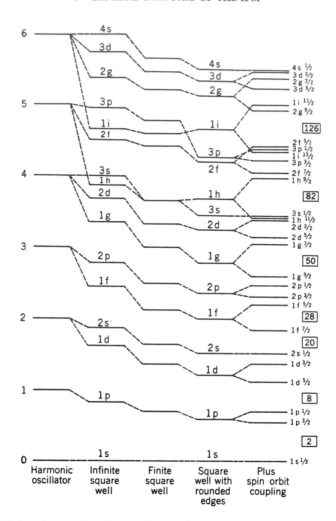

Fig. 3. Order of energy levels according to the independent particle model of nuclei under various assumptions concerning the shape of the nuclear potential and including the effects of spin orbit coupling.

(The energy is not to scale, nor should the exact order of the levels within a given shell be taken too seriously.)

raise or depress the individual particle levels to an extent which depends upon the numbers of occupants of the levels. Nevertheless, it is possible to represent schematically the energy levels of nuclei by a filling order diagram which indicates information which is quite useful. Figure 4 is such a schematic diagram. The neutron orbitals shown are based upon the assignments of Klinkenberg (1952), which have been arrived at on the basis of the shell model studies with the aid of spin and magnetic moment data. The proton orbitals have been positioned in relation to the neutron orbitals with schematic consideration given to the effects of the Coulomb interactions as well as the experimental spin and magnetic moment data. Competing orbitals are grouped together. In nuclear physics this diagram may be used for all nuclei as a guide in assigning ground state configurations and possible low lying excited state configurations.

To pursue seriously the single particle shell model, we must use a potential which at least has the property of vanishing at $r \to \infty$. The spherical well is the simplest function of this type which is analytically solvable for all values of l. Here we take

$$V = -V_0 \quad (r < a) \quad \text{and} \quad V = 0 \quad (r > a). \tag{23}$$

Since the interior potential is just like that of the spherical box, the interior wave equation and solutions have the same forms as those given at the beginning of this section.

However, since V now vanishes as r goes to infinity, the wave function no longer vanishes identically outside the well. Instead the exterior wave function for S waves must satisfy

$$G_e'' - \varepsilon^2 G_e = 0 \tag{24}$$

where the subscript e denotes the word exterior. The solution of this equation which vanishes at infinity is

$$G_e = C_e \exp(-\varepsilon\rho) \tag{25}$$

where C_e is a normalization constant. The interior wave equation and interior wave function are given by Eqs. (7) and (8) just as in the spherical box. To satisfy the good-behavior requirement, the interior and exterior wave functions must now join smoothly at $\rho = 1$. We may impose the condition $G_i(1) = G_e(1)$ and $G_i'(1) = G_e'(1)$. These two equations would furnish two algebraic relations between C_i and C_e in terms of ε_0 and ε. A third relation follows from the normalization condition. In general the three equations for C_i and C_e can be satisfied only for special values of ε in relation to ε_0. However, the simplest and most direct method for finding the eigenvalue condition is to use

$$\left. \frac{G_i'}{G_i} \right|_{\rho=1} = \left. \frac{G_e'}{G_e} \right|_{\rho=1}. \tag{26}$$

The C_i's and C_e's cancel in this equation, and we obtain immediately the eigenvalue equation

$$\varepsilon' \cot \varepsilon' = -\varepsilon \quad \text{or} \quad (\tan \varepsilon'/\varepsilon')^{-1} = -\varepsilon. \tag{27}$$

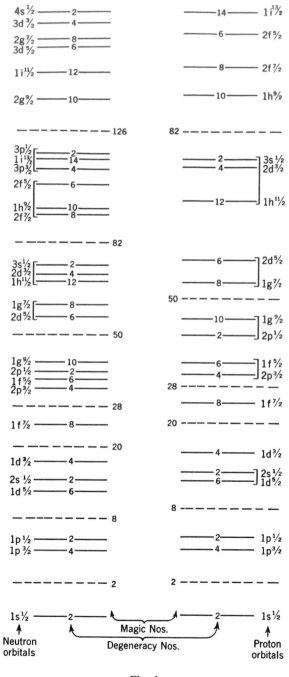

Fig. 4.

For a well which has a large ε_0, ε will be close to ε_0 for low lying states, and hence the right side of Eq. (27) will be small. Hence for this case Eq. (9) will furnish a good approximation for the energy values of the low lying states. When the well is shallow, it is impossible to express the energy levels in terms of an explicit formula. Instead for a given ε_0 we must find the roots of Eq. (27) by approximate numerical or graphical methods. The number of ε roots which exist depends upon the value of the well parameter ε_0. In Table I we

TABLE I

ROOTS OF EIGENVALUE EQUATION

ε_0	No.	ε			
		$1s$	$2s$	$3s$	$4s$
0	None				
$1.5708 = \pi/2$	One	0			
$4.7124 = 3\pi/2$	Two	3.950	0		
$7.8540 = 5\pi/2$	Three	7.345	5.600	0	
$10.9956 = 7\pi/2$	Four	10.612	9.382	6.931	0

show the number of ε roots and their values for small critical values of ε_0. In the range of ε_0 between critical values the number of roots is the same as for the lower ε_0 value. By inserting $\varepsilon = 0$ into Eq. (27) we obtain

$$\tan \varepsilon_0 = -\infty. \tag{28}$$

The roots of this equation are the critical values which give rise to an S state of zero energy. These are $\varepsilon_0 = \pi/2, 3\pi/2, 5\pi/2, (n + \frac{1}{2})\pi$. The ε values corresponding to the more stable S states at the critical ε_0 values are listed in the four right-hand columns.

Once the roots of the eigenvalue equation for any given well parameter ε_0 are found, we can readily construct the S wave eigenfunctions corresponding to each root. If this is done, it is again found that the ground S state has no intermediate nodes. In Fig. 5 we indicate schematically the energy values and the radial wave functions for the several low lying S states in the case of a particle in a box and for the case of a particle in a deep well. We note that in each of the latter cases the wave function extends into the external

---

Fig. 4. The filling order of nuclear orbitals, the degeneracy numbers, and the magic numbers of the nuclear periodic table.

(The neutron orbitals follow approximately the level assignments of Klinkenberg (1952). The proton orbitals are positioned in relation to the neutron orbitals so as to include schematically the effects of the Coulomb interactions.)

region. This region would be inaccessible to the particle if classical laws were obeyed, since here the classical kinetic energy ($T = E - V$) would be negative.

To treat P, D, and higher orbital angular momentum states, we note now that the exterior radial wave equation is

$$G'' - [\varepsilon^2 + l(l + 1)\rho^{-2}]G = 0 \qquad (\rho > 1) \qquad (29)$$

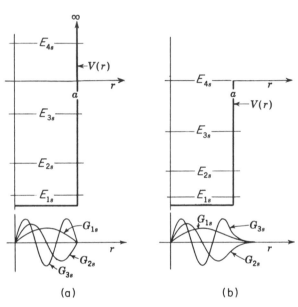

(a)   (b)

Fig. 5. Schematic diagram showing low lying S states and the corresponding wave functions when $\varepsilon_0 = 7\pi/2$ in (a) a spherical box, and (b) a spherical well.

where prime denotes differentiation relative to ρ. The internal solution, which is well behaved at $\rho = 0$, is given again by Eq. (13). The external solution which is well behaved as $\rho \to \infty$ may be expressed in terms of modified Hankel functions. Denoting these functions by $K_{l+\frac{1}{2}}$ the external solution may be written as

$$G_e = A_e \rho^{1/2} K_{l+\frac{1}{2}}(\varepsilon\rho). \qquad (30)$$

The eigenvalues may be obtained without consideration of the normalization constants by imposing at the boundary $\rho = 1$ the requirement

$$-G_i'/G_i = -G_e'/G_e \qquad \text{or} \qquad I_l(\varepsilon') = E_l(\varepsilon) \qquad (31)$$

where $I_l(\varepsilon')$ and $E_l(\varepsilon)$ are defined as the negatives of the logarithmic derivatives of the internal and external radial wave functions.

To facilitate the solutions of this transcendental equation, subject to the condition $\varepsilon' = (\varepsilon_0{}^2 - \varepsilon^2)^{1/2}$, Green and Lee (1955) prepared tables of I_l and E_l using the recurrence relations

$$I_l(x) = l - [x^2/(I_{l-1} + l)] \qquad (32)$$

and

$$E_l(x) = l + [x^2/(E_{l-1} + l)] \qquad (33)$$

which follow from the usual recurrence relations between Bessel functions. Using Eq. (33) and $E_0(x) = x$ the higher integral order $E_l(x)$ were generated. To obtain higher order $I_l(x)$, tabulated Bessel functions were first used to generate the corresponding I_l functions. Then Eq. (32) was used to generate the higher order functions. Green and Lee then used graphical techniques to satisfy Eq. (31). By doing so they obtained functional relationships between ε^2 and $\varepsilon_0{}^2$ for various l's. Figure 6 shows the results of the work. The form of presentation follows that of Moszkowski (1953), who had previously prepared a similar graph for a somewhat narrower range of well parameters. Essentially Fig. 6 gives the energy eigenvalues in units of E_0 measured relative to the bottom of the well. The parameter $\varepsilon'^2 = \varepsilon_0{}^2 - \varepsilon^2$ goes over to the results of the infinite spherical well as $\varepsilon_0{}^2$ goes to infinity. These infinite well eigenvalues are shown on the right side of Fig. 6. Some noteworthy points which are apparent in this figure are the 3s–1h and 1j–2g cross overs as well as the fact that the approximate equality of spacing in the low lying levels breaks down above the 1g state.

The work of Ford and Bohm (1950) on S wave neutron size resonances provides a direct basis for fixing the two parameters r_0 and V_0 of the square well model of nuclear potentials. They noted S wave size resonances in the neighborhood of $A = 55$ and $A = 155$, and identified $A = 55$ with a potential which would bind a 3S state at zero energy, and $A = 155$ as one which would bind a 4S state at zero energy. Next assuming a fixed neutron well depth V_0 and the relationship $R = r_0 A^{1/3}$, they determined the two parameters.

As we shall see in the next section, these parameters imply that $V_0 = 45$ MeV and $r_0 = 1.40$ F. A 2S size resonance occurs near $A \approx 12$. Since the parameters V_0 and r_0 uniquely define the IPM potential for all nuclei, we are now in a position to study all other bound states to see whether such a model can be used as a realistic system of potentials which leads to proper level ordering and energies for particles in each nucleus.

It turns out, however, that the level ordering so obtained is not good for all nuclei, even after allowance is made for possible spin orbit effects. It is, however, possible to secure a good level ordering if the boundary of the nuclear potential is diffuse.

A schematic drawing of a diffuse potential is shown in Fig. 7. In order to obtain well-behaved wave functions and corresponding eigenvalues, we

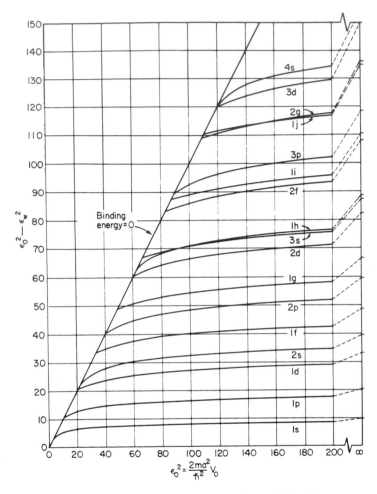

Fig. 6. The energy levels of a spherical well ($\delta = 0$).

(The abscissa corresponds to values of ε_0^2, that is, V_0 in the natural unit $\hbar^2/2ma^2$. The ordinate gives $\varepsilon_0^2 - \varepsilon^2$, or $V_0 - |E|$ in the same unit. The vertical scale on the right side gives the levels for a spherical box (Green and Lee, 1955; after Moszkowski, 1953).)

have in general to integrate numerically the radial equation using standard techniques of integration such as a Runge–Kutta method. Figure 7 illustrates the method of inward integration. Choosing an appropriate initial value E_a for E, we start at a sufficiently far point r where the asymptotic form of Eq. (25) is valid. In the region where the potential becomes important, $G_a(r)$ will deviate quite appreciably from Eq. (25). In fact, at the classical turning point, the curvature reverses and G_a becomes concave. Proceeding further inwardly to the origin, thereby making sure that the number of intermediate nodes is right, the value of G_a at the origin can finally be determined. The value $G_a(0)$ thus obtained will be different from zero in general since we have chosen a particular value E_a. We repeat the process with a slightly different value E_b and find $G_b(0)$. Interpolating or extrapolating the

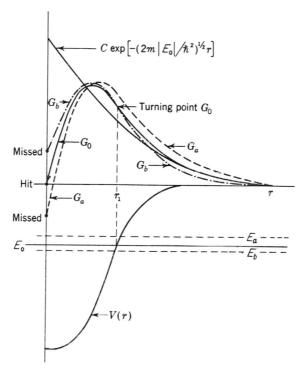

Fig. 7. Diagram illustrating the inward integration of the radial wave equation for a bound state from its long range solution for an arbitrary energy.

(E_a and E_b lead to solutions which miss the origin and hence are unacceptable. E_0 leads to a well-behaved solution.)

values $G_a(0)$ and $G_b(0)$, we can guess a value of E which brings the value of G at the origin closer to zero. The whole process is repeated until the solution converges within a required accuracy. Rather than working on the wave function itself, however, numerical integration of the logarithmic derivative of the wave function is often advantageous in the process for finding an eigenvalue.

Numerical integration can also be performed outwardly starting from the origin with the initial condition

$$G_l(r) = \text{const} \times r^{l+1}.$$

With a value of E, the outward integration is carried out to a sufficiently far distance r_m and the internal logarithmic derivative is computed as well as the number of nodes inside the potential well. The external logarithmic derivative at r_m is calculated using Eq. (25) with the same value of E. In general, the logarithmic derivatives do not match each other, and hence it is required to vary the initial value of E and repeat the process until the matching is achieved.

It is straightforward to modify the above methods so that, instead of searching the energy eigenvalue for a given potential, one of the potential parameters is searched to yield a given eigenvalue. We will return to such realistic potential problems in Chapter II and consider instead elastic scattering by square well potentials.

1.4   The Optical Model

We consider in this section the scattering states of the IPM model for simple potentials. We first treat the case of real potentials giving attention to the phase shift formalism which is described in greater detail in many works on scattering theory. The scattering problem has a simplifying feature with respect to the bound state problem. Thus the energy E in the center of mass system is given at the outset and is related to the energy E_{lab} in a coordinate system in which the target is at rest (laboratory system) by

$$E = \frac{M}{m_1 + M} E_l. \tag{1}$$

The quantum mechanical calculation of the elastic scattering cross sections is based upon the solution of the Schroedinger time independent wave equation for the equivalent one body system having the total energy

$$E = p^2/2m = \hbar^2 k^2/2m. \tag{2}$$

Consequently the propagation constant is given by

$$k^2 = 2mE/\hbar^2. \tag{3}$$

In the wave analysis the nucleus is regarded as a refractive and/or absorptive region which distorts the incident plane waves, causing waves to be scattered out of the incident beam. The wave function describing the entire continuous scattering process must satisfy the Schroedinger amplitude equation (Eq. (4), Section 1.2). The mathematical problem now is quite different from the bound state problem where we simultaneously sought the allowed energy eigenvalues and the corresponding energy eigenfunctions by appealing to the good-behavior requirement. In the scattering problem, the energy constant is given at the outset, and the problem is to find the solution of Schroedinger's equation which at long ranges has the form (we let $z = r \cos \theta$)

$$\psi(r, \theta, \phi) = \exp(ikr \cos \theta) + r^{-1}f(\theta, \phi) \exp ikr. \tag{4}$$

We may identify the two parts of this asymptotic wave function with the incident and scattered waves. The basic quantum mechanical procedure for obtaining the differential cross section is to find an exact solution of Schroedinger's equation and to investigate the asymptotic form in order to identify the function $f(\theta, \phi)$. Using the general interpretive postulate for wave functions, we observe that the probability for finding an incident particle in any element of volume of the beam at great distances from the scatterer is

$$P_i \, d\tau = \psi_i^* \psi_i \, d\tau = dx \, dy \, dz. \tag{5}$$

This probability flows a distance dz through the area $dx \, dy$ in the time $dt = dz/v$, where v is the velocity of the particles in the incident beam. Consequently the probability current per unit area, or the incident flux density, is

$$\frac{P_i \, d\tau}{dx \, dy \, dt} = v. \tag{6}$$

The probability of finding a scattered particle in the volume element $d\tau' = r^2 \sin \theta \, d\phi \, d\theta \, dr = r^2 \, d\Omega \, dr$ is

$$P_s \, d\tau' = f^*(\theta, \phi)f(\theta, \phi) \, d\Omega \, dr. \tag{7}$$

Thus the probability current at the point (r, θ, ϕ) due to the scattered particles moving radially outward with the velocity v into the solid angle $d\Omega$ is (letting $dt = dr/v$)

$$\frac{P_s \, d\tau'}{dt} = vf^*(\theta, \phi)f(\theta, \phi) \, d\Omega. \tag{8}$$

Using the basic definition for the differential cross section

$$\sigma(\theta, \phi) \, d\Omega = \frac{\text{probability current into solid angle } d\Omega}{\text{incident probability-current density}} \tag{9}$$

we obtain finally for the differential cross section per unit solid angle

$$\sigma(\theta, \phi) = f^*(\theta, \phi)f(\theta, \phi) = |f(\theta, \phi)|^2. \tag{10}$$

From Eq. (4) we see that we may express $f(\theta, \phi)$ in terms of the components of the asymptotic wave function using

$$f(\theta, \phi) = \lim_{r \to \infty}[\psi(r, \theta, \phi) - \exp(ikr \cos \theta)]r \exp(-ikr). \tag{11}$$

Alternatively we may view the fact that both sides of Eq. (11) must be independent of r as the formal expression of the boundary condition upon the exact solution of Schroedinger's wave equation.

The exact solution of Schroedinger's equation can be carried out analytically only in a few special cases. Accordingly we must usually resort to some numerical method. A method of solving Schroedinger's equation that is particularly suited to nuclear optical model studies is the so-called method of partial waves. Here the incoming plane waves are expressed as

$$\psi_i = \exp(ikr\cos\theta) = \sum_{l=0}^{\infty} (2l + 1)i^l j_l(kr)P_l(\cos\theta) \qquad (12)$$

where P_l are the Legendre polynomials, and j_l are the spherical Bessel functions.

$$j_l(\rho) = (\pi/2\rho)^{1/2} J_{l+\frac{1}{2}}(\rho) \qquad (13)$$

where $J_{l+\frac{1}{2}}$ are Bessel functions of half integral order. Equation (12) can be shown to be an exact solution of Schroedinger's equation when the potential vanishes. When the potential exists the solution is assumed to have the expansion

$$\psi(r, \theta, \phi) = \sum_{l=0}^{\infty} (2l + 1)i^l R_l(kr)P_l(\cos\theta), \qquad (14)$$

where R_l is an as yet unknown radial wave function for each value of l. Inserting this into Schroedinger's equation and using the properties of the Legendre polynomials, it is simple to show that each function

$$G_l(r) = krR_l(kr) \qquad (15)$$

must satisfy the radial equation for the lth partial wave,

$$\frac{d^2 G_l}{dr^2} + \left[k^2 - \frac{2mV(r)}{\hbar^2} - \frac{l(l + 1)}{r^2} \right] G_l = 0. \qquad (16)$$

From the theory of Bessel functions it is known that

$$\lim_{r \to \infty} krj_l(kr) = \sin[kr - (\pi l/2)]. \qquad (17)$$

We may view the phase factor in Eq. (17) as the cumulative effect at long ranges of the centrifugal force term in the radial equation. The effect of the potential function of Eq. (16) will cause an additional phase shift as $r \to \infty$, and an amplitude change; hence we may let

$$\lim_{r \to \infty} G_l(kr) = A_l \sin[kr - (l\pi/2) + \delta_l] \qquad (18)$$

where δ_l is called the lth partial wave phase shift. If now we require that Eq. (14) with $R_l(kr)$ given by Eqs. (15) and (18) satisfy the asymptotic form given by Eq. (11), then, using also Eqs. (12) and (17), it follows by a series of algebraic steps that

$$A_l = e^{i\delta_l} \tag{19}$$

and furthermore, that

$$f(\theta, \phi) = (1/2ik) \sum_{l=0}^{\infty} (2l + 1)(e^{2i\delta_l} - 1)P_l(\cos \theta). \tag{20}$$

Using this amplitude, we see that it follows from Eq. (10) that

$$\sigma(\theta, \phi) = (1/k^2) \left| \sum_{l=0}^{\infty} (2l + 1)e^{i\delta_l} \sin \delta_l P_l(\cos \theta) \right|^2. \tag{21}$$

We find the total cross section by integrating over the total solid angle and using the orthogonality properties of the Legendre functions. It becomes

$$\sigma = (4\pi/k^2) \sum_{l=0}^{\infty} (2l + 1) \sin^2\delta_l. \tag{22}$$

As it was introduced the phase shift of the lth partial wave is the difference in phase between the asymptotic form of the actual wave function and the wave function which would exist if there were no scattering potential. The collection of phase shifts completely determines both the differential cross sections and the total cross section.

In view of the identity of the angular dependent factor $P_l(\cos \theta)$ with the $m_l = 0$ spherical harmonic which arose in the bound state problem, we may assume the lth partial wave is associated with an orbital angular momentum $[l(l + 1)]^{1/2}\hbar$ and a vanishing z component of orbital angular momentum. It is customary to designate the wave functions as follows: that associated with $l = 0$ is the S wave, that with $l = 1$ is the P wave, that with $l = 2$ is the D wave, etc.

The interpretation of partial waves in terms of angular momentum suggests the use of a semiclassical picture, which may be used gainfully to develop an intuitive understanding. Suppose we consider an incident particle moving with the momentum p and directed relative to the center of mass so as to have an impact parameter b_l ahd hence the angular momentum pb_l. Using this expression, we may identify an impact parameter with each partial wave by

$$b_l p = b_l \hbar k = [l(l + 1)]^{1/2}\hbar \approx (l + \tfrac{1}{2})\hbar. \tag{23}$$

The last approximation when used with a semiclassical description (the WJKB approximation) frequently leads to better accuracy than the exact quantum mechanical relation.

Now if the forces which cause the scattering have a distinct range R beyond which these forces are negligible, then the lth partial wave will not be scattered if $b_l \gg R$ or [using the unit given by Eq. (2), Section 1.3]

$$l + \tfrac{1}{2} = kb_l > kR = (E/E_0)^{1/2} \approx (E/10)^{1/2} A^{1/3}. \tag{24}$$

For a typical nucleus (say $A^{1/3} \sim 5$) and a typical energy $E \sim 10$ we see that $l > 5$ would not be scattered. Thus at low and moderate energies, the method of partial waves is particularly useful since only a few partial waves are phase shifted and they decrease rapidly with l so that the contributions of the P, D, F, $\ldots$, waves to the total cross section decrease rapidly. We should note, however, that the higher partial waves may manifest themselves more effectively in the differential cross section because of the cross product terms with the lower partial waves.

The square well has been a great favorite of physicists because the solutions of the radial wave equation can be given in terms of known functions, and the problem of extracting the phase shifts from the solutions is particularly simple (see Mott and Massey, 1933, 1965). Because of its important role in the work of Ford and Bohm (1950), we shall consider here in detail the calculations of the S wave phase shift for the real square well potential.

Now letting $\varepsilon = kR = (E/E_0)^{1/2}$ and $\varepsilon' = (\varepsilon_0{}^2 + \varepsilon^2)^{1/2}$, the S wave radial wave equation for the square well becomes

$$G_i'' + \varepsilon'^2 G_i = 0 \qquad \text{for} \qquad \rho < 1 \tag{25}$$

$$G_e'' + \varepsilon^2 G_e = 0 \qquad \text{for} \qquad \rho > 1. \tag{26}$$

The interior solution which satisfies the condition $G_i(0) = 0$ is

$$G_i = C_i \sin \varepsilon' \rho. \tag{27}$$

The general exterior solution is (letting $\delta_0 = \delta$)

$$G_e = C_e \sin(\varepsilon \rho + \delta). \tag{28}$$

Since this already is in the form of the asymptotic solution, we do not have to make an analysis of the limit of this function to extract the phase shift. To meet the requirements on wave functions, that G must be continuous and have a continuous first derivative, we might equate the value of G_i and G_e and G_e' and G_i' at $\rho = 1$. However, the phase shift can be obtained most simply by insisting that

$$\frac{G_i'}{G_i} = \frac{G_e'}{G_e} \qquad \text{at} \quad \rho = 1. \tag{29}$$

We obtain immediately

$$\varepsilon' \cot \varepsilon' = \varepsilon \cot(\varepsilon + \delta) \tag{30}$$

or

$$\tan(\varepsilon + \delta) = \varepsilon[(\tan \varepsilon')/\varepsilon']. \tag{31}$$

Consequently the phase shift is given by

$$\delta = [\tan^{-1} \varepsilon T(\varepsilon')] - \varepsilon \tag{32}$$

where we let $T(x) = x^{-1} \tan x$.

For a given ε_0 we can use this equation to evaluate δ for every value of ε. The corresponding S wave cross section is then given by

$$\sigma^0 = \frac{4\pi R^2 \sin^2 \delta(E)}{(E/E_0)}. \tag{33}$$

The variation of the S wave cross section with energy (through δ and through E) takes on an interesting variety of forms according to the value of ε_0. Figure 1 shows several examples of the variation of the S, P, and D total

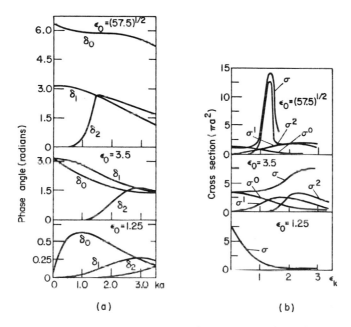

Fig. 1. Variations of the phases and total cross sections with E.
((a) Variation of phases $\delta_0, \delta_1,$ and δ_2 with velocity $\varepsilon_k = (2ma^2E/\hbar^2)^{1/2}$ for different well strengths $\varepsilon_0 = (2ma^2 V_0/\hbar^2)^{1/2}$ for spherical wells of depth V_0 and radius a. (b) Variation of $S, P,$ and D total cross sections with ε_k for several fixed values of ε_0 (adapted from Mott and Massey, 1933).)

cross sections with ε for several fixed values of ε_0. The fact that, for extremely large values of E, the S wave cross section vanishes, follows immediately from Eq. (32). Since ε_0 may be ignored, it is obvious that $\delta = 0$. Of course, the cross sections for the P, D, F, ... waves become important at large values of E.

The minima that occur in the total cross section for certain large values of ε_0 correspond to the Ramsauer–Townsend (Mott and Massey, 1933) effect of atomic physics. These minima arise for deep wells at particular low energies when the S wave phase shift is π, 2π, 3π, ... If such phase shifts occur for small values of E when the P and D wave cross sections are negligible, then the total cross section will vanish and the substance will be transparent to the incident particles at these energies.

Of more immediate interest from the nuclear physics viewpoint is the problem of the single particle resonances and in particular the S wave size resonances. Let us therefore consider the variation of σ^0 given by Eq. (33) with radius and with energy. Using $\varepsilon' = (\varepsilon_0^2 + \varepsilon^2)^{1/2}$ and the notation $T' = T(\varepsilon')$ and $T(\varepsilon) = T$ and the trigonometric rules for sums of angles, it is simple to show that

$$\tan \delta = \varepsilon \frac{T' - T}{1 + \varepsilon^2 TT'}. \tag{34}$$

Proceeding then to determine $\sin^2\delta$ from this expression, we find

$$\sigma = 4\pi R^2 \frac{1}{\varepsilon^2 + [\Omega(1 + \varepsilon^2 T^2) + \varepsilon^2 T]^2} \tag{35}$$

where

$$\Omega = 1/(T' - T). \tag{36}$$

For small values of ε, $T \approx 1$. However, T' can be large, and indeed, near the infinities of T' which occur when $\varepsilon' = (n + \frac{1}{2})\pi$, Ω vanishes, and σ reaches its peak values. In the neighborhood of such a "resonance" we may let $\varepsilon = \varepsilon_n + \Delta$, in which case $\varepsilon' = \varepsilon_n' + (\varepsilon_n\Delta/\varepsilon_n')$. Expanding Ω in the neighborhood of $\varepsilon \approx \varepsilon_n$, it follows then that

$$\Omega = \tfrac{1}{2}[\varepsilon^2 - \varepsilon_n^2]. \tag{37}$$

Inserting this into Eq. (35) we obtain

$$\sigma = \frac{4\pi R^2}{\varepsilon_n^2 + [\frac{1}{2}(\varepsilon^2 - \varepsilon_n^2)(1 + \varepsilon_n^2 T_n^2) + \varepsilon_n^2 T_n]^2}. \tag{38}$$

This may be rewritten in the well-known form of the Lorentz dispersion formula

$$\sigma = \frac{\pi}{k^2} \frac{\Gamma_n^2}{(\varepsilon^2 - \varepsilon_r^2)^2 + (\Gamma_n^2/4)} \tag{39}$$

where $\varepsilon_r{}^2 = \varepsilon_n{}^2 - \Delta\varepsilon_n{}^2$ is the slightly shifted position corresponding to zero of the bracket in the denominator of Eq. (38),

$$\Delta\varepsilon_n{}^2 = 2\varepsilon_n{}^2 T_n/(1 + \varepsilon_n{}^2 T_n{}^2) \tag{40}$$

and

$$\Gamma_n = 4\varepsilon_n/(1 + \varepsilon_n{}^2 T_n{}^2). \tag{41}$$

Accordingly we see that the S wave cross sections display maxima at locations near $\varepsilon' = (n + \tfrac{1}{2})\pi$. Note that the larger $\varepsilon_n{}^2$, the larger the width of the resonance. If ε_0 itself $\approx (n + \tfrac{1}{2})\pi$, then these conditions on ε' occur near $\varepsilon \approx 0$. Then, since $1/k^2 = R^2/\varepsilon^2$, it follows that these zero energy cross sections are infinite. As we have indicated earlier in our bound state discussions, these so-called size resonances were introduced in nuclear physics by Ford and Bohm (1950). They identified the expected infinities at $\varepsilon_0 = 3\pi/2$, $5\pi/2$, and $7\pi/2$ with experimental maxima in slow neutron cross sections in the neighborhood of $A \sim 12$, 55, and 155, and in doing so they arrived at the potential parameters $r_0 = 1.40$ F and $V_0 = 45$ MeV. In Fig. 2 a similar calculation by

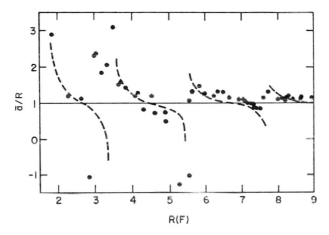

Fig. 2. The points show the variation of the average scattering length $\bar{a}$ divided by the nuclear radius R, as a function of R. The dashed curve represents the variation of $\bar{a}/R$ to be expected from a well with the parameters: $V = -42$ MeV, $0 \leq r < R$; $V = 0$, $r > R$; $R = 1.45 A^{1/3}$ F (Adair, 1954).

Adair (1954) is shown, where the scattering length $\bar{a}$, defined by $4\pi\bar{a}^2 = \sigma (E = 0)$, divided by the nuclear radius R is given as a function of R. The parameters used in plotting Fig. 2 are $V_0 = 42$ MeV and $r_0 = 1.45$ F.

The success of this work suggests that we determine the phase shifts and cross sections associated with the higher partial waves. Here it is somewhat more convenient to work with spherical Bessel functions and the radial wave function R_l rather than G_l. The phase shift δ_l is computed by fitting the radial wave function $R_l(r)$ for $r = R$ to the exterior solution. The boundary condition at $r = R$ is that $(1/R_l)(dR_l/dr)$ be continuous. Thus if $\Gamma_l = R[(dR_l/dr)/R_l]$ is the dimensionless logarithmic derivative of the interior function, we have

$$\Gamma_l = \frac{\varepsilon j_l'(\varepsilon) \cos \delta_l - n_l'(\varepsilon) \sin \delta_l}{j_l(\varepsilon) \cos \delta_l - n_l(\varepsilon) \sin \delta_l} \tag{42}$$

where j_l and n_l are spherical Bessel and Neumann functions. This may be solved for $\tan \delta_l$ to give

$$\tan \delta_l = \frac{\varepsilon j_l'(\varepsilon) - \Gamma_l j_l(\varepsilon)}{\varepsilon n_l'(\varepsilon) - \Gamma_l n_l(\varepsilon)}. \tag{43}$$

We may solve this for $\sin^2 \delta$ to relate the partial cross section directly to the values of ε^2 and the constant Γ_l. For the real square well potential, the interior solution in terms of spherical Bessel functions is

$$R_l = B_l j_l(\varepsilon' \rho) \tag{44}$$

hence

$$\Gamma_l = \varepsilon' j_l'(\varepsilon')/j_l(\varepsilon'). \tag{45}$$

Some examples of phase shifts and the corresponding cross sections for several values of the parameter ε_0 are shown in Fig. 1. These are illustrative of the diversity of possible forms of total cross sections.

After the work of Ford and Bohm (1950), Le Levier and Saxon (1952) applied a low energy nuclear optical model for 18 MeV protons on aluminum. They introduced an imaginary component of about 20 MeV in the optical model potential along with the parameters $r_0 = 1.42$ F, $V_0 = 45$ MeV. Later Feshbach, Porter and Weisskopf, for neutrons in the 1–3 MeV region, used similar real potential parameters $r_0 = 1.45$ F, $V_0 = 42$ MeV, but incorporated a much smaller imaginary part $W \sim 1$–2 MeV.

Some insight is provided as to the effects of the imaginary term if we consider the propagation of a Schroedinger wave in a homogeneous nuclear medium characterized by a constant complex potential, $U + iW$. A plane wave describing the motion of a particle in the direction $\hat{\mathbf{n}}$, with the energy $E > U$, is then given by

$$\psi = \exp(ik\hat{\mathbf{n}} \cdot \mathbf{r}) \tag{46}$$

where k is the complex propagation constant

$$k = [(2m/\hbar^2)(E - U - iW)]^{1/2} = \text{Re } k + i \text{ Im } k. \tag{47}$$

We see that if W is negative, k has a positive imaginary part and the wave is attenuated as it advances. The attenuation constant α, which is twice the imaginary part of k, is then seen to be

$$\alpha = 2Imk = -2\frac{(2m)^{1/2}}{\hbar^2}[(E-U)^2 + W^2]^{1/4}\sin\left(\frac{1}{2}\tan^{-1}\frac{W}{E-U}\right) \quad (48)$$

which, when $W \ll E - U$, as is usually the case, simplifies to

$$\alpha \simeq -\left(\frac{2m}{\hbar^2}\right)^{1/2}\frac{W}{(E-U)^{1/2}} = -k\frac{W}{E}\frac{1}{[1-(U/E)]^{1/2}} \quad (49)$$

where $k = (2mE/\hbar^2)^{1/2}$ is the free particle wave number. The reciprocal of α, is the *mean free path* Λ, and is given by

$$\Lambda \simeq -\left(\frac{\hbar^2}{2m}\right)^{1/2}\frac{(E-W)^{1/2}}{W} = -\frac{\lambda E}{W}[1-(U/E)]^{1/2} \quad (50)$$

where $\lambda = 1/k$ is the free space reduced wavelength. Thus, we see that at high energies, a mean free path which is independent of energy requires W to increase as $\sqrt{E}$. On the other hand, a constant value of W means that the mean free path increases as $\sqrt{E}$, which is qualitatively what is observed in the case of nuclear scattering.

Although we have introduced the mean free path by discussing propagation in a fictitious homogeneous nuclear medium, the concept furnishes a useful qualitative guide in nuclear scattering where U and W are functions of position. If we think of the solution of Schroedinger's equation in terms of a semiclassical, or ray optical, approximation, the Λ can be regarded as the local mean free path for absorption along the ray.

Returning now to Schroedinger's equation we will indicate briefly the procedure used when the potential is a square well with the form

$$V(r) = U(r) + iW(r) = -V_0(1 + i\xi) \quad (r < R) \qquad V(r) = 0 \quad (r > R). \quad (51)$$

The exterior solutions are unchanged by this so that the Eq. (42) is preserved. However, ε' has now become a complex quantity and hence Γ_l given by Eq. (45) is a complex quantity. The real and imaginary parts of the logarithmic derivatives can be generated using the same recurrence relations as pertain to spherical Bessel functions of real variables. The results when inserted into Eq. (43) now lead to complex phase shifts. For small values of ξ the influence upon the cross sections is not very great, mainly tending to dampen out the hills and valleys of the cross section surface.

To gain somewhat more detailed insight into the influence of the imaginary term in the optical model potential, let us compute the various fluxes using the quantum mechanical expressions

$$\mathbf{j} = (\hbar/2mi)(\psi^* \, \nabla\psi - \psi \, \nabla\psi^*). \quad (52)$$

From the first part of Eq. (4) the probability flux or number of particles/cm^2 sec in the incident beam is

$$\mathbf{j}_i = \hat{\mathbf{n}}_0(\hbar k/m) \tag{53}$$

where $\hat{\mathbf{n}}_0$ is a unit vector along the incident direction. From the second part of Eq. (4) the flux of the radially outgoing wave into the solid angle $d\Omega$ is

$$N \, d\Omega = j_s r^2 \, d\Omega = (\hbar k/m) f^*(\hat{\mathbf{n}}_0, \hat{\mathbf{n}}) f(\hat{\mathbf{n}}_0, \hat{\mathbf{n}}) \, d\Omega \tag{54}$$

where $\hat{\mathbf{n}}$ is a unit vector along the outgoing direction. Accordingly, the differential elastic scattering cross section per unit solid angle is

$$\sigma_e(\hat{\mathbf{n}}_0, \hat{\mathbf{n}}) = N/j_i = f^*(\hat{\mathbf{n}}_0, \hat{\mathbf{n}}) f(\hat{\mathbf{n}}_0, \hat{\mathbf{n}}) . \tag{55}$$

The total elastic cross section is defined as the integral of the differential elastic cross section over the entire solid angle, i.e.,

$$\sigma_e = \int \sigma(\hat{\mathbf{n}}_0, \hat{\mathbf{n}}) \, d\Omega = \int f^* f \, d\Omega. \tag{56}$$

Because the optical potential is not hermitian, the quantum mechanical laws governing the conservation of probability are modified. The form of these modifications follows upon multiplying Schroedinger's equation by ψ^* and subtracting from the result its complex conjugate. In this way we find

$$\nabla \cdot \mathbf{j} = -(i/\hbar)(\psi^* V\psi - \psi V^*\psi^*) = (2/\hbar)\psi^*\psi W. \tag{57}$$

We thus see that there is a local volume absorption if W is negative.

A formal expression for the total cross section for absorption is now easily derived as follows. The total number of particles absorbed per second N_α is simply obtained by integrating the net flux of particles into a large sphere surrounding the scattering center. The absorption cross section σ_r is then defined as the number of particles absorbed per second per unit incident-flux. Hence with $\hat{\mathbf{n}}$ the outward normal

$$\sigma_r = \frac{N_\alpha}{(\hbar k/m)} = -\frac{m}{\hbar k} \int \mathbf{j} \cdot \hat{\mathbf{n}} \, dS = -\frac{m}{\hbar k} \int \nabla \cdot \mathbf{j} \, d\mathbf{r} = -\frac{2m}{\hbar^2 k} \int W\psi^*\psi \, d\tau. \tag{58}$$

Again we see that if V has a negative imaginary part we obtain absorption. For the square well problem we see that

$$\sigma_r = \frac{2mV_0}{\hbar^2 k} \xi \int_0^R \psi^*\psi \, d\tau. \tag{59}$$

This shows that the absorption is proportional to $|W| = V_0 \xi$ as might have been expected.

Since we will describe the numerical attack on the general complex central field problem in Chapter III, we will not go into the specialized details of the complex square well problem. Results of the Feshbach *et al.* (1953) calculation are illustrated in Fig. 3.

Let us now turn our attention to the search for realistic N–$\mathscr{N}$ potentials.

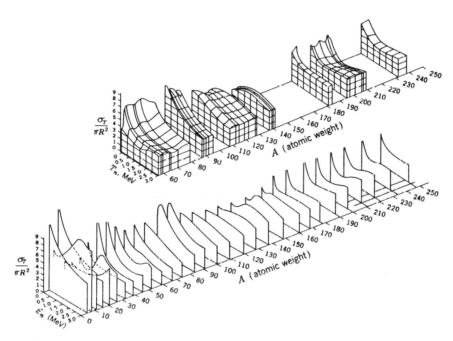

Fig. 3. Total cross sections of neutrons as a function of mass number and energy, upper profiles [Barschall (1952)], lower profile, early optical model results with constants $V_0 = 19.0$ MeV, $R = 1.45 \times 10^{-13} A^{1/3}$, $\zeta = 0.05$ [from Feshbach *et al.* (1953)].

II

Realistic Shell Models

2.1 The Nuclear Energy Surface

The painstaking measurements of nuclear masses by experimentalists using mass spectrographic and nuclear techniques have brought forth an impressive array of precision data whose interpretation has been of great help to the development of quantitative shell models. Let us now consider the information of measurements of nuclear energies.

It is a well-known fact that the total energy content of every complex nucleus is negative, i.e., every nucleus has less energy or mass than the total energy or mass of its unassembled constituents. For practical purposes (in view of the smallness of atomic binding energies) the energy of a nucleus may be defined by

$$E = M - Zm_h - Nm_n, \tag{1}$$

where M is the atomic mass of the neutral atom, m_h and m_n are the masses of the hydrogen atom and the neutron, respectively. The general trend of these nuclear energies for beta stable nuclei is shown in Fig. 1. The smooth curve corresponds to an empirical formula defined later; the dots represent averages of experimental data for beta stable nuclei in the neighborhoods of mass numbers 10, 20, ..., 250, i.e., the normal places. The large magnitudes of the nuclear energies, ranging to about -2000 MeV are indicative of the strength of nuclear forces. It is important to note from the diagram that nuclear energies vary almost linearly with the number of particles, and that the scatter of the experimental points is extremely small compared with the absolute values of the nuclear energies. Also shown in Fig. 1 is the quantity

$$\varepsilon = E/A, \tag{2}$$

the nuclear energy per particle. The extent to which ε is constant is an indication of the degree of saturation of nuclear energies. From the diagram it is clear that while the nucleus is approximately saturated there are definite systematic departures from the constancy of the nuclear energy per particle. The two straight lines in Fig. 1 represent the general trends of the nuclear

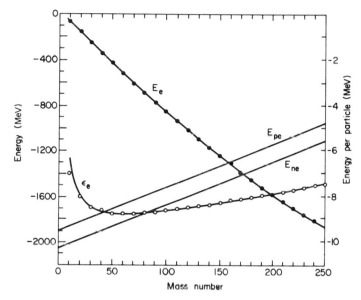

Fig. 1. Nuclear energies (E), nuclear energies per particle (ε), and nuclear energies of the last proton and neutron (E_p) and (F_n) for beta stable nuclei.

(The circles represent averages of the experimental values in the neighborhoods of $A = 10, 20, \ldots$, etc. The smooth curves are all based upon an empirical expression for mass decrements (see Eq. (6)) (Green, 1958a).)

energies of the last neutrons and protons. The agreement and departure of E_n and E_p, the last neutron and proton energies, from ε are even better measures of the degree of saturation of nuclear energies. These particle energies are defined by

$$E_n(A, N, Z) = M(A, N, Z) - M'(A - 1, N - 1, Z) - m_n = -B_n \qquad (3)$$

and

$$E_p(A, N, Z) = M(A, N, Z) - M'(A - 1, N, Z - 1) - m_h = -B_p \qquad (4)$$

where B_n and B_p are usually called the particle binding energies.

When an important physical quantity exhibits so great a regularity as E or ε, it is often helpful to examine it in fine detail with the help of a smooth

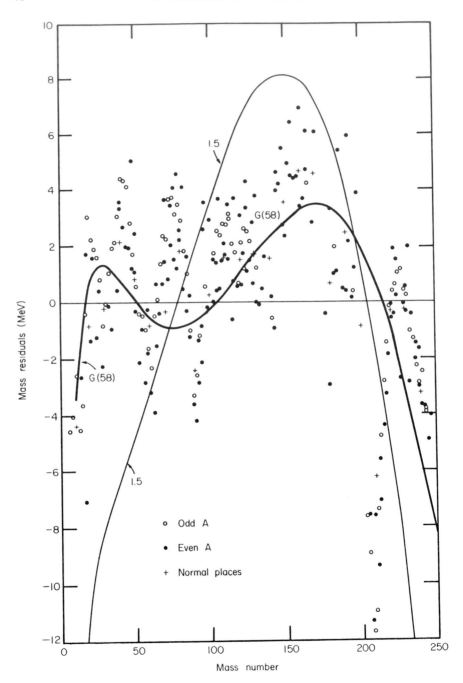

Fig. 2.

reference function which fits the general trend. A convenient function which fits the mass decrements of nuclei,

$$\Delta = M - A \tag{5}$$

is (Green, 1951; Green *et al.*, 1952; Green and Engler, 1953)

$$\Delta_e = 0.01(A - 100)^2 - 64 \quad \text{(in mMU)}. \tag{6}$$

where here the mMU relates to the old O^{16} standard (1 mMU = 0.93116 MeV). This reference function has served as a tool for the purposes of making microscopic examinations of the fits of various theoretical expressions to the nuclear energy data. We, therefore, define the mass residual by

$$R = M - M_e = \Delta - \Delta_e. \tag{7}$$

The mass residuals of all beta stable nuclei are presented in Fig. 2. The horizontal base line corresponds to the smooth curve of Fig. 1 and the crosses represent the normal points in the same figure.

It should be clear that the residual presentation of nuclear mass or energy data provides a tremendous magnification of the nuclear energy surface. The diagram is helpful in illustrating the fact that irregularities in the mass surface which may be identified with shell effects are relatively small effects compared to the overall regularities of the nuclear energy surface. The curve labeled 1.5 is representative of pre-1952 fits using the Bethe–Weizsäcker equation which will be discussed shortly. The curve labeled $G(58)$ is representative of post-1952 fits.

The general trend of last particle energies may, in the light of Eqs. (3), (5), and (6), be represented by the empirical expressions

$$E_{ne}(A) = -B_{ne}(A) = -10.23 + 0.0186A \quad \text{(in MeV)} \tag{8}$$

and

$$E_{pe}(A) = -B_{pe}(A) = -9.45 + 0.0186A \quad \text{(in MeV)}. \tag{9}$$

These are the linear functions labeled E_{ne} and E_{pe} in Fig. 1.

In addition to the information content of the magnitudes of the total nuclear energy and neutron and proton energies the collection of nuclear masses provides very sensitive information on the experimental line of beta

---

Fig. 2. Experimental mass residuals of beta stable nuclei.
(The circles correspond to even A nuclei, the dots to odd A nuclei. The crosses represent the averages of the experimental data for beta stable nuclei in the neighborhoods of mass numbers 10, 20, ..., 250, i.e., "the normal places." The curve $r_0 = 1.5$ is representative of pre-1952 fits with the B.W. formula. The curve $G(58)$ is representative of post-1952 fits, adapted from Green (1954).)

stability. This line may be represented by the neutron excess $D = N - Z$ for various A associated with beta stability. It conforms approximately to a simple empirical formula

$$(N - Z)_e = D_e(A) = \frac{0.40A^2}{A + 200} \tag{10}$$

which is also useful for the purposes of studying various theoretical equations for the line of beta stability. Figure 3 is a neutron excess diagram indicating how odd A stable nuclei follow the smooth line which represents Eq. (10). Figure 4 is a graph of $D - D_m{}^e(A)$ for the odd A stable nuclei. It should be clear from the small values of the departures that $D_e(A)$ is a good fit. The curve labeled B represents a best smooth fit to the experimental data. The curve labeled $G(58)$ is a representative fit using the Bethe–Weizsäcker mass formula.

Among the earliest efforts to explain nuclear energies, nuclear densities, and nuclear stabilities, the work of Weizsäcker (1935) brought forth a number of concepts which still prevail. He divided the total nuclear energy obtained from mass data into parts called the volume energy, the surface energy, the Coulomb energy, and the symmetry energy. While Weizsäcker initially attempted to determine these coefficients from the two-body interaction, in view of the difficulties encountered, he instead adjusted certain coefficients in his mass formula empirically in the light of stability and mass data. In his original work and in subsequent theoretical efforts the expression for total energy contained a number of small terms whose dependences upon the nuclear numbers A, Z, N, and $D = N - Z$ were quite complicated and intractable. Since the complications were then unwarranted, Bethe and Bacher (1936) chose the somewhat simplified form

$$E = -a_1 A + a_2 A^{2/3} + \frac{a_3 Z^2}{A^{1/3}} + \frac{a_4 D^2}{4A} \tag{11}$$

where the successive terms represent the volume energy, the surface energy, the Coulomb energy, and the symmetry energy. If we assume a uniformly distributed nuclear charge over a radius

$$R_c = r_c A^{1/3}, \tag{12}$$

it then follows from classical electrostatics that

$$a_3 = \frac{3e^2}{5r_c} = \frac{U_c}{r_c} \tag{13}$$

where $U_c = 0.8639$ MeV when r_c is in fermis. From Eqs. (1) and (5) it follows

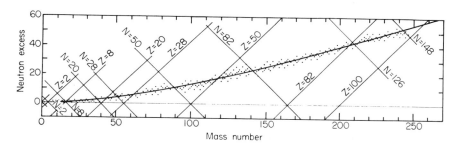

Fig. 3. The line of beta stability, i.e., the location of stable nuclei on a *D* vs. *A* plot in relationship to zones defined by magic numbers. The smooth curve corresponds to Eq. (10) (Green and Edwards, 1953).

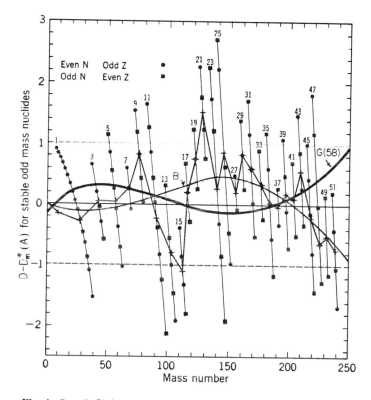

Fig. 4. $D - D_m^e(A)$ vs. mass number for beta stable odd *A* nuclides.

(*B* locates an improved smooth representation of the line of beta stability relative to the base line, which corresponds to the empirical function $D_m^e(A)$. G(58) is a representative line of beta stability based upon the Bethe–Weizsäcker formula.)

that the Bethe–Weizsäcker decrement corresponding to the Bethe–Weizsäcker energy is

$$\Delta^w(A, D) = A\,\frac{\Delta_n + \Delta_h}{2} + D\,\frac{\Delta_n - \Delta_h}{2} - a_1 A + a_2 A^{2/3}$$

$$+ \frac{a_3}{4}\,\frac{(A - D)^2}{A^{1/3}} + \frac{a_4}{4}\,\frac{D^2}{A}. \tag{14}$$

To obtain the equation for the neutron excess at the minimum of the mass decrement valley we solve $\partial \Delta^w / \partial D = 0$ to obtain

$$D_m{}^w(A) = \frac{a_3 A^{5/3} - (\Delta_n - \Delta_h)A}{a_4 + a_3 A^{2/3}}. \tag{15}$$

Defining the coordinate θ^w for any nuclide by $\theta^w = D - D_m{}^w(A)$ and substituting $D = D_m{}^w(A) + \theta^w$ into Eq. (14) we obtain after considerable cancellation

$$\Delta^w(A, D) = \Delta_m{}^w J^w (D + - D_m{}^w)^2 \tag{16}$$

where

$$\Delta_m{}^w = \Delta_m{}^w(A) = \left(\frac{3\Delta_n + \Delta_h}{4} - a_1\right)A + \left(\frac{\Delta_n - \Delta_h}{4} + \frac{a_4}{4}\right)D_m{}^w + a_2 A^{2/3} \tag{17}$$

and

$$J^w = J^w(A) = \frac{a_4 + a_3 A^{2/3}}{4A}. \tag{18}$$

Mass data, beta decay data, and various theoretical models of the nucleus suggest that, apart from shell and pairing discontinuities, a surface of the general form given by Eq. (16) may be used as an approximate representation of nuclear mass decrements. The function $\Delta_m(A)$ fixes the depth of the valley of the mass surface. The term $J(A)[D - D_m(A)]^2$ suggests that, apart from the shell and pairing discontinuities, isobaric sections of the mass surface are parabolas. $D_m(A)$ fixes the neutron excess of the vertex and $J(A)$ characterizes the width of the parabola.

Prior to 1950 the customary method of adjusting the constants of the Bethe–Weizsäcker formula was to choose a_3 from estimates of r_c usually obtained from mirror nuclei studies. Then a_4 was adjusted to make Eq. (15) fit the experimental line of beta stability. Finally a_1 and a_2 were determined to fit mass excesses of beta stable nuclei. With such techniques it was customary to use $r_c \approx 1.45$ or $a_3 = 0.58$ MeV in accord with the then assumed radii of nuclei. When the other constants in the mass equation were then adjusted to fit total nuclear energies and nuclear stability data, the nuclear energy surface constants prevalent at the time were (in MeV) $a_1 \sim 14.0$, $a_2 \sim 13$, $a_3 \sim 70$. Around 1950 when the shell model was revived there was a clear need for a good reference mass surface from which to examine shell related discontinuities. Green (1951) and Green *et al*., (1952) while attempting to study shell and pairing regularities noted that the then published studies of the Bethe–Weizsäcker formula corresponded to surfaces which departed rather grossly (~ 10 MeV) from the then available mass data. To serve as a base surface from which irregularities of the experimental mass surface may be charted the theoretical justification of the expression used for the nuclear surface is unimportant as compared to the accuracy and simplicity of the mathematical representation. Thus they began their studies of shell irregularities by first seeking out a simpler and more accurate reference mass formula. It was in this connection that Eqs. (6) and (10) were determined. However, during the course of these studies Green and Engler (1953) found that they could achieve a very considerable improvement in the fit of the Bethe–Weizsäcker surface if a_3 was treated as a free parameter in fitting the mass data. When they did so they found $a_3 \approx 0.71$ MeV which corresponds to $r_c \approx 1.24$. This result turned out to be very close to the radius constants of the nuclear charge distribution obtained about the same time from electron scattering (Hofstadter *et al*., 1953), mu mesonic X-ray measurements (Fitch and Rainwater, 1953; Cooper and Henley, 1953), and from atomic spectra isotopic shift studies (Brix and Kopfermann, 1951). The fact that these various radii determinations represented a large decrease of nuclear size with respect to earlier determinations was noted by Bitters and Feshbach (1953). These works led to a more intensive effort to sharpen up various nuclear radius determinations. The Stanford Conference (Hofstadter, 1958[1]) presents a comprehensive summary of the various efforts in the 1952–1958 period which greatly clarified our understanding of nuclear sizes and distributions.

In relation to the Bethe–Weizsäcker formula, extensive analyses (Green, 1958a) of the influence of various perturbations led to the following results. The Coulomb self-energy, exchange and radius compression effects each led to a deterioration of fit. A surface symmetry term of the type $E_{ss} = \gamma_{ss} D^2/A^{4/3}$ and a symmetry dependent term of the form $E_{sym} = \gamma_d D$ improved matters if their coefficients were negative. In no case did the readjusted Coulomb constant a_3 deviate greatly from those determined from electron scattering. The coefficients a_1 and a_2 were also relatively stable with respect to reasonable perturbations. The symmetry term was influenced considerably by a surface symmetry term. However, the equivalent combination $a_4' = a_4 - \gamma_{ss}/\overline{A}^{1/3}$ was quite stable with respect to large changes in γ_{ss}.

Table I lists various sets of the Bethe–Weizsäcker constants (or equivalent constants) taken from published studies.

The pairing correction may be viewed as representing the additional energy due to unpaired nucleons. If the reference surface is taken as the *EE* surface

---

[1] Further reference to this work will be by place and date, i.e., Stanford (1958).

TABLE I

SOME BETHE–WEIZSÄCKER CONSTANTS (IN MeV)

a_1	a_2	a_3	a_4	r_c	Reference
13.86	13.20	0.580	78.0	1.49	Bethe and Bacher (1936)
14.66	15.36	0.602	82.2	1.44	Mattauch and Flügge (1946)
14.00	13.10	0.584	72.4	1.48	Feenberg (1947)
14.00	13.03	0.584	77.3	1.48	Fermi (1949)
15.58	17.23	0.698	93.1	1.24	Green–Engler (1953)
15.82	17.90	0.718	94.1	1.203	Green (1958a)
15.68	18.56	0.664^a	93.0^a	1.301^a	Myers and Swiatecki (1966)

^{a} See Eq. (22).

(i.e., N and Z even) we may denote the additional energies of an EO, or OE nuclide as π and v, respectively (Coryell and Suess, 1952). To allow for the possible interaction of the odd proton and odd neutron, we denote this by τ, and we do not restrict our τ to $\pi + v$. In Table II we show an analysis of the

TABLE II

THE PAIRING CORRECTION TO BINDING ENERGIES

N, Z	Neutron binding			Proton binding		
	$\tau \neq \pi + v$	$\tau = \pi + v$	$\pi = v = H$	$\tau \neq \pi + v$	$\tau = \pi + v$	$\pi = v = H$
E, E	$+v$	$+v$	$+H$	$+\pi$	$+\pi$	$+H$
O, O	$-\tau + \pi$	$-v$	$-H$	$-\tau + v$	$-\pi$	$-H$
E, O	$+\tau - \pi$	$+v$	$+H$	$-\pi$	$-\pi$	$-H$
O, E	$-v$	$-v$	$-H$	$\tau - v$	$+\pi$	$+H$

pairing correction for the binding energies of protons and neutrons as they depend upon the nuclear type given in column 1. In columns 2 and 5 we indicate the pairing energy differences involved in these cases under the general assumption that the pairing energies take on the values 0, π, v, and τ. In columns 3 and 6 we indicate what these differences would be if $\tau = \pi + v$. In columns 4 and 7 we indicate what these differences would be if $\pi = v = \tau/2 = H$. If we referred masses to the odd mass surface, which is customary, then the E, $E(O, O)$ surface would have the pairing correction $-H$ $(+H)$.

In Eq. (11) we usually take as a reference the surface which lies halfway between the EE and OO surfaces. For the case $\pi \neq v$ we may let $H = \frac{1}{2}(\pi + v)$. Various functions of A have been proposed for this pairing correction. Green and Edwards (1953) tested three of these functions, $H_1(A) = 140/A$ (Blatt and Weisskopf, 1952), $H_2(A) = 36/A^{3/4}$ (Fermi, 1949), and $H_3 = 10/A^{1/2}$ (Green et al., 1952). The last appeared to best follow the variation with A although the function $12/A^{1/2}$ is still better. Recently Kümmel *et al.* (1966) found $H = \Delta/A^{1/2}$ for *nn* and *pp* pairing with $\Delta = 11.3$ MeV $= 12.1$ mMU. However, for *np* pairing he uses $H = \mu/A$ with $\mu \approx 30$ MeV.

Mayer (1950), on the assumption of a delta function attractive potential for the spin orbit coupling model, obtains formulas for the pairing energy which may be expressed as

$$\pi = -C(j_\pi + \tfrac{1}{2})/A \qquad \text{and} \qquad \nu = -C(j_\nu + \tfrac{1}{2})/A \qquad (19)$$

where j_π or j_ν is the total angular momentum of each proton or neutron in a given subshell and $C \sim 25$ MeV. The experimental evidence has indicated that these simple shell model expressions are not obeyed between major shells.

The discontinuities in the nuclear mass surface have been the subject of many studies. Green and Edwards (1953) from an analysis of neutron and proton separation energies arrived at the shell correction term

$$S_{ij}(N, Z) = -\alpha_i(N - N_i)^2 - \alpha_j(Z - Z_j)^2 + k_{ij}. \qquad (20)$$

This shell function thus has the shape of an inverted cup with the peak value at N_i and Z_j, points which usually lie intermediate between the boundaries of the zone. It contrasted with the earlier shell function of Wapstra (1952) which carried the mass surface smoothly through closed shell regions. For qualitative purposes they noted that the empirical constants could be taken as

$$\begin{aligned} \bar{\alpha}_i &= (N_u - N_l)^{-1} \quad \text{mMu} & \bar{\alpha}_j &= (Z_u - Z_l)^{-1} \quad \text{mMu} \\ \bar{N}_i &= (N_u + N_l)/2, & \bar{Z}_j &= (Z_u + Z_l)/2. \end{aligned} \qquad (21)$$

where the subscripts u and l refer to the upper and lower magic numbers of the particular zone. In using these simple expressions for the parameters in the shell correction, they exploited the latitude then available.

Such a shell correction imposes sharp breaks at the major magic numbers. Shell correction functions which have been developed over the subsequent 15 years (Baker and Baker, 1956; Levy, 1957; Cameron, 1957, Mozer, 1959; Wing and Fong, 1964; Seeger, 1961; Zeldes, 1965; Kümmel *et al.*, 1966; and Myers and Swiatecki, 1966) have similar overall features to the Green–Edwards function. We refer the reader particularly to the work of Myers and Swiatecki which contains a derivation of a shell correction function using IPM concepts, which has the same qualitative features of Eq. (20). They embody in their work the deformation of nuclear shapes which occurs between major shells and use for this the Nilsson type spheroidal potential (see Section 2.4). Figure 5 shows a two-dimensional contour picture of their shell function. Figure 6 shows this shell function along the approximate valley defined by Eq. (10).

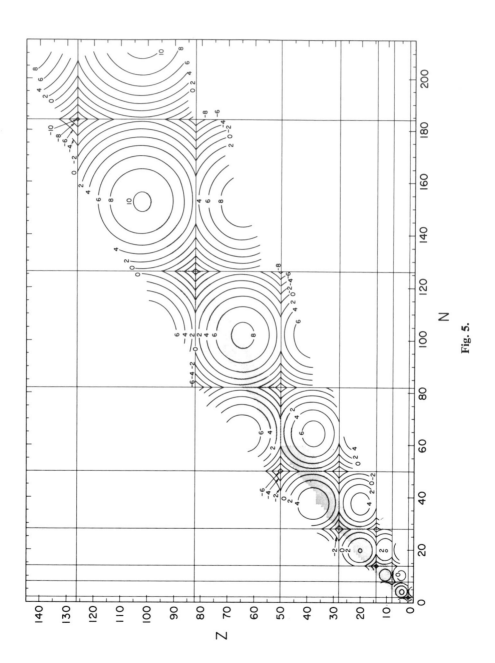

Fig. 5.

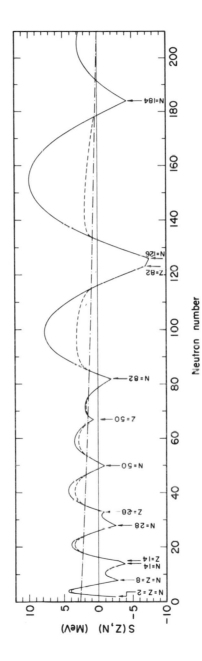

Fig. 5. The level lines, in MeV, of the two-dimensional shell function $S(N, Z)$ are shown. (The gray band corresponds to the region of nuclei with measured masses. The doubly magic combinations $N = 184$, $z = 82$, 126 are hypothetical (Myers and Swiatecki, 1966).)

Fig. 6. The shell function $S(Z, N)$ is shown along Green's approximation to the valley of stability (solid line). (The dot and dash line corresponds to the critical value S_{crit} which, when exceeded, leads to the appearance of deformations and a flattening out (of the humps in S, given by the dashed lines (Myers and Swiatecki, 1966).)

The quality of various mass formulas in current use largely depends on the number of free parameters used. Roughly speaking, Bethe–Weizsäcker formulas with five parameters or so give average deviations of the order of 2.8 MeV. Formulas using an order of magnitude more parameters (~ 50) (Kümmel *et al.*, 1966) achieve an order of magnitude improvement in fit (~ 0.3 MeV). The work of Myers and Swiatecki, which harmoniously blends the liquid drop model and the shell model, appears to be a reasonable compromise between good data fitting and economical use of parameters. As their reference liquid drop model equation for spherical nuclei, they use

$$\frac{E}{A} = -(a_1 - a_2 A^{-1/3})\left[1 - k\left(\frac{N-Z}{A}\right)^2\right] + C_3 \frac{Z^2}{A^{1/3}} - C_4 \frac{Z^2}{A}. \quad (22)$$

They find $a_1 = 15.677$ MeV, $a_2 = 18.56$ MeV, $C_3 = 0.717$ MeV ($r_0 = 1.205$ F), $C_4 = 1.211$ MeV, $k = 1.79$. The values for the equivalent Bethe–Weizsäcker parameters listed in Table I use the approximations $a_4 = 4[a_1 - (a_2/A^{1/3})] \approx 93.0$ and $a_3 = C_3 - C_4/A^{2/3} \approx 0.664$.

The Bethe–Weizsäcker mass formula has had an important influence upon nuclear physics. It serves very conveniently as an accurate summary of nuclear energy and nuclear stability data. It has also been used as a basis for inferring the quantitative properties of a hypothetical substance known as infinite nuclear matter. Thus the volume coefficient a_1, the coefficient of D^2/A, and the radius constant r_0 have frequently been used as representative of the properties of infinite nuclear matter. In this latter regard we note that caution must be exercised since $A^{1/3}$ is a rather slowly varying expansion parameter (see Green, 1958a). In the former regard we note that the Bethe–Weizsäcker formula may be imposed as a rigid constraint upon theoretical investigations of allowable potential energy functions. Let us consider qualitatively the relation of the mass formula to the IPM.

If we discard the Coulomb energy and the symmetry energy, then on the basis of the Bethe–Weizsäcker formula, a typical nucleus (say $A^{1/3} = 5$) should have the average energy per nucleon

$$\varepsilon = \frac{E}{A} = -a_1 + \frac{a_2}{A^{1/3}} \approx -12.4 \quad \text{MeV}. \quad (23)$$

This result might be chosen as a reasonable goal for a finite nucleus calculation when Coulomb and symmetry effects are ignored. Let us consider now what might be expected from the shell model.

If the energy of the nucleons in a nucleus arises from two body interactions, it is given by

$$E = \sum_i \langle T_i \rangle + \tfrac{1}{2} \sum_{ij} \langle v_{ij} \rangle. \quad (24)$$

Assuming the potential energy of the ith particle arises from the two body interactions, it follows that

$$V_i = \sum_j v_{ij}. \tag{25}$$

Thus

$$E = \sum_i \langle T_i \rangle + \tfrac{1}{2} \sum_i \langle V_i \rangle$$

$$= \sum_i E_i - \tfrac{1}{2} \sum_i \langle V_i \rangle \tag{26}$$

and the average energy per nucleon is

$$\varepsilon = E/A = \bar{E} - \tfrac{1}{2}\langle \bar{V} \rangle \tag{27}$$

where the averages are carried out, not only with respect to the quantum mechanical wave functions, but also with respect to the number of particles in the nucleus. Now let us ignore the Coulomb and symmetry effect and sum up eigenvalues for our typical heavy nucleus. The eigenvalues in a static well would range from about -35 in the lowest state to about -8 in the uppermost occupied state. Since the occupancy number of the upper states on the average are much greater than the occupancy number of the lower states the weighted averages might be expected to be the order of -18 MeV. On the other hand, the average $\langle \bar{V} \rangle$ for a well about 40 MeV deep is about -32 MeV when one considers the leakage of the particle into the diffuse region of the well. Accordingly, the difference in Eq. (27) which would be the average energy per particle comes out only of the order of -2 MeV. This compares to a desired value on the basis of studies of the Weizsäcker mass formula of the order of -12 MeV.

One of the lines of attack which has been used in an effort to overcome this difficulty of insufficient binding has been the introduction of a velocity dependent potential. We shall consider this problem in Chapter V. Let us, however, consider in detail the development of realistic static potentials.

2.2   Realistic Potentials for Neutrons

In Chapter I, Section 1.3, we considered various primitive potentials which have been used to account for the general properties of nuclear energy levels. In the present section we shall describe phenomenological efforts to use realistic potentials to fit the bound state data in a detailed way. Here we must recognize that self-consistent nuclear field studies indicate that each nucleus presents its own unique potential to the nucleons contained in it. However, such a potential might be expected to vary slowly on the average as one proceeds through the periodic table from the light to the heavy elements. Of course, there will be local fluctuations superposed on the smooth average. However, we shall now concern ourselves with an attempt to find the general trends of the real potentials which characterize bound state data. This effort is the analog of the attempts to find the general trends of the optical model potentials which account for the scattering data.

The most important characteristics of a realistic potential in relation to the primitive potentials discussed in Chapter I, Section 1.3, relate to the diffuseness of the nuclear potential surface. In this regard the harmonic oscillator model which is so appealing because of its simple eigenvalue formula and its convenient analytic wave functions is physically objectionable because the potential goes to infinity as the radial separation between a nucleon and the nucleus becomes large. Furthermore, the states of a harmonic oscillator form an infinite set of discrete states whereas a realistic model has a finite number of discrete states followed by a continuum of positive energy states.

The square well model also has the advantage of analytic functions and furthermore leads to a discrete and a continuum set of states. However, the abrupt onset of nuclear force inherent in the square well model is now recognized to be a crude description.

Early studies by Feenberg (1950), Malenka (1952), and others suggested that better level ordering in individual nuclei can be achieved by using a potential model with a diffuse boundary.

A systematic attempt to treat the bound state problem with a realistic set of potentials which vary in a gradual way from nucleus to nucleus was begun by Green and Lee (1955) in 1953. To retain the feature of analytic wave functions they initially utilized a potential well with an exponentially diffuse boundary which may be characterized by $V(r) = -V_0 \xi(r)$ where

$$\xi(r) = 1 \quad (r < a) \qquad \xi(r) = \exp[-(r-a)/d] \quad (r > a). \tag{1}$$

This three parameter (V_0, a, and d) potential form is illustrated in Fig. 1. Using graphical and analytic techniques to find approximate solutions for this type of potential, Green and Lee generated a large collection of eigenvalues for various parameters V_0, a and d which were believed to encompass the range of these parameters in nuclei.

A diffuse potential introduced first in scattering studies (Woods and Saxon, 1954) has also been used in bound state studies. Here $\xi(r)$ is given by

$$\xi(r) = \{1 + \exp[(r-R)/d]\}^{-1}. \tag{2}$$

Ross et al. (1956a) used this potential in conjunction with an analog computing device to explore some of the upper states of nucleons in nuclei. This function avoids the somewhat unaesthetic sharp corner of the exponentially diffuse edge potential, although it does so at the sacrifice of the analyticity of the wave functions.

In an effort to improve the convergence of the numerical solutions Green, (Florida, 1959), and Wyatt, *et al.* (1960), explored another class of rounded diffuse boundary potentials. Here the potential is represented by the form

$$\xi(r) = 1 \qquad (r < a)$$
$$\xi(r) = 0 \qquad (r > b)$$
$$\xi(r) = \frac{1}{2} - \frac{15}{16}Z + \frac{10}{16}Z^3 - \frac{3}{16}Z^5 \qquad (a < r < b)$$

$$(3)$$

where

$$Z = [r - \tfrac{1}{2}(a + b)]/\tfrac{1}{2}(b - a). \tag{4}$$

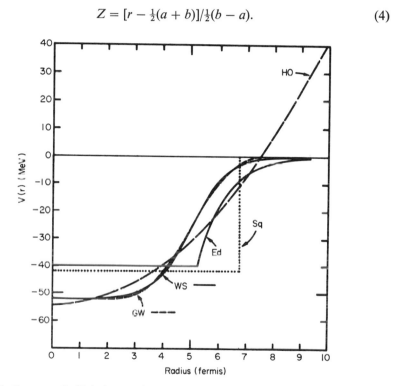

Fig. 1. Square well (Sq), harmonic oscillator (HO), and exponentially diffuse (Ed). Woods and Saxon (WS), and Green and Wyatt (GW) potential forms corresponding to $A = 100$.

While the solutions for this potential are analytic in the internal and external region, numerical solutions are needed in the intermediate region. The characteristics of these three diffuse boundary potentials are illustrated in Fig. 1. Also shown are a harmonic oscillator (HO) and a square well (Sq) potential.

From the standpoint of physical phenomena related to the last few particles in a nuclear potential which are bound in the neighborhood of about 8 MeV, the differences in the form of the diffuse potentials are relatively small. This is particularly true when considered in relation to the change in going from a harmonic oscillator potential or square well potential to any of the diffuse boundary potentials indicated in Fig. 1. Accordingly we might expect that the phenomenological consequences of any of the three diffuse potentials would be representative of the other two. Since the exponentially diffuse potential has received the most systematic treatment we will devote some detailed attention to it.

In treating this potential we note that in the interior of the well the wave functions have precisely the analytic form of the square well which we discussed in Section 1.3. On the other hand, in the external region, Eq. (5), Section 1.3, takes the form

$$G'' + [\varepsilon_0{}^2 \exp(-(\rho - 1)/\delta) - l(l + 1)\rho^{-2} - \varepsilon^2]G = 0 \qquad (5)$$

where $\delta = d/a$. Because of the presence of both the exponential and the centrifugal term this equation is not solvable exactly in analytical form for $l > 0$. Malenka (1952) dealt with a similar problem by effectively replacing ρ^{-2} by 1. The centrifugal energy is then taken together with ε^2 and the solutions are then expressible in terms of ordinary Bessel functions. To improve upon this rather crude approximation, Green and Lee (1955) let

$$\rho^{-2} \approx \alpha^2 + (1 - \alpha^2) \exp[-(\rho - 1)/\delta] \qquad (6)$$

where α^2 is chosen to accomplish a suitable match of the function on the right to the function on the left. These two functions automatically have the same value (unity) at $\rho = 1$ or $r = a$. As a prescription for a second crossing point between the approximate representation and the exact representation of the centrifugal energy, Green and Lee forced a match at

$$\rho = 1 + \delta + 0.1. \qquad (7)$$

Their investigations of the error in the external regions occasioned by this approximate treatment of the centrifugal energy indicated that the errors in eigenvalues due to this approximation were small.

If we now introduce the approximate representation of the centrifugal energy the external radial wave equation becomes

$$4\delta^2 G'' + \{k^2 \exp[-(\rho - 1)/\delta] - n^2\}G = 0 \qquad (8)$$

where

$$k^2 = 4\delta^2[\varepsilon_0{}^2 - l(l + 1)(1 - \alpha^2)] \qquad (9)$$

and

$$n^2 = 4\delta^2[\varepsilon^2 + l(l + 1)\alpha^2]. \qquad (10)$$

Letting

$$x = \exp[-(\rho - 1)/2\delta] \qquad (11)$$

the radial equation becomes the Bessel equation

$$x^2 \frac{d^2G}{dx^2} + x \frac{dG}{dx} + (k^2x^2 - n^2)G = 0. \tag{12}$$

The solution of Eq. (12) which is well-behaved as $\rho \to \infty$, i.e., as $x \to 0$ is

$$G_e = A_e J_n(kx) = A_e J_n\{k \exp[-(\rho - 1)/2\delta]\}. \tag{13}$$

To establish the energy eigenvalues, Green and Lee again used an analytic graphical technique for matching the logarithmic derivatives of the interior and exterior functions. Representative eigenvalues obtained as a result of this effort are shown in Fig. 2. We come next to the application of this library of eigenvalues to nuclear physics.

The fundamental assumption of the phenomenological approach is to identify the eigenvalues with experimentally observed particle separation energies. Characteristically neutron separation energies run from about 10 MeV in the lightest nuclei to about 6 MeV in the heaviest nuclei. These general trends may be characterized by the approximate formula (Eq. (8), Section 2.1),

$$E_n = -10.23 + 0.0186A \quad \text{MeV} \tag{14}$$

which fits most nuclei within 1 or 2 MeV. Green (1956a,b) chose the parameters of his potential wells so that the last neutron in any nucleus resides in a state which is bound in approximate accord with this formula. It might be noted that despite the crudeness of this general formula it imposes a very severe constraint upon acceptable potential families. Since nuclear potentials have depths of the order of 50 MeV, the requirement that the last particle reside within a 1 or 2 MeV band around the values computed from Eq. (14) constitutes a genuinely restrictive condition.

Two additional constraints used by Green were the A values of the 3s and 4s size resonances. Developments subsequent to the work of Ford and Bohm (1950) placed these at mass numbers 55 and 170. A parameter study indicated that relatively few families of potentials could simultaneously satisfy all of these constraints. The unusual characteristics of these were: (1) the diffuseness distance was approximately constant for all nuclei, (2) the well depth as seen by a neutron appeared approximately constant for all nuclei, (3) the characteristic radius expanded linearly with $A^{1/3}$. The simplest model of this general type within the framework of the representation chosen is illustrated in Fig. 3. Also shown are the diffuse shell model potential of Ross et al. (1956a) and the real part of the optical model potential of Weisskopf (1956).

The Ed model is characterized by

$$V_0 = 40 \quad \text{MeV} \qquad d = 1 \quad \text{F} \qquad \text{and} \qquad a = 1.32A^{1/3} - 0.8 \quad \text{F}. \tag{15}$$

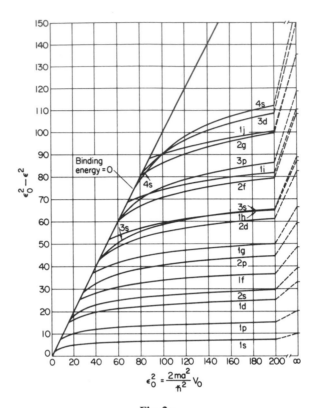

Fig. 2a.

Fig. 2. Dimensionless eigenvalues for Ed forms corresponding to (a) $\delta = d/a = 0.2$, and (b) $\delta = d/a = 0.4$. Compare with case $\delta = 0$ given in Fig. 6, Section 1.3 (Green and Lee, 1955).

The radial distance to $\frac{1}{2} V_0$ is $R_{1/2} = 1.32 A^{1/3} - 0.10 \simeq 1.30 A^{1/3}$. In Fig. 4 we show the neutron energy eigenvalues for various A according to the Ed model. Note that the $3s$ state and the $4s$ state approach the zero energy axis in the neighborhood of $A = 55$ and $A = 170$, respectively. These A numbers were points of adjustment of the model. The additional "built in" characteristic of the model is the fact that the last neutron in beta stable nuclei resides in states whose energies agree approximately with their observed separation energies. It was gratifying that so simple and reasonable a model could satisfy the experimental requirements. In a subsequent work all the wave function parameters (A_i, A_e, ε, k, and n) for both the inner regions and outer regions which are needed to characterize bound states in this family of potentials were determined. These wave functions were then available for the pursuit of the physical consequences of this model.

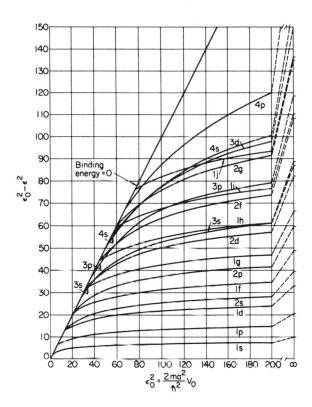

Fig. 2b.

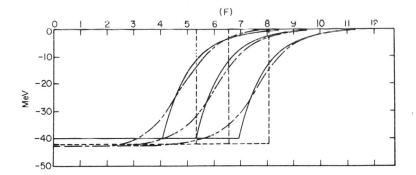

Fig. 3. Neutron–nuclear potentials for $A = 50$, 100, and 200 according to static models of Green (1956a), Ross *et al.* (1956a), and Weisskopf (1956).

    The spin orbit term was introduced using the Thomas–Frenkel type term

$$V_{so} = -a_{so}^2 \left| \frac{1}{r} \cdot \frac{\partial V}{\partial r} \right| \frac{(\mathbf{L} \cdot \mathbf{S})}{\hbar^2} \tag{16}$$

where a_{so} is here taken as an adjustable length. Equation (21), Section 1.3, may be deduced from Eq. (16) if we use an unrealistic three-dimensional harmonic oscillator potential.

    The problems of establishing quantitatively the magnitude of the spin orbit splitting in conjunction with a realistic family of potentials involve much

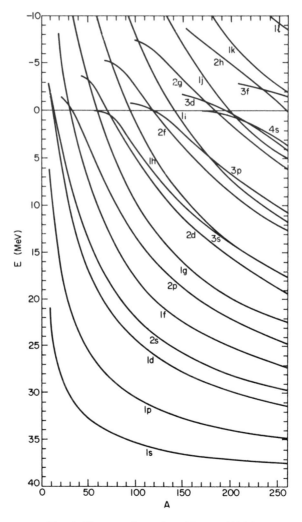

Fig. 4. Neutron eigenvalues (Green, 1956a).

greater complications. For the exponentially diffuse potentials the spin orbit radial function is

$$\xi(r) = -(a_{so}^2/dr)V_0 \exp[-(r-a)/d] \qquad r > a \qquad (17)$$

and $\xi(r) = 0$ for $r < a$. Since states of like l are widely separated in this model, sufficient accuracy may be attained if one uses

$$\langle\xi(r)\rangle = -(a_{so}^2/a^2\delta)V_0\, 2\, dA_e^2 \int_0^1 (x^2\rho^{-1})x^{-1}J_n^2(kx)\, dx. \qquad (18)$$

These factors were evaluated using several approximate analytical techniques. Figure 5 presents graphs of these splitting factors for $a_{so} = 1$ (in units of F)

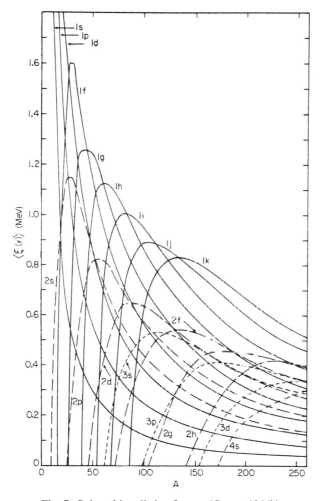

Fig. 5. Spin orbit splitting factors (Green, 1956b).

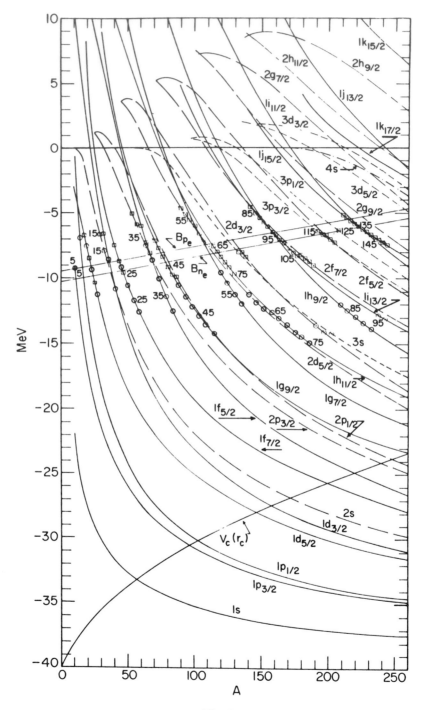

Fig. 6.

for the various states. The extensive variation of these splitting factors with A and from state to state is noteworthy, particularly in view of the fact that in early shell model studies (Mayer, 1950), a single constant was used. The general shapes of these curves are quite reasonable when they are viewed as the overlap between a series of probability distributions and the surface "window curve" represented by Eq. (17).

In an effort to determine a_{so} empirically, an investigation was made of the positions of various states in the neighborhood of the neutron magic numbers 20, 28, 50, 82, and 126. A careful examination of these neighborhoods indicated that a_{so}^2 cannot range very far from 1 and still generate all of the magic numbers. The locations of the states at $N = 20$ and $N = 126$ particularly restrict the value of a_{so}^2. The latter effect may, however, be due to the rather high location of the $3p$ state relative to the $1i$ state and may indicate a need for a small change in well shape in this region. In any event, it would appear that the convenient choice of $a_{so} = 1$ does yield the magic numbers and apparently is as good as any other possibility. If the spin orbit term were strictly the Thomas–Frenkel relativistic effect, one would have $\hbar^2/2m^2c^2 = 0.022$ F^2 in place of a_{so}^2. Thus the chosen spin orbit coefficient is about 45 times larger than that called for by the relativistic electrodynamic effect.

It might be noted that the sizes of the discontinuities obtained were somewhat larger than the experimentally determined values which range from 1 to 3 MeV. However, it must be remembered that any further splittings of the energy states, such as are caused by aspherical distortions or interparticle couplings, will tend to reduce the sizes of energy discontinuities. Thus, it is to be expected that the discontinuities derived from a strict central IPM will be somewhat larger than the actual discontinuities.

The neutron energy levels obtained when spin orbit splitting with $a_{so} = 1$ is included are shown in Fig. 6. The locations of last neutrons and protons in beta stable nuclei are also shown in Fig. 6, under the assumption that no additional perturbations act upon these nucleons. Note that the $3s$ and $4s$ states still go to zero binding at $A = 55$ and $A = 170$ since these states are unaffected by the spin orbit splitting. The fact that the binding energies of the last neutrons in beta stable nuclei fluctuate about the line E_{ne} demonstrates that the efficacy of the original well parameter adjustment procedure was not destroyed by the introduction of spin orbit splitting.

In the work it was recognized that the family of neutron potentials would merely represent a frame of reference which was more realistic than a family

---

Fig. 6. (Nuclear energy levels after spin orbit are included. The locations of last neutrons in beta stable nuclei are indicated by squares. The location of the last protons, if no extra force acted upon them, are indicated by circles. The curve labeled $v_c(r_c)$ indicates the major correction associated with classical Coulomb perturbation (Green, 1956b).)

of harmonic oscillators or square wells. It was expected that there would be many additional effects over and above those embodied in the chosen family of potentials. The spin orbit effect is one example which has been handled by first order perturbation theory. Here one uses the unperturbed wave functions to arrive at the energetic influence of the perturbation. However, many perturbations arise which are large enough so that one should consider the influence of the perturbation upon the wave function.

While in principle standard second order perturbation theory is available for such investigations, nevertheless, the practical utilization of perturbation theory would entail the use of computing machines directly and accordingly negate the analytic approach. When using the harmonic oscillator as a reference set some perturbations are handled by readjusting the oscillator parameter and using the altered wave functions so obtained. In an analogous way, Green (1956a) devised a perturbation technique which utilized the set of eigenvalues and eigenfunction parameters already determined.

The square well problem provides a guide for the determination of a perturbation method to handle the diffuse boundary nucleus problem. The parameters which characterize a square well enter the radial equation only through the dimensionless well strength parameter

$$\varepsilon_0{}^2 = V_0\, 2ma^2/\hbar^2. \tag{19}$$

Since nuclear potentials fall off rather sharply one might as a first step seek a procedure for finding an equivalent square well strength of an arbitrary well with a diffuse boundary. Green essentially proposed that $\varepsilon_0{}^2$ be generalized to the form

$$S = 2(2m/\hbar^2) \int_0^\infty V(r)r\, dr. \tag{20}$$

For example on this basis the equivalent well strength of the model under study turns out to be

$$S = \varepsilon_0{}^2(1 + 2\delta + 2\delta^2). \tag{21}$$

The values of S for our family of potentials for the various values of A are shown in Fig. 7. It turns out for small δ this definition leads to a reasonable correspondence of energy levels particularly in the sense that the 2s, 3s, and 4s size resonances occur at wells with approximately the same equivalent well strength. To apply the method to small perturbations in such a manner as to minimize the uncertainty of the definition of the equivalent well strength we may calculate the shift in A due to a change of well strength ΔS by means of

$$\Delta A = (dA/dS)\, \Delta S \approx (6.32A/S)\, \Delta S. \tag{22}$$

The value of dA/dS for the model family is given rather precisely by the last expression. For a given perturbation the shifted A should be used to obtain the altered wave function parameters appropriate for the perturbed state.

If we wish the new energies we may use Fig. 4 or Fig. 7 at the shifted A value provided corrections are made for the fact that these figures are based upon the standard correspondence between mass number and radius parameter. Accordingly, we would use the eigenvalue diagram at the shifted value A but correct these values by the factor a'^2/a^2, i.e.,

$$E = E(A')[a'^2/a^2] \approx E(A + \Delta A)[1 + 2a^{-1}(da/dA)\,\Delta A]. \qquad (23)$$

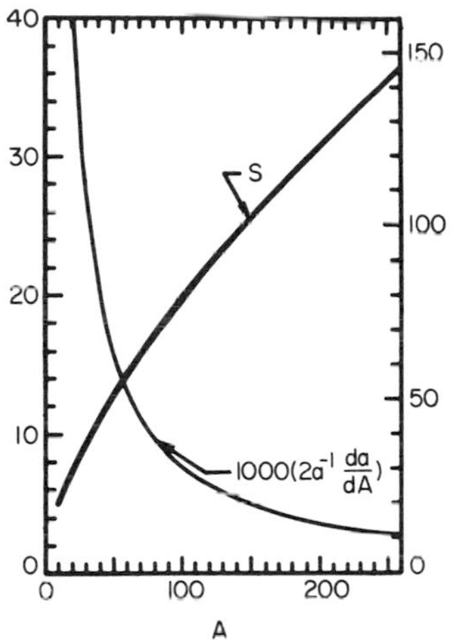

Fig. 7. Functions needed to calculate perturbations by the A shift method. S is to be read on right scale, $2a^{-1}(da/dS) \times 10^3$ on the left scale.

The value of $2a^{-1}(da/dA)$ is also given on Fig. 7. This perturbation scheme in effect represents a simple way of exploiting the model family of potentials and its eigenvalues and eigenfunctions for slightly perturbed potential forms. It serves thereby as a simple means to extend the usefulness of the model family and its eigenvalues and wave functions. While subsequent investigations of bound states have for the most part utilized numerical techniques, nevertheless, this simple procedure has served to illustrate the influence of perturbations upon any family of potentials which is similar to the model family chosen.

2.3   Realistic Potentials for Protons

Having found a reasonable family of potentials for neutrons we come next to the problem of establishing the family of potentials acting upon the protons in a nucleus. It had been customary to assume that a proton sees the Coulomb potential due to the remaining protons in addition to the proper nuclear potential seen by neutrons. To establish the additional Coulomb potential seen by a proton, one must first consider the distribution of the proton charges within the nucleus. This, of course, implies additional assumptions which might be expected to influence the character of the result. However, it turns out that the Coulomb potential is relatively insensitive to the assumed form of proton charge distribution. Accordingly any reasonable form may be utilized for this purpose. The procedure followed by Green and Lee (1955) was to assume that $Z - 1$ protons which act upon the last proton are distributed according to the charge density

$$\rho(r) = \rho_0 \, \xi(r) \tag{1}$$

where $\xi(r)$ is the same form function as the potential but with slightly altered parameters (i.e., a and d). On the basis of the classical solution of Poisson's equation, the Coulomb potential of the single proton is then

$$V_c(r) = \frac{(Z-1)e^2}{a_c \lambda_c} \left[\mu_c - \frac{r^2}{6a_c{}^2} \right] \qquad (r < a)$$

$$V_c(r) = \frac{(Z-1)e^2}{r} \left[1 - \frac{\delta_c{}^2}{\lambda_c a_c} (r + 2\delta_c a_c) \exp\left(\frac{a_c - r}{d_c}\right) \right] \qquad (r > a) \tag{2}$$

where

$$\mu_c = \tfrac{1}{2} + \delta_c + \delta^2{}_c \tag{3}$$

and

$$\lambda_c = \tfrac{1}{3} + \delta_c + 2\delta_c{}^2 + 2\delta_c{}^3. \tag{4}$$

This function falls off rather slowly with increasing r and at radii immediately outside the nuclear surface it still has an appreciable value of about

$$V_c(r_c) \approx \frac{(Z-1)e^2}{a+d}. \tag{5}$$

Now the fact that the Coulomb perturbation dies down very slowly prejudices somewhat the use of the A shift perturbation method. However, it is reasonable to replace the perturbation by a constant plus a residual function, i.e.,

$$V_c(r) = \frac{(Z-1)e^2}{a+d} + V_{cr}(r). \tag{6}$$

The presence of such a constant in Schroedinger's equation simply leads to a raising of the energy levels by the corresponding amount, with no alterations of the wave function parameters. On the other hand, the residual potential leads not only to a small additional shift in energy, but also, to a shift in the wave functions. To calculate these effects, the well strength change associated with the residual perturbation and the corresponding A shifts were determined.

Prior to 1955 it was customary to assume that protons sensed the same nuclear potential as that seen by neutrons and that the Coulomb potential represented the only difference. However, since there had not been studies with realistic nuclear potentials, no one had really verified whether this common hypothesis was consistent with experiment.

In their first attempts to embody the Coulomb effect within a realistic family of nuclear potentials, Lee and Green (1956a) in mass formula studies,

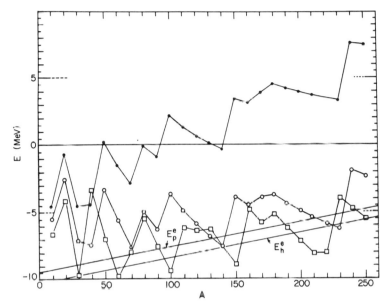

Fig. 1. The energies of the outermost protons and neutrons in beta stable nuclei.
(The open circles denote values computed with one-half the classical Coulomb potential. The closed circles denote values computed with the full classical Coulomb potential. The squares denote neutron energies. The straight lines represent the empirical energies (Green, 1956a).)

and Green (1955) in particle binding energy studies, argued that the IPM Coulomb potential energy of a proton should approximate one-half the classical Coulomb energy of a single proton in the electrostatic field of the other $Z - 1$ protons. The factor one-half was related to the two body nature of the Coulomb interaction in the sense that only one-half the Coulomb interaction energy of a single proton with the remaining protons may be taken as the "share" of this proton. The efficacy of this argument from an empirical viewpoint is illustrated in Fig. 1. Here the location of the outermost neutrons in beta stable nuclei with 10, 20, 30, ... neutrons is indicated by square symbols. The line E_n^e represents the general trends of experiment (see

Eq. (8), Section 2.1). The line E_p^e represents the empirical equation (Eq. (9), Section 2.1),

$$E_p^e = -9.45 + 0.0186A \quad (MeV) \tag{7}$$

based upon an analysis of nuclear energies (Green and Engler, 1953). The open circles denote proton energy values computed with one-half the classical Coulomb energy. It should be clear that the use of $\frac{1}{2}V_c(r)$ occasions reasonable agreement between the IPM proton energies and experimental separation energies. On the other hand, if we use the full Coulomb potential, we obtain the results indicated by the closed circles in Fig. 1. Here we see that in typical heavy nuclei the last proton would be unbound by about $+5$ MeV rather than bound by about -5 MeV, i.e., $E_p = +5$ MeV. Another way of expressing the result is to note that in a typical heavy nucleus the last proton in the bare nuclear potential would be bound by about 15 MeV. The application of the full Coulomb repulsion would raise the last proton by something about 20 MeV throwing the particle about 5 MeV out of binding. The use of $\frac{1}{2}V_c$ would cut the Coulomb effect to about 10 MeV leaving the proton bound by about 5 MeV.

While use of $\frac{1}{2}V_c$ gives the right reduction of the Coulomb effect, it must be noted that the IPM Coulomb potential energy, as represented by the sum of all the two body Coulomb interactions acting on a single proton, is the full Coulomb potential energy. It should be clear, however, that an equivalent device for reducing the effect of the Coulomb potential would be to introduce an anomalous attractive potential which cancels approximately one-half of the classical Coulomb potential acting upon an individual proton. In the absence of a fundamental understanding as to the origin of the nuclear potential this interpretation seemed less objectionable than an interpretation which implied the breakdown of electrostatics. The proton scattering studies of Melkanoff et al. (1956) indicating proton well depth at low energies ~ 55 MeV as contrasted with a neutron well depth ~ 45 MeV also supported the idea of an anomalous nuclear attraction to protons.

To facilitate a quantitative study the total proton potential was represented by Green (1956a,b,c) as

$$V_p = V + V_c + V_a \tag{8}$$

where V is the IPM potential seen by a neutron, V_c is the full classical Coulomb perturbation, and V_a is the additional anomaly. It was assumed that the classical Coulomb potential was given by Eq. (2) on an individual proton. Since the inner radius function $a = 1.32A^{1/3} - 0.8 \approx 1.164A^{1/3}$ was slightly smaller than the radii of the nuclear charge distribution as observed in electron scattering and μ-mesonic x-ray studies, the approximation $a_c \approx a$ was taken in conjunction with a decay length, which was smaller than the decay length of the nuclear potential. Specifically, the choice $d_c = \frac{1}{2}d$ was taken as a reasonable way of embodying observed proton distributions into the analytic model. A comparison of the classical expression $6(Z - 1)e^2/5R$, based upon the assumption that the outermost proton and the remaining protons are uniformly distributed over the radius R, suggests that the first term in Eq. (6) accounts for the bulk of the classical Coulomb effect. To correct for the small residual influences on both the wave functions and the eigenvalues, the approximate method outlined in Section 2.1 may be used. The Coulomb A shifts so computed are given in Table I.

TABLE I

COULOMB A SHIFTS

A	Z	ΔA_{cr}	ΔA_a	ΔA_{net}	$V_c(a_c)$
25	12	$-$ 1.44	2.95	1.51	3.90
50	23	$-$ 4.26	9.63	5.37	6.26
75	33	$-$ 7.84	18.60	10.77	7.99
100	43	-12.18	29.83	17.65	9.56
125	53	-17.20	43.11	25.90	11.01
150	62	-22.49	57.36	34.87	12.18
175	71	-28.30	73.22	44.92	13.29
200	80	-34.61	90.59	55.98	14.36
225	89	-41.38	109.44	68.06	15.40
250	97	-48.11	128.36	80.25	16.23

In view of the previously noted success, from the particle binding energy standpoint, of the simple device of reducing the Coulomb interaction by one-half, the possibility that the anomaly is indeed associated with a direct distortion of the Coulomb interaction was investigated first. For greater realism, it was assumed that the proton anomaly is the product of the Coulomb interaction and a dimensionless function $\phi(r)$ which is close to zero at a_c and which builds up rapidly to $-k$ as one proceeds towards $r = 0$. For simplicity this function was taken as

$$\phi(r) = -k \quad (r < a) \qquad \phi(r) = -k \, \exp[(a - r)/d_a] \quad (r > a). \tag{9}$$

After investigation of the consequences of a number of choices of k, the value $k = 0.7$ was found to yield proton binding energies in approximate accord with the experimental trends. The A shifts associated with this anomaly and the net A shifts are also given in Table I. Particle binding energies based upon the net A shifts given by

$$\Delta A = \Delta A_a + \Delta A_{cr} \tag{10}$$

in conjunction with the formula

$$W = W(A + \Delta A)\left[1 + \frac{2}{a}\frac{da}{dA}\Delta A\right] + \frac{(Z-1)e^2}{a+d}. \qquad (11)$$

ΔA's conform quite closely to the E_{ep} line in Fig. 1. An illustration of the general nature of the potentials which are assumed to act in a typical heavy nucleus ($_{80}$Hg^{200}) is shown in Fig. 2. Here V denotes the nuclear potential,

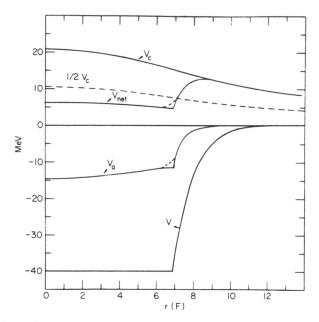

Fig. 2. Illustration of the general nature of the potentials assumed to act in a heavy nucleus ($_{80}$Hg^{200}).
   (V denotes the nuclear potential, v_c the Coulomb potential, v_a the anomaly based upon Eqs. (2) and (9) with $k = 0.7$, and v_{net} the net perturbation.)

V_c the Coulomb potential, V_a the anomaly based upon $V_a = \phi(r)\,V_c(r)$ with $k = 0.7$. V_{net} is the net perturbation acting upon a proton. Also shown on this diagram is $\frac{1}{2}V_c$, which clearly provides a moderately good average representation of the net perturbation.

The overall agreement between $\frac{1}{2}V_c$ and V_{net} indicates that both devices would be about equally effective from the standpoint of particle binding energies. The differences between these two perturbations would, however, influence the wave functions. Because of the slow decline of V_c, this perturbation would push out the proton probability distribution relative to the neutron distribution in the same quantum state. On the other hand, the abrupt rise in V_{net} indicates that with the alternative interpretation the proton is pulled in relative to a neutron in the same quantum state. Since there was no reason to suspect a breakdown of electrostatics at distances of the order of nuclear radii, the interpretation in terms of a nuclear anomaly is favored. Accordingly, the characterization of the anomaly in terms of Eqs. (9) and (2) or the A shifts given in Table I were used as a basis for an extensive study of IPM neutron and proton distributions by Green *et al.* (1956). At the end of this section we shall return to a more detailed consideration of the proton potential anomaly.

One of the important orbital parameters that enters into many physical problems is the expectation value of r^2 for various single particle orbitals. On the basis of the wave functions developed in the previous section,

$$\langle r^2 \rangle = a^2 \left\{ A_i^2 \int_0^1 \rho^4 j_l^2 (\varepsilon' \rho) \, d\rho + 2 \, d A_e^2 \int_0^1 x^{-1} \rho^2 J_n^2 (kx) \, dx \right\}. \qquad (12)$$

The first integral can be evaluated exactly and the second integral by the use of an approximate polynomial method. The values of $\langle r^2 \rangle a^{-2}$ obtained from this formula have been determined, and a comparison has been made with the harmonic oscillator radii which are given by

$$\langle r^2 \rangle_{nl} a_h^{-2} = [2(n-1) + l + \tfrac{3}{2}] \qquad (13)$$

where $a_h = (\hbar/m\omega)^{1/2}$ is the natural length associated with the harmonic oscillator. Equation (13) implies that the radii of states belonging to the same oscillator number, $N = 2(n-1) + l$, should be identical. This, however, is not the case for the radii derived from this realistic potential, although a tendency towards the harmonic oscillator grouping occurs among the particular states which are just filling in any mass region. (For example, the 2s and 1d radii near $A \sim 30$; the 2p and 1f levels near $A \sim 60$; the 3s, 2d, and 1g levels near $A \sim 100$; and the 3p, 2f, and 1h levels near $A \sim 180$.) This grouping tendency may well account for the efficacy of the harmonic oscillator potential as a starting point in deriving magic numbers and in other ordering considerations. The departures from the harmonic oscillator groupings suggest, however, that the convenient and widely used harmonic oscillator wave functions must be used with considerable caution in quantitative discussions.

The spin orbit effect also influences nuclear radii, acting to draw in the state $j = l + \tfrac{1}{2}$, and to push out the state $j = l - \tfrac{1}{2}$. An approximate estimate of the changes in radii may be made by the method of A shifts. The values of $\langle r^2/a^2 \rangle$ as a function of A for various nuclear orbitals are shown in Fig. 3. The central line here represents the radius of the uniform part of the well. To give some idea as to the scale, two heavy solid lines have been plotted corresponding to points 1 F on the outside and inside of the boundary. The rectangles on this diagram indicate the radii of the last neutrons determined

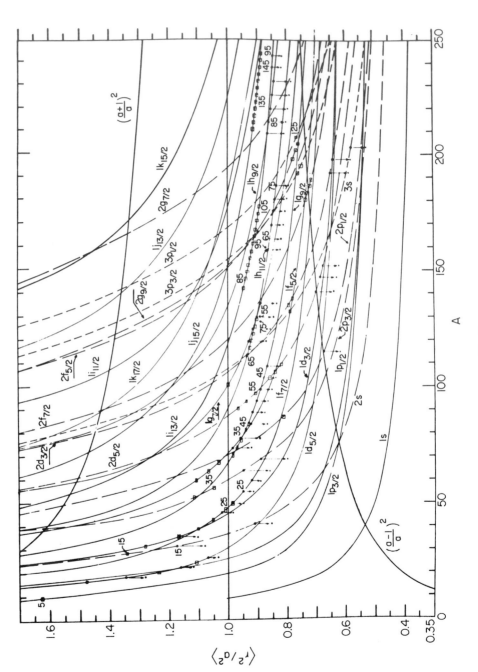

Fig. 3.

on the basis of the model family of potentials. The open circles denote the location of the last protons under the assumption that no additional forces act upon protons. The solid circles represent the shifted radii of these protons under the assumption that the net perturbation conforms to that needed to hold protons in binding at the observed energies. Note that these protons are pulled inward by the combined action of the Coulomb potential and the proton potential anomaly. In earlier work it was almost universally assumed that the Coulomb potential alone perturbed the proton states and that it acted to push the protons outward.

One of the most interesting physical properties which may be investigated with the aid of the analytic wave functions is the question of the overall radii of the neutron and proton distributions. For neutrons in the unperturbed model potential these may be calculated in the following way (Green, 1956b). Choosing a particular A, and an N corresponding to a nucleus near the line of beta stability, one places these N neutrons in the lowest states which are permitted by the exclusion principle. The radii of these states are then obtained from Fig. 3 at the particular A value. The rms radius of the neutron distribution ($\bar{R}_n$) then follows from

$$\bar{R}_n = a[N^{-1} \sum_i \langle \rho^2 \rangle_i]^{1/2}. \tag{14}$$

Such calculations have been carried out for nuclei with mass numbers 25, 50, ..., 250. Similar calculations have also been carried out for the proton distributions. To clarify the influence of the various perturbations upon the proton distribution, the calculations have been made under the assumptions (a) that no perturbation acts upon the protons ($\bar{R}_u$), (b) that only the Coulomb perturbation acts upon the protons ($\bar{R}_c$), and (c) that the Coulomb and anomalous potentials act upon the protons ($\bar{R}_p$). The results so obtained have been fitted by least squares by functions of the form $\bar{r} = \bar{r}_0 A^{1/3} + b$ and $\bar{r} = \bar{r}_0 A^{1/3}$ in each of the four cases. These results are

$$\bar{R}_n = 1.0009A^{1/3} + 0.0434 \approx 1.0092A^{1/3}$$
$$\bar{R}_p = 0.9147A^{1/3} + 0.2428 \approx 0.9616A^{1/3}$$
$$\bar{R}_u = 0.9495A^{1/3} + 0.1719 \approx 0.9827A^{1/3}$$
$$\bar{R}_c = 0.9737A^{1/3} + 0.1524 \approx 1.0031A^{1/3}. \tag{15}$$

Fig. 3. Nuclear radii when spin orbit splitting is included.
(The squares represent the radii of the orbitals of the last neutrons in beta stable nuclei. The open circles represent the radii of last protons under the assumption that only the nuclear potential acts upon them. The closed circles give the proton radii after all perturbations have acted (Green, 1956b).)

The radii of the equivalent uniform distributions are used most frequently as parameters to characterize radii of neutron and proton distributions. These may be obtained by multiplying the rums radii by $(5/3)^{1/2}$. The equivalent radii so obtained from the RIPM effort were

$$R_n \approx 1.303A^{1/3} \qquad R_p \approx 1.241A^{1/3}. \tag{16}$$

The unshifted and Coulomb shifted radii are

$$R_u \approx 1.269A^{1/3} \qquad R_c \approx 1.295A^{1/3}. \tag{17}$$

These results not only indicate that the proton distribution is smaller than the neutron distribution, but also suggest in detail the origin of this effect. In part, the effect is associated with the existence of a neutron excess in beta stable nuclei as indicated by the comparison of R_u with R_n. This tendency of the neutron excess to enlarge the radius of the neutron distribution has previously been noted by Johnson and Teller (1955). A comparison of R_c and R_n indicates that if the proton and neutron nuclear potentials were the same, and the protons felt, in addition, only the Coulomb perturbation, they would be "pushed out" until the proton radius would be almost identical with the neutron radius. This is contrary to the Johnson–Teller argument. The proton potential anomaly, however, pulls the proton distribution in from R_c to R_p and leads to a thin surface layer of neutrons in heavy nuclei. This is in agreement with the Johnson–Teller conclusion, although the analysis suggests the neutron membrane is only $0.06A^{1/3}$ F thick. The fact that proton radii given by $R_p = 1.241A^{1/3}$ were in good agreement with radii obtained from μ-mesonic x-ray studies, high energy electron scattering, and Coulomb energy calculations (Stanford, 1958) was quite satisfying in view of the fact that these experimental data were not used at all in arriving at the phenomenological potentials.

If we wish to compare the radius of the proton distributions with the radius of the original potential well we are confronted with the problem of choosing an appropriate radius parameter to assign to the diffuse boundary potential. From the standpoint of the locations of the 3s and 4s wave maxima, the equivalent square well radius might be taken as Emmerich's (1955) function,

$$R_w = 1.26A^{1/3} + 0.7 \approx 1.40A^{1/3} \tag{18}$$

where in the right-hand expression the constant has been incorporated into the A term to produce agreement at $A = 125$. Alternatively, we might use the definition of equivalent square well radii based upon the perturbation method previously described. This leads to

$$R^2 = V_0^{-1} \times 2 \int_0^\infty V(r)r \, dr. \tag{19}$$

These have been calculated and found to conform fairly well to

$$R_w = 1.29A^{1/3} + 0.45 \approx 1.38A^{1/3}. \tag{20}$$

Another convenient well radius is the distance at which the potential falls to about e^{-1} of its central value. According to this model,

$$R_w = a + d = 1.32A^{1/3} + 0.20 \approx 1.36A^{1/3}. \tag{21}$$

The slight difference between these equivalent well radii is probably not as significant as the fact that all of them are appreciably larger than the proton distribution radii. This is quite satisfactory from the standpoint of a number of experimental observations as well as from the standpoint of a number of theoretical considerations. We may explore these considerations in detail by going to the nucleon density distributions directly.

Using the realistic IPM it is possible also to investigate in detail the expected neutron and proton density distributions in nuclei. The particle densities may be obtained from the radial wave functions (Green *et al.*, 1956)

$$\rho_m = (4\pi a^3 \rho^2)^{-1} G^2. \tag{22}$$

Figure 4 shows a set of inferred proton densities based upon this model. Also shown is a family of curves interpolated from high energy electron scattering measurements at Stanford. Note the rather good agreement of the interpolated experimental curves in relation to the theoretically derived charge distributions in the neighborhood of the surface. The dotted curve for mass number 250 represents a density curve corresponding to a 5% smaller radius parameter extrapolated from the Stanford results. Its purpose is to show that small residual differences can be eliminated by adjustments of radius parameters which are almost within the realm of experimental uncertainty. Note, however, the fluctuations in the theoretically inferred distributions which were not indicated in the earliest measurements at Stanford. It should be remarked, however, that subsequent measurements of electron scattering at Stanford did indicate charge density variation in light nuclei having the character which might be expected from a shell model, although in heavier nuclei the resolution has not yet been adequate for the purpose.

In Fig. 5 we show the total nuclear densities computed from the RIPM for a set of typical nuclei. Also shown are the potential functions which underlie the model. The observed deviation of total particle densities from the potential functions may be of considerable physical significance. Note that the density functions show marked hills and valleys as compared to the simple family of potential functions. One should not expect, of course, the potential function and density functions to be self-consistent in the sense of direct proportionality since these are two physically different quantities. A more

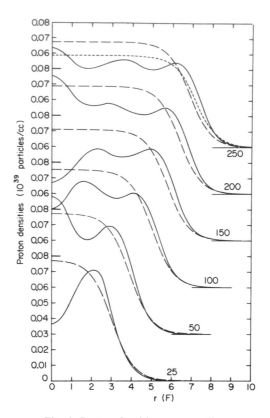

Fig. 4. Proton densities versus radius.

(The solid curves are proton density distributions for mass numbers 25, 50, 100, 150, 200, and 250 calculated on the basis of the family of potentials arrived at in an earlier work (Green, 1956a). The dashed curves are density curves inferred from the Stanford electron scattering experiments. To avoid overlap, the curves for successive mass numbers are shifted upwards by 0.03 scale units. The heavy markers denote the ordinates at which the scale is broken. The dotted line for mass number 250 represents a density curve with a radius parameter 5% smaller than the radius parameter extrapolated from the Stanford experimental results (Green *et al.*, 1956).)

reasonable approach, following the ideas of the simplest form of meson theory, would be to assume that

$$\nabla^2 V - a_\pi^{-2} V = 4\pi g \rho_m(r) \tag{23}$$

where a_π represents the natural length $(\hbar/m_\pi c)$ of the nuclear force meson. Then it can be shown by integration by parts that

$$\langle r^2 \rangle_V - \langle r^2 \rangle_d = 6 a_\pi^2 \approx 12 \quad \text{F.} \tag{23a}$$

It is somewhat satisfactory that the difference between the derived rms density radii and the initially assumed rms potential radii are in qualitative correspondence with this simple result.

In summary, it has been shown that the family of potentials inferred from a limited amount of particle binding energies and some neutron scattering considerations leads to a rather self-consistent model for nuclear properties.

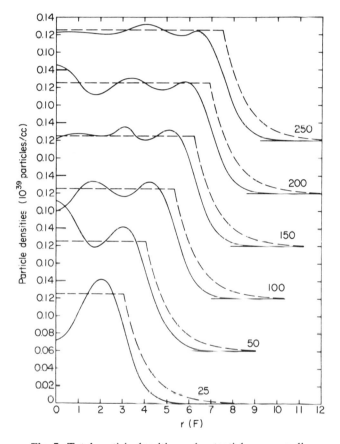

Fig. 5. Total particle densities and potentials versus radius.
(The solid curves are calculated total particle densities. The dashed curves represent the form of the potential functions which underlie the work. The heavy markers indicate ordinates at which the scale is broken by 0.06 scale units (Green *et al.*, 1956).)

Furthermore, the deduced proton densities agree in general with those inferred directly from a host of essentially different experimental measurements. The family of potentials so obtained extends consistently beyond the deduced density function as might be expected from an elementary form of meson theory. One might also expect, on the basis of experience with atomic self-consistent fields, that the self-consistent nuclear potential should also display local variations similar to, but somewhat smoother than, those exhibited by the density fluctuations. Such fluctuations would be expected to significantly influence the details of energy level ordering, surface diffuseness, radii, and other nuclear properties. It is not unlikely that observed fluctuations of nuclear properties from their general trends are related to the fluctuations expected from a self-consistent calculation.

Let us return now to a more detailed consideration of the character and magnitude of the proton potential anomaly.

To unfold the characteristics of the proton potential anomaly, Green (1956c) used Eqs. (10) and (11) in conjunction with Fig. 6, Section 2.2, to determine the net A shift required to bring the protons to approximately their binding energy in known nuclei. An iterative process was used for finding the roots of this transcendental equation. The results are shown by the dots in Fig. 6. The most interesting aspect of these "experimental" shifts is that they are positive, which implies that, inside the cutoff, the net perturbing force acting upon the proton is an attractive one whereas the balance of the classical Coulomb interaction is, of course, repulsive. The local value of these points may not be meaningful since they were computed on the basis of general trends of proton binding energies rather than specific proton binding energies. However, these A shifts serve as a systematic measure of the attractive proton anomaly on the basis of a scale established by the classical Coulomb effect.

Figure 6 also presents the results of a number of theoretical calculations. The curve labeled V_{ca} represents the net A shifts computed under the assumption that the anomaly corresponds to a direct distortion of the Coulomb interaction inside the nucleus. A single parameter is available to characterize this distortion, and we note that the fit achieved is fairly good. However, for small mass numbers a systematic departure between the points and curve seems evident.

The curve labeled V_{pa} represents the net A shifts when the anomaly is assumed to be simply 25% of the nuclear potential. This would correspond to the assumption of a fixed ratio between a proton well and a neutron well as suggested in some scattering studies (Melkanoff et al., 1956). It should be clear that this type of anomaly is unsatisfactory.

The curve V_e represents the net A shift computed under the assumption that the additional potential seen by the proton is proportional to the neutron excess. Assuming a reasonable distribution for the neutron excess which tends to peak near the surface, we can readily compute a functional formula for the A shift which is approximately proportional to the symmetry parameter $(N - Z)/A$ and is dependent upon one adjustable constant. It should be clear in this case that the agreement throughout the range is rather good so that a proton potential anomaly directly related to the neutron excess density might well account for the anomalous attraction of protons.

The curves labeled V_{hp} and V_{hn} represent the net A shifts for a proton and neutron under the assumption that a Heisenberg exchange force acts upon these particles. Such an exchange force was implicit in many early studies of

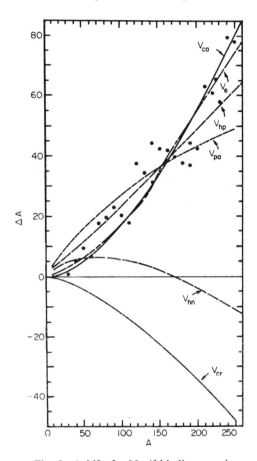

Fig. 6. A shifts for N–$\mathcal{N}$ binding energies.

(The dots represent the net A shifts needed to account for the general trends of proton binding energies. The curve labeled V_{cr} represents the net A shifts associated with the residual Coulomb repulsion. The curve labeled V_{ca} indicates the net A shift assuming the Coulomb potential is distorted inside the nucleus. The curve labeled V_{pu} is the net A shift computed under the assumption that the proton potential is uniformly 10 MeV deeper than the neutron potential. The curve labeled V_e is based upon the assumption that the proton potential anomaly is proportional to the neutron excess density. The curves labeled V_{hp} and V_{hn} are based upon the assumption that the neutron and proton see an additional potential given by Eq. (25) (Green, 1956c; Green and Sood, 1958).)

nuclear forces. Specifically in a context similar to that of the present discussion, Drell (1955) showed that an N–N interaction of the type

$$V(r) = V_d(r) + V_\tau(r)\tau_1 \cdot \tau_2 \tag{24}$$

upon summation, leads to an N–$\mathcal{N}$ interaction which we may place in the form

$$V(r) = V_0(r) + [(N - Z)/A]\langle T_{z1}\rangle[V_1(r)] \tag{24a}$$

where $\langle T_{z1}\rangle = +1$ for a proton and -1 for a neutron, and $V_1 = V_\tau(r)$. If $V_1(r)$ is attractive such a Heisenberg force would introduce an additional repulsion for neutrons as well as an additional attraction for protons. Thus one must introduce an additional attractive nonexchange term to the model to maintain the carefully adjusted neutron potential which underlies the earlier work. Accordingly, the anomaly was written in the form (Green, 1956c)

$$v = -\lambda(1 \pm K_\tau D/A)V_0\,\xi(r) \tag{25}$$

where $D = N - Z$, the upper sign is for protons and the lower sign for neutrons, V_0 is the unperturbed well depth for the neutron case, and $\xi(r)$ is the form function used in the neutron case. The constant $k_\tau \approx 5.6$ minimizes the overall A shifts for neutrons. The value $\lambda = 0.125$ then leads to the good overall set of A shifts for protons shown in Fig. 6. The residual neutron A shifts suggest that this perturbation would increase slightly the well depth of neutrons in light nuclei and decrease the well depth in heavy nuclei. In current notation (see Eq. (30)), $\lambda k_\tau V_0 \to V_1 \approx 26.5$ and $\lambda V_0 + V_0 \to V_0 \approx 45$.

While the foregoing phenomenological study excluded the possibility of a constant potential difference between protons and neutrons, i.e., V_{pa}, it did not convincingly discriminate between the $Z/A^{1/3}$ dependent anomaly V_{ca} and the two $(N - Z)/A$ dependent anomalies V_e and V_h. To rectify this, a detailed study was made of mirror nuclei (Sood and Green, 1958) for which an $(N - Z)/A$ effect would be expected to cancel but a $Z/A^{1/3}$ dependent effect should survive. The results were negative. This study thus not only rejected a strictly $Z/A^{1/3}$ dependent effect but also more convincingly rejected the possibility of a constant potential difference. Furthermore, the study indicated that the small increase in the neutron well depth was helpful.

Having explored the general nature of the proton potential anomaly, Green and Sood (1958) next attempted a more detailed study based on the properties of particular nuclei. To this end the following procedure was adopted to estimate the difference between the potential well depths for the cases of neutrons and protons. The radius constant and the diffuseness and spin orbit splitting parameters were assumed to be the same for both cases and are taken from the systematic neutron study described in Section 2.2. However, the neutron well depth was adjusted for each individual nucleus to get the predicted last neutron binding energy in agreement with experiment, thus in part taking into account the local variations of the potential. To treat protons, the neutron well was altered by the full Coulomb perturbation and the proton potential anomaly was adjusted so as to secure the experimental binding energy for the last proton. For simplicity the form function of the corrections was assumed to be the same as for the major nuclear potential. With this assumption the change in the well depth is given in terms of the needed A shift by

$$\Delta V_0 = \Delta A V_0/(S \, dA/dS). \tag{26}$$

For the proton case we must find the A shift after allowing for the constant shift associated with the Coulomb perturbation as well as the residual A shift. In Fig. 7 we show the potential anomaly defined by

$$V_{0a} = \Delta V_{0p} - \Delta V_{0n} \tag{27}$$

as a function of the parameter D/A. The results of such calculations for individual nuclei are shown by circles. Even–even nuclei have been chosen in an effort to equalize pairing energy effects. Since the results are quite sensitive to the details of the energy level spacings and the latter cannot be completely verified against the experimental data, appreciable uncertainty can enter into the calculations, particularly in the light elements. Thus, most cases with only a slight neutron excess were omitted. Furthermore, the assumption that the radii and spin orbit constants and the diffuseness length conform to the family of parameters previously selected was open to question since certainly these parameters also undergo local variations. Accepting these reservations, it should be clear in a qualitative way from Fig. 7 that the potential anomaly does indeed vary approximately linearly with D/A. The proportionality constant determined by least squares was

$$C_A = 57 \pm 4. \tag{28}$$

The sum of the neutron and proton well anomalies is fairly independent of the neutron excess parameter and is given approximately by

$$\Delta V_{0n} + \Delta V_{0p} = 12.1. \tag{29}$$

This detailed result tends to confirm Eq. (25) and leads to the parameter values $\lambda = 0.151$, $k_\tau = 4.75$. The particular cases of calcium isotopes are quite interesting since in these cases the symmetry parameter D/A undergoes appreciable variation. It was noteworthy that these conformed reasonably well to the systematics of the determinations from other nuclei.

In conclusion, the studies upon static potentials indicated that last particle proton and neutron binding energies could be accounted for quite

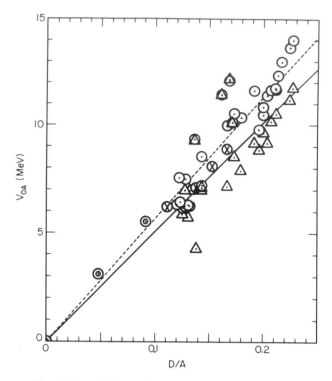

Fig. 7. Potential anomaly versus symmetry parameter.

(The circles represent the potential anomaly computed for individual nuclei on the basis of static potentials. The double circles indicate the isotopes of Ca^{40}, Ca^{44}, and Ca^{48}, the crossed circles the isotopes of Sn. The dotted line represents a least squares fit to the static anomalies. The triangles refer to potential anomalies computed for the case of a velocity dependent well with a reduced mass of the order of 0.6. The solid line represents a least squares fit to these points (see Chapter V) (Green and Sood, 1958).)

well using a basic IPM potential of the form

$$V(r) = -\left[V_0 \pm \frac{N-Z}{A} V_1\right]\xi(r) \qquad (30)$$

with $V_0 \approx 46$ and $V_1 = 28.5 \pm 2$.

By the time this study based upon static potentials was completed, a number of works had appeared (Johnson and Teller, 1955; Lane, 1957; Satchler, 1958) which suggested that the proton–neutron potential difference might be attributed to the velocity dependence of the N–$\mathcal{N}$ potential. Green (1956c), using an adaptation of the method of A shifts, investigated this possibility and found that unless an extremely high degree of velocity dependence was assumed there still remained a rather substantial anomaly. At the same time the mass surface studies (Lee and Green, 1956b; Green, 1958b) showed that the derived symmetry energy is improved if an $(N - Z)/A$ dependent term is introduced. The problem was treated more definitively with the aid of the Oak Ridge Oracle, using a numerical program for finding eigenvalues for velocity dependent potentials (Green, 1957). We shall return to this discussion in Chapter V when we treat the velocity dependent N-$\mathcal{N}$ potential in some detail. We will, however, note the conclusion was again reached (Green and Sood, 1958) that the need for an $(N - Z)/A$ dependent term does not change very much as we proceed from a static to a velocity dependent potential. This result is illustrated by the triangular points on Fig. 7 and the solid line which represents a least square fit to these points. These results implied that the principal term in a velocity dependent potential should have the form given by Eq. (30) but with $V_0 = 62$ MeV and $V_1 = 25$ MeV.

In view of the foregoing, the problem remains of explaining the funda-mental origin of such a symmetry dependent term. We come, therefore, to the consideration of various possible physical explanations for the proton anomaly.

a   Possible Failure of Koopmans' Theorem

It appeared possible at first that the proton potential anomaly might have its origin in the breakdown of the approximate theorem relating last particle separation energies to eigenvalues. For the case of atoms and mole-cules, the work of Koopmans (1933) shows that separation energies, computed by taking the difference of the total energies between the initial and final systems, are approximately equal to the eigenvalues for the single particle in the field of force established by its interactions with all the other particles. Expressed in other terms, we might say that rearrangement energies are small compared to the eigenvalues. By virtue of the strong and complex nature of the N–N interaction, Koopmans' theorem might well fail for the nuclear case. Unfortunately, papers attempting self-consistent nuclear field calculations have found rearrangement energies which have varied from 40 to 0 MeV per particle. It should be clear that this problem will not be settled until the definitive self-consistent field calculation based upon realistic N–N interactions has been carried out.

b   Breakdown of Electrostatic Laws inside the Nucleus

If the potential anomaly were due to a breakdown of electrodynamic laws inside the nucleus, we would expect it to have a $Z/A^{1/3}$ dependence rather than an $(N - Z)/A$ dependence. Studies of mirror nuclei appear to preclude this possibility. On the other hand, to the accuracy of our current investigations, we could not exclude a short-range modification of electro-dynamics, such as might be characterized by the alteration of the Coulomb Green's function to the form

$$G = (1 - e^{-\kappa r})/r \tag{31}$$

(Podolsky, 1942). Here κ corresponds to the regulator mass now used in discussions of the possible breakdown of electrodynamics. If one chooses κ to be large enough, then the short-range modification should have relatively little effect on the proton potential anomaly. Studies of electron scattering have indeed revealed proton size effects at distances corresponding to vector meson force ranges (~ 0.3 F). These effects, however, appear too short-ranged to explain the phenomenon in question.

c   Presence of Heisenberg Forces

If the N–N interaction contains an appreciable component of Heisenberg exchange forces, then as Drell (1955) has shown a perturbation of the type given by Eq. (24a) would be present. The success of this equation has already been evident. Heisenberg forces also arise from the exchange of isovector mesons. In view of the interrelationships between space, spin, and isotopic spin wave functions, imposed by the generalized exclusion principle for nucleons, it is likely that other types of exchange forces would also lead to nucleon–nuclear potential anomalies; thus the Heisenberg force explanation of the anomaly is not unique.

d   Effect of the Exclusion Principle

The exclusion principle influences the interaction of a nucleon with a nucleus in a variety of ways. Ross et al. (1956b) have proposed a simplified version of the effect of the exclusion principle, reasoning in the following fashion. Assuming the exclusion principle prevents like particles of the same spin from getting within the range of the nuclear forces, they conclude that

$$V_p(r) = \left(\frac{N + \frac{1}{2}Z}{Z + \frac{1}{2}N}\right) V_n(r). \tag{32}$$

Replacing N by $(A + D)/2$ and Z by $(A - D)/2$, it follows readily that

$$V_{p\alpha} = \frac{2}{3}\frac{D}{A} V_n(r). \tag{33}$$

Quantitative estimates of this effect suggest, however, that it is insufficient by itself.

Another effect of the exclusion principle is implicit in the works of Brueckner (1955), Bethe (1956a), and Moszkowski and Scott (1960), which indicate that the effect of the repulsive core terms in conjunction with the exclusion principle manifests itself in a self-consistent field calculation as inducing a modification of the effective N–N interaction in complex nuclear matter. The effective N–N potential is caused to have a nonlocal character, and in consequence the N–$\mathcal{N}$ potential has also a nonlocal or velocity dependent character. However, in the work of Green and Sood (1958), using nonlocal potentials as the basis of estimates of the proton potential anomaly, a part of the influence of the exclusion has already been considered. The additional need for an anomaly thus seems to demand a more positive $(N - Z)/A$ dependent effect.

e   Spin Dependence of Nuclear Forces

As early as 1936, Wigner recognized in the low energy n–p scattering data that the two body interaction is dependent upon the relative orientations of the spins, and that the ^3S state interaction is somewhat stronger than the ^1S state interaction. Bethe (1956b) has pointed to this spin dependence in conjunction with the exclusion principle as the explanation for the proton potential anomaly. The argument may be formalized as follows. Let us assume, for simplicity, that the two body interaction acts only in the S state of relative motion. Now let us consider a heavy nucleus consisting of a saturated core of nucleons and the neutron excess. A neutron or proton should be acted upon in a similar way by the core. On the other hand, the proton can interact with the neutron excess in both ^1S and ^3S states, whereas the incident neutron can interact only in ^1S states. Estimates of the combined influence of the extra interactions and the extra strength of ^3S interactions do indeed lead to a sufficiently large difference to explain the anomaly. However, until realistic N–N forces are successfully embodied in a self-consistent nuclear calculation, one could not make quantitative estimates of this effect.

In summary we may conclude that experimental information on neutron and proton separation energies, after allowing for the classical Coulomb effect, reveal systematic differences between the proton and neutron well depths which vary with the symmetry parameter $(N - Z)/A$. The variations are suggestive of the presence of a Heisenberg force. However, it would appear that the most reasonable explanation of these variations comes when one considers the effect of the exclusion principle in conjunction with the spin and isotopic spin dependence of the two body interaction. The proton potential anomaly inferred from bound state studies undergoes relatively small change as one goes to a velocity dependent potential or nonlocal potential. Green and Sood (1958) suggested that the optical model parameters utilized in nucleon–nuclear scattering should also reveal a similar dependence upon the symmetry parameter. These effects will be discussed in later sections.

In closing this discussion of the proton potential anomaly we call attention to the recent work of Perey and Schiffer (1966) on the isospin dependence of the nuclear charge radius. This investigation was stimulated by a series of precise measurements of muonic x-rays (Anderson et al., 1963, 1966; Devons et al., 1964, 1965, 1966), electron scattering studies (Hofstadter, 1965, 1966; Hofstadter et al., 1965), as well as earlier optical isotope shift measurements (Brix and Kopfermann,1958). All of these experimental observations indicate that the charge radius of the isotopes of an element does not increase as $A^{1/3}$ but at a rate which is considerably smaller. The $(N - Z)/A$ effect which we have discussed in this section provides a natural explanation for this anomalous behavior since a series of isotopes with increasing neutron excess would present successively deeper potentials to protons. Perey and Schiffer (1966) particularly examined the data on the calcium-40, -42, and -48 isotopes and the nickel-58, -60, -62, and -64 isotopes and compared charge radius measurements with calculated radii using shell model potentials which reproduce last particle binding energies. Their calculations were performed with a Woods–Saxon potential using the Abacus II program (Auerbach, 1962) for the determination of proton bound state wave functions and eigenvalues. Their results indicated that the symmetry term in the shell model potential explains the major characteristics of the observed anomalies. Similar calculations and results have been obtained with the exponentially diffuse potential using the A shift techniques described in this section (Sharma, 1964). Swift and Elton (1966) have also studied this problem.

2.4   Individual Particle States in Spheroidal Nuclei

In the previous sections we considered the energy level structure of spherical nuclei giving consideration to the influence of the spin orbit effect, diffuseness of the nuclear boundary, and the symmetry effect. During the same period in which these effects were studied, investigations initiated by Rainwater (1950), A. Bohr and Mottelson (1953), and others developed the so-called collective model of the nucleus. Here nucleons are pictured as undergoing collective motions similar to the vibrations and rotations of a liquid drop. These motions are in addition to the independent particle motion in an average nuclear potential which is now deformed from spherical form. It would take us outside the scope of this monograph to discuss in detail this collective motion or the interweaving of the independent particle motion with this collective motion. However, we shall consider a limiting case studied first by Nilsson (1955), Gottfried (1956), and others in which the two motions are sufficiently well separated so that we can meaningfully investigate the independent motion of individual particles in a deformed field which may be considered as stationary.

We shall restrict ourselves to states of cylindrical symmetry, that is, particle states in a field of spheroidal nature. The choice of the spheroidal field has varied in the many investigations. In one of the earliest definitive works Nilsson utilized the harmonic oscillator as his basic set. Gottfried in his investigations also used the harmonic oscillator although Uretsky (1957) used a spheroidal square well of finite depth. Later, Lemmer and Green (1960) treated the problem of independent particle motion in a nonlocal diffuse boundary spheroidal potential.

In dealing with spheroidal wells we might reasonably make the assumption that the spheroidal field is but a modification of the spherically symmetric field in which the equipotentials have been deformed from spheres to spheroids. We may characterize such a spheroid by the equation

$$r'^2 = \frac{x^2 + y^2}{c^2} + \frac{z^2}{b^2} = \frac{r^2 - z^2}{c^2} + \frac{z^2}{b^2}. \tag{1}$$

If $b = 1$ and $c = 1$, the equipotentials are spheres. Let us now characterize a deformation by a small deviation parameter ε so that

$$b - 1 + \varepsilon. \tag{2}$$

If now we agree that any deformed spheroid contains the same volume as the sphere, we have

$$bc^2 = 1 \quad \text{or} \quad c = (1 + \varepsilon)^{-1/2}. \tag{3}$$

Letting $z = r \cos \theta$ and

$$P_2 = P_2(\cos \theta) = \tfrac{1}{2}(3 \cos^2 \theta - 1) \tag{4}$$

and eliminating $\cos \theta$ it follows that Eq. (1) may be written

$$r'^2 = \left[\frac{2}{3}(1 + \varepsilon) + \frac{1}{3(1 + \varepsilon)^2} \right] r^2 - 2\left[\frac{1}{3}(1 + \varepsilon) - \frac{1}{3(1 + \varepsilon)^2} \right] r^2 P_2 \tag{5}$$

or

$$r'^2 - r^2 = (\alpha_0 - 2\alpha_2 P_2) r^2 \tag{6}$$

where

$$\alpha_0 = \frac{2}{3}(1 + \varepsilon) + \frac{1}{3(1 + \varepsilon)^2} - 1 \approx \varepsilon^2 - \frac{4}{3} \varepsilon^3 \tag{7}$$

and

$$\alpha_2 = \frac{1}{3}(1 + \varepsilon) - \frac{1}{3(1 + \varepsilon)^2} \approx \varepsilon - \varepsilon^2 + \frac{4}{3} \varepsilon^3. \tag{8}$$

If the potential at the deformed coordinate r' is chosen to be the same as the potential of a spherical well at the coordinate r it follows that

$$V(r'^2) = V(r^2) + (r'^2 - r^2)\frac{dV}{d(r^2)} + \frac{(r'^2 - r^2)^2}{2}\frac{d^2V}{d(r^2)^2} + \cdots \tag{9}$$

or

$$V(r') = V(r) + \frac{r'^2 - r^2}{2}\frac{1}{r}\frac{dV}{dr} + \frac{(r'^2 - r^2)^2}{2}\left[-\frac{1}{4r^3}\frac{dV}{dr} + \frac{1}{4r^2}\frac{d^2V}{dr^2}\right] + \cdots \tag{10}$$

Hence

$$V(r') = V(r) + (\alpha_0 - 2\alpha_2 P_2)\frac{r}{2}\frac{dV}{dr}$$

$$+ \frac{1}{2}[\alpha_0 - 2\alpha_2 P_2]^2\left[-\frac{r}{4}\frac{dV}{dr} + \frac{r^2}{4}\frac{d^2V}{dr^2}\right] + \cdots \tag{11}$$

We might note that the first two terms in this expression constitute an exact result for the case of the harmonic oscillator potential, since for this potential the last term and higher order terms vanish identically. In treating spheroidal distorted nuclei it is customary to expand the potential and to carry terms up to quadratic in the distortion parameters. Thus we may write

$$V(r') = V(r) - \varepsilon r\frac{dV}{dr}P_2 + \frac{\varepsilon^2}{2}r\frac{dV}{dr}$$

$$+ \varepsilon^2 r\frac{dV}{dr}P_2 + \frac{1}{2}\left[-r\frac{dV}{dr} + r^2\frac{d^2V}{dr^2}\right]\varepsilon^2 P_2{}^2. \tag{12}$$

The linear term in ε in this series is a common element in all treatments of spheroidal nuclei. The quadratic terms differ from treatment to treatment partly because of differences in the choice of the deformation parameter and partly because of inconsistencies in approximation. We shall concentrate the remainder of our discussion on the work of Nilsson (1955) since his work has been quoted most extensively.

Nilsson chooses the harmonic oscillator as his unperturbed Hamiltonian and treats the spheroidal deformation effect as a perturbation which is represented by

$$H_\delta = -\delta\hbar\omega_0(\delta)\frac{4}{3}\left(\frac{\pi}{5}\right)^{1/2}r^2 Y_{20} \tag{13}$$

where

$$\omega_0(\delta) = \mathring{\omega}_0\left(1 - \frac{4}{3}\delta^2 - \frac{16}{27}\delta^3\right)^{-1/6}. \tag{14}$$

Here $\dot{\omega}_0$ is a constant which differs from $\omega_0(\delta)$ because of the volume preserving requirement. This differs from the linear perturbation which we have just developed partly in the use of

$$Y_{20} = [5/4\pi]^{1/2}P_2(\cos\theta) \tag{15}$$

and a deformation parameter $\delta = 3\varepsilon/2 + \mathcal{O}\varepsilon^2 + \cdots$. Nilsson also introduces a spin orbit perturbation

$$H_{so} = C\mathbf{L}\cdot\mathbf{S} \tag{16}$$

and the oscillator orbital perturbation

$$H_l = D\mathbf{L}\cdot\mathbf{L} \tag{17}$$

which we discussed in Section 1.3. The total perturbation is represented by

$$H - H_0 = k\hbar\dot{\omega}_0\,R \tag{18}$$

where

$$R = -\eta\,\frac{4}{3}\left(\frac{\pi}{5}\right)^{1/2} r^2 Y_{20} - 2\mathbf{L}\cdot\mathbf{S} - \mu\mathbf{L}^2 \tag{19}$$

and

$$k = -\tfrac{1}{2}(C/\hbar\dot{\omega}_0) \tag{20}$$

$$\mu = 2D/C \tag{21}$$

$$\eta = \frac{\delta}{k}\,\frac{\omega_0(\delta)}{\dot{\omega}_0} = \frac{\delta}{k}\left(1 - \frac{4}{3}\delta^2 - \frac{16}{27}\delta^3\right)^{-1/6}. \tag{22}$$

Note that other than η the only parameter in R is μ which is independent of the deformation. This parameter is chosen for each oscillator shell to obtain the observed order of spherical well levels. For $N = 0$, 1, and 2, $\mu = 0$ is adequate so that this perturbation can be ignored. However, for $N = 3\text{--}7$, values between 0.35 and 0.55 are needed. The final calculation consisted of an exact diagonalization of the matrix of the perturbation in the chosen representation. We may recall from the standard discussions of second order perturbation theory that we must find the linear combination of the unperturbed wave functions which correspond to a representation which diagonalizes the perturbation. For the harmonic oscillator Hamiltonian, states with different j, l, and m_j (in the usual notation) are degenerate in the zero order. The spin orbit effect breaks the degeneracy on j, the orbital effect breaks the degeneracy on l, and now the spheroidal distortion effect partially breaks the degeneracy on m_j. For spheroidal deformation this term is independent of the sign of m_j and hence the perturbation introduces a splitting which depends upon the values of the quantum number

$$\Omega = |m_j|. \tag{23}$$

Now in actuality in the presence of a spheroidal distortion perturbation the quantum numbers N, l, and j are no longer good quantum numbers since the perturbation term connects states which have different values of these quantum numbers. However, the nondiagonal terms which connect states of different N are relatively small compared to the energy separation between such states and accordingly Nilsson discards such terms and hence N may still be used as a good quantum number. While the three perturbations destroy the meaningfulness of the quantum numbers l and j they do not influence the component operator

$$J_z = L_z + S_z \tag{24}$$

or the corresponding quantum number

$$m_j = m_l + m_s \tag{24a}$$

or

$$\Omega = |m_j| = |\Lambda + \Sigma|, \tag{25}$$

the latter equation representing the current notation.

Nilsson carried out his diagonalization for various values of the deformation parameter η and from this diagonalization or rather its submatrices belonging to certain N and Ω the eigenvalues $r_\alpha^N(\eta)$ were deduced. Nilsson presents these eigenvalues as graphs of

$$\frac{E_\alpha}{\hbar\omega_0(\delta)} = N_\alpha + \frac{3}{2} + \frac{\mathring{\omega}_0}{\omega_0(\delta)} r_\alpha^N(\eta). \tag{26}$$

Adjusting $\hbar\mathring{\omega}_0$ to produce mean radii in accord with electron scattering results Nilsson chooses

$$\hbar\mathring{\omega}_0 \approx 41 A^{-1/3} \quad \text{MeV}. \tag{27}$$

The matrix diagonalizations were carried out with the aid of a digital computer. Nilsson's results are illustrated in Fig. 1.

A number of features of Fig. 1 are worthy of note. In the neighborhood of the spherical state ($\delta = 0$) the states can be labeled by the l and j quantum numbers. The degeneracy with respect to m_j is then partially removed by the distortion term in such a manner that the energies increase with increasing $\Omega = |m_j|$ for positive δ(or η). The level order is the opposite for negative δ. With increasing deformation, states of different j and l, but with the same

Ω and parity, are coupled together. For intermediate deformations the situation becomes quite complex as illustrated by the peculiar variations of the energy levels with δ.

When the deformations are sufficiently large, a simplification again sets

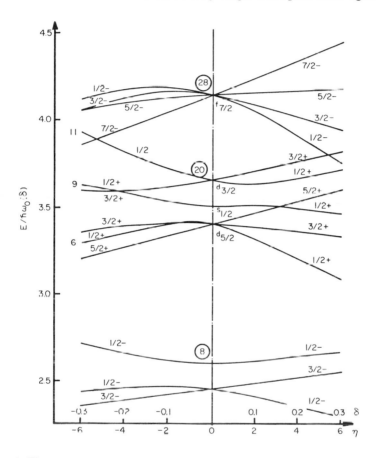

Fig. 1. The energy levels of a single particle in an axially symmetric deformed well with spin orbit coupling.

(The parameter δ is defined in Eq. (13). Nilsson's parameter η is defined in terms of δ and the spin orbit coupling constant. The numbers at the left of the $\frac{1}{2}^+$ curves are Nilsson's labels for the orbits. The Ω value for each orbit is given at the right and left.)

in, in that the zero order approximation may be considered to be the levels of a pure anisotropic harmonic oscillator in which the spheroidal distortion term is the principle perturbation and the H_{so} and H_l are minor perturbations. In this case the good quantum numbers are N, n_z, m_l, and m_s. In addition to the eigenvalues, Nilsson also finds the corresponding eigenfunctions as a sequence of coefficients defined by

$$|N\Omega\alpha\rangle = \sum_{l} \{A_{l,\,\Omega-\frac{1}{2}}|Nl(\Omega - \tfrac{1}{2})+\rangle + A_{l,\,\Omega-\frac{1}{2}}|Nl(\Omega + \tfrac{1}{2})-\rangle\}. \quad (28)$$

Table I illustrates an example of these results. For example the state of

TABLE I
EIGENVALUES AND EIGENFUNCTIONS FOR THE DEFORMED FIELD[a,b]

	$\eta = -6$	-4	-2	2	4	6
11	8.719	6.379	4.368	2.630	3.298	4.394
	1.000	1.000	1.000	1.000	1.000	1.000
	0.649	0.591	0.432	−0.717	−1.143	−1.287
	−0.428	−0.605	−0.907	−1.066	−0.675	−0.454
9	2.568	1.693	0.667	0.120	−0.237	−0.853
	1.000	1.000	1.000	1.000	1.000	1.000
	2.203	2.227	2.828	−15.696	15.901	6.635
	5.672	3.827	2.449	11.489	−25.472	−16.609
6	−4.287	−3.072	−2.035	−3.751	−6.069	−8.542
	1.000	1.000	1.000	1.000	1.000	1.000
	−1.319	−1.227	−0.927	0.503	0.622	0.662
	0.336	0.453	0.662	0.600	0.428	0.325

[a] $N = 2$, $\Omega = \frac{1}{2}$, base vectors: $|220+\rangle$, $|200+\rangle$, $|221-\rangle$.
[b] Nilsson (1955).

$N = 2$, $\Omega = \frac{1}{2}$ is used, with the base vectors from 2s and 1d orbitals $|220+\rangle$, $|200+\rangle$, and $|221-\rangle$. The eigenvalues r_1, r_2, and r_3 are listed for each value of η. Below each eigenvalue are three numbers which give the coefficients. The normalization has been taken so that the first listed coefficient is equal to 1. For example when $\eta = 6$ the largest eigenvalue is 4.394. This corresponds to the eigenfunction

$$1.000|220+\rangle - 1.287|200+\rangle - 0.454|221-\rangle. \quad (29)$$

An essential part of the Nilsson calculation is a determination of the total energy and the equilibrium deformation. We might indicate briefly the nature of this approach. Assuming only two body forces the Hamiltonian for the ith particle may be written

$$H_i = T_i + V_i = T_i + \sum_{i \neq j} v_{ij}. \quad (30)$$

On the other hand, the Hamiltonian for the total nucleus is (Eq. (24), Section 2.1)

$$H_T = \sum T_i + \tfrac{1}{2} \sum{}' v_{ij} = \sum E_i - \tfrac{1}{2} V_i. \tag{31}$$

Accordingly to find the total energy E_T we must have the expectation of H_T with respect to an appropriately antisymmetrized combination of the calculated single particle wave functions. The equilibrium deformation then follows from the solution of

$$\frac{\partial E_T(\delta)}{\partial \delta} = 0 \tag{32}$$

and the value δ_{eq} which satisfies this at the total minimum energy $E_T(\delta_{eq})$. The energy minimum may be found for each single particle combination of levels. The lowest minimum gives the ground state. Other level combinations for the given set of particles would correspond to excited states.

Perhaps it is important at this point to emphasize again that the total nuclear excitation spectrum will have three distinct modes. On each single particle level characterized by Ω, there will be superimposed vibrational bands. They will be analogous to the vibrational bands of molecular spectra. Furthermore, on each level is superimposed a rotational band associated with the collective motion of the nucleus as a whole. For a heavy nucleus the level distance of the particle spectrum is of the order of 100 keV, that of the vibrational spectrum is of the order of a few MeV (in contrast to molecular spectra, the vibrational spectra of nuclei are much more widely spaced). Finally, the rotational energies depend upon the nuclear deformation, but for heavy nuclei and for large deformation they are much smaller than the vibrational energies.

We shall not go into the successes of the spheroidally distorted nucleus from the standpoint of ground state spin and magnetic moments. Let it suffice to say that when a spheroidal deformation is introduced to single particle states one finds that the magnetic moments are moved away from the Schmidt limits in the direction indicated by experiment. Furthermore, when a reasonable allowance is made for the collective contributions of the deformed core, the total quadrupole moments are in very nice agreement with experiment.

III

Realistic Optical Models

3.1 Partial Wave Analysis for Neutral Spinless Particles

3.1a Partial Wave Expansions

The problem of finding the solutions of Schroedinger's equation with the appropriate asymptotic form in the presence of a complex potential in general is a difficult one. For the most part a numerical technique must be invoked to treat this problem. The most important technique from the standpoint of low energy nuclear physics is the method of partial waves. This is of particular interest to us because of its relationship to many of the techniques used in bound state problems. In this method we take advantage of an exact expansion for an incident plane wave as given by Eq. (12), Section 1.4,

$$\psi_{\text{inc}} = \exp(ik\hat{\mathbf{n}}_0 \cdot \mathbf{r}) = \sum_l (2l + 1)i^l j_l(kr)P_l(\cos \theta). \tag{1}$$

We now consider a somewhat more convenient partial wave formalism than the usual phase shift formalism which involves complex scattering amplitudes (η_l). The spherical Bessel functions are decomposed as

$$j_l(kr) = \tfrac{1}{2}[h_l^{(2)}(kr) + h_l^{(1)}(kr)] \tag{2}$$

where $h_l^{(1)(2)}$ denote spherical Hankel functions of the first and second kind. The asymptotic forms of these spherical Hankel functions are

$$h_l^{(1)}(kr) \simeq -(i/kr)\exp[i(kr - l\pi/2)] \tag{3}$$

and

$$h_l^{(2)}(kr) \simeq (i/kr)\exp[-i(kr - l\pi/2)] \tag{4}$$

Accordingly $h_l^{(2)}(kr)$ may be identified as a radially incoming wave and $h_l^{(1)}(kr)$ as a radially outgoing wave.

The above representation for an unperturbed plane wave is now used as a guide for seeking the exact solution of Schroedinger's equation. Essentially we assume that the solution of the optical model Schroedinger equation has the same dependence upon angle but an altered radial dependence. Therefore we write

$$\psi = \tfrac{1}{2} \sum_l (2l + 1)i^l(G_l(r)/kr)P_l(\cos \theta). \tag{5}$$

It follows then from the orthogonality of angular momentum eigenfunctions that each radial function must satisfy

$$\frac{d^2 G_l}{dr^2} + \left\{ k^2 - \frac{l(l+1)}{r^2} - \frac{2m}{\hbar^2} V \right\} G_l = 0. \tag{6}$$

As a boundary condition we require G_l to be zero at the origin. This apart from the normalization constant serves to uniquely determine the radial wave functions. The normalization is determined by examining the asymptotic form of the wave function which must be expressible in terms of the incident plane wave plus a radially outgoing scattered wave. In the partial wave treatment, this implies that as $V \to 0$

$$\frac{G_l(kr)}{kr} \simeq h_l^{(2)}(kr) + \eta_l \, h_l^{(1)}(kr). \tag{7}$$

Essentially we assume that the lth partial wave function at long distances differs from the lth partial wave in the incident plane wave only in the complex amplitude of the radially outgoing wave. The magnitude of this amplitude cannot be greater than unity since we are assuming that we are dealing with an absorptive (i.e., not emissive) medium. Writing $\eta_l = 1 + \eta_l - 1$ we see that the solution of Schroedinger's equation at large distances is

$$\psi \simeq \psi_{\text{inc}} + \tfrac{1}{2} \sum_l (2l + 1)i^l h_l^{(1)}(kr)[\eta_l - 1]P_l(\cos \theta). \tag{8}$$

In view of the asymptotic form of $h_l^{(1)}(kr)$ we see that this is in conformity with the original requirement that

$$\psi = \psi_{\text{inc}} + f(\hat{n}_0, \hat{n})(e^{ikr}/r) \tag{9}$$

where

$$f = (1/2ik) \sum_l (2l + 1)(\eta_l - 1)P_l(\cos \theta). \tag{10}$$

3.1b   The Cross Sections

It follows from Eq. (10), Section 1.4, that the differential scattering cross section is given by

$$\sigma(\hat{n}_0, \hat{n}) = (1/4k^2) \left| \sum_l (2l + 1)(\eta_l - 1)P_l(\cos \theta) \right|^2. \tag{11}$$

The total scattering cross section obtained by integrating over the entire solid angle is

$$\sigma_e = \int f^* f \, d\Omega = \sum_l \sigma_e^{(l)} \tag{12}$$

where

$$\sigma_e^{(l)} = (\pi/k^2)(2l+1) |\eta_l - 1|^2 \tag{13}$$

is the elastic scattering cross section for the lth partial wave. Our characterization of the wave function permits us to solve for the absorption cross section. Thus, to calculate the flux which enters a large sphere surrounding the scatterer, we note that the asymptotic wave function may be written in the form

$$\psi \simeq (i/2kr) \sum_l (2l+1)[e^{-ikr} - \eta_l e^{ikr}]P_l(\cos\theta). \tag{14}$$

Thus it follows upon integration over the entire solid angle that the number of incoming particles with orbital angular momentum l are

$$N_{\text{inc}} = (2l+1)\pi\hbar/mk \tag{15}$$

whereas from the outgoing wave we find

$$N_{\text{out}} = (2l+1) |\eta_l|^2 \pi\hbar/mk. \tag{16}$$

The net flux which flows in, i.e., the absorbed particles, is

$$N_a = (\pi\hbar/mk) \sum_l (2l+1)[1 - |\eta_l|^2]. \tag{17}$$

Hence the absorption cross section is

$$\sigma_r = N_a/(\hbar k/m) = \sum_l \sigma_r^{(l)} \tag{18}$$

where

$$\sigma_r^{(l)} = (\pi/k^2)(2l+1)[1 - |\eta_l|^2]. \tag{19}$$

The quantity $T_l \equiv 1 - |\eta_l|^2$ is called the absorption coefficient. The total cross section may now be expressed as

$$\sigma_t = \sigma_e + \sigma_r = \sum_l [\sigma_e^{(l)} + \sigma_r^{(l)}]. \tag{20}$$

Thus we see that all of the major measurable quantities may be related to the complex scattering amplitudes η_l. As an example we note that the S state ($l = 0$) scattering cross sections for spinless particles are seen to be

$$\sigma_e = (\pi/k^2) |1 - \eta|^2 \tag{21}$$

and

$$\sigma_r = (\pi/k^2)(1 - |\eta|^2) \tag{22}$$

while from Eq. (14), the asymptotic form of the S wave part of the field is, for the particular normalization we have chosen,

$$\psi = (i/2kr)(e^{-ikr} - \eta e^{ikr}). \qquad (23)$$

These results will form the starting point of our discussion in Chapter IV, Section 4.1, concerning scattering at low energies. We might mention that the formulas given in this section are model independent. Nuclear models enter into the calculation of η_l.

If there is no absorption, $|\eta_l| = 1$. It is customary in many treatments to introduce the partial wave phase shifts δ_l by writing

$$\eta_l = \exp(2i\delta_l). \qquad (24)$$

Even when the potential is absorbing, this representation is still frequently used, but the phase shifts are then complex and must have positive imaginary parts.

3.1c   The Cross Section Theorem

An important theorem which has a rather general validity is the so-called cross section theorem

$$\sigma_t = (4\pi/k) \operatorname{Im} f(0) \qquad (25)$$

which relates the total cross section to the imaginary part of the forward scattering amplitude. We shall demonstrate the validity of this theorem for the case of spinless particles using the partial wave analysis. Thus with a little algebra, we obtain

$$\sigma_t = \sigma_r + \sigma_e = (2\pi/k^2) \sum_l (2l + 1)(1 - \operatorname{Re} \eta_l). \qquad (26)$$

Since $P_l(\cos \theta = 1) = 1$ we have from Eq. (10)

$$f(0) = (1/2ik) \sum_l (2l + 1)(\eta_l - 1) \qquad (27)$$

whence

$$(4\pi/k) \operatorname{Im} f(0) = (2\pi/k^2) \sum_l (2l + 1)(1 - \operatorname{Re} \eta) = \sigma_t. \qquad (28)$$

We remark that this theorem is a general one and not as restricted as our particular method of verification makes it appear. The theorem is a consequence of the conservation law; it is a mathematical statement of the fact that any particles which are elastically scattered or absorbed must necessarily have been removed from the incident beam. Its form follows from the fact that, for conservation, interference between the incident and scattered wave must account for the total scattering. The incident wave picks out the forward direction and hence we see the origin of the linear relationship between the total cross section and the forward scattering amplitude which is embodied in the theorem. For a more detailed discussion of the optical theorem we refer the reader to the article by Gerjuoy and Saxon (1954).

3.2   Partial Wave Analysis for Charged Spinless Particles

We now discuss the scattering of particles of charge ze by a nucleus of charge Ze. At small distances the form of the electrostatic interaction depends on the assumed nuclear charge distribution, while for large values we must go over to the Coulomb interaction of two point charges. Since the scattering turns out to be insensitive to the precise form of the charge distribution, for simplicity, the potential is frequently taken to be that of a uniformly charged sphere of radius equal to the nuclear radius. The potential in this case is

$$V_{\text{coul}} = \frac{zZe^2}{R_c} \left(\frac{3}{2} - \frac{r^2}{2R_c{}^2} \right) \qquad \text{for} \qquad r \le R_c \tag{1}$$

and

$$V_{\text{coul}} = \frac{zZe^2}{r} \qquad \text{for} \qquad r \ge R_c \tag{2}$$

where R_c corresponds to the equivalent charged sphere distribution.

Charged particle scattering can be treated in analogy to the neutral particle case by introducing first the Coulomb wave function ψ_c, corresponding to the scattering of two point charges, which is a solution of the Schroedinger equation,

$$-(\hbar^2/2m) \nabla^2 \psi_c + (zZe^2/r)\psi_c = E\psi_c. \tag{3}$$

For a wave incident along $\hat{\mathbf{n}}_0$, ψ_c has the familiar form

$$\psi_c = \Gamma(1 + i\eta) \exp(-i\eta\pi/2) \exp(ik\hat{\mathbf{n}}_0 \cdot \mathbf{r})F(-i\eta, 1, ik\xi) \tag{4}$$

where η is the dimensionless Coulomb parameter

$$\eta = mzZe^2/\hbar^2 k \tag{5}$$

and

$$\xi = r - \hat{\mathbf{n}}_0 \cdot \mathbf{r} = r(1 - \hat{\mathbf{n}}_0 \cdot \hat{\mathbf{n}}) \tag{6}$$

is the parabolic coordinate, while F is a confluent hypergeometric function (Schiff, 1955), and Γ is the gamma function.

The asymptotic form of ψ_c is, at $r \to \infty$,

$$\psi_c \simeq \left(1 - \frac{\eta^2}{ik(r - \hat{\mathbf{n}}_0 \cdot \mathbf{r})} \right) \exp\{i[k\hat{\mathbf{n}}_0 \cdot \mathbf{r} - \eta \ln k(r - \hat{\mathbf{n}}_0 \cdot \mathbf{r})]\}$$
$$+ r^{-1} f_c(\theta) \exp[i(kr - \eta \ln 2kr)] \tag{7}$$

where f_c is the Rutherford scattering amplitude,

$$f_c = -\frac{\eta}{2k \sin^2 \theta/2} \exp[-i\eta \ln(\sin^2 \theta/2) + 2i\sigma_0] \tag{8}$$

and $\sigma_0 = \arg \Gamma(1 + i\eta)$. The expansion of ψ_c in angular momentum eigen-functions is

$$\psi_c = \sum_{l=0}^{\infty} (2l + 1)i^l \exp(i\sigma_l) \frac{\mathscr{F}_l(\eta, kr)}{kr} P_l(\cos \theta) \tag{9}$$

where $\mathscr{F}_l$ is the Coulomb function, regular at the origin, and where σ_l is the Coulomb phase shift given by

$$\sigma_l = \arg \Gamma(l + 1 + i\eta). \tag{10}$$

The functions $\exp(i\sigma_l)\mathscr{F}_l/kr$ then play the same role as the spherical Bessel functions in the neutral particle case. We express them in terms of their in-coming and outgoing parts by writing

$$\mathscr{F}_l = \tfrac{1}{2}i(M_l^{(2)} - M_l^{(1)}) \tag{11}$$

where, in more customary notation,

$$M_l^{(1)} = \mathscr{G}_l + i\mathscr{F}_l \tag{12}$$

$$M_l^{(2)} = \mathscr{G}_l - i\mathscr{F}_l \tag{13}$$

with $\mathscr{G}_l$ the irregular Coulomb function. The normalization is such that, $r \to \infty$,

$$M_l^{(1)} \simeq \exp\{i[kr - \eta \ln 2kr - l\pi/2 - \sigma_l]\} \tag{14}$$

and

$$M_l^{(2)} \simeq \exp\{-i[kr - \eta \ln 2kr - l\pi/2 - \sigma_l]\}. \tag{15}$$

The actual optical model Schroedinger equation contains only short range nuclear interactions in addition to the Coulomb potential due to a nuclear charge distribution. Consequently, just as in the neutral case, only the out-going waves are modified by the short range interaction and the extended charge distribution. Writing, in analogy with Eq. (9),

$$\psi = \tfrac{1}{2}i \sum (2l + 1)i^l \exp(i\sigma_l)(G_l/kr)P_l(\cos \theta) \tag{16}$$

we see that G_l are the regular solutions of the radial equations

$$\frac{d^2 G_l}{dr^2} + \left\{ k^2 - \frac{l(l + 1)}{r^2} - \frac{2m}{\hbar^2} [V_{\text{coul}} + V] \right\} G_l = 0, \tag{17}$$

with the asymptotic form

$$G_l \simeq M_l^{(2)}(kr) - \eta_l M_l^{(1)}(kr) \tag{18}$$

where $|\eta_l| \leq 1$. The η_l contains the effect of nuclear interactions and the effect of extended charge distribution. The subsequent analysis now proceeds exactly as in the neutral particle case and leads to the result that, as $r \to \infty$,

$$\psi \simeq \left[1 - \frac{\eta^2}{ik(r - \hat{\mathbf{n}}_0 \cdot \mathbf{r})} \right] \exp\{i[k\hat{\mathbf{n}}_0 \cdot \mathbf{r} - \eta \ln k(r - \hat{\mathbf{n}}_0 \cdot \mathbf{r})]\}$$

$$+ f(\hat{\mathbf{n}}_0, \hat{\mathbf{n}}) \frac{\exp\{i[kr - \eta \ln 2kr]\}}{r} \tag{19}$$

where, with f_c given by Eq. (8), we have

$$f(\hat{\mathbf{n}}_0, \hat{\mathbf{n}}) = f_c + \frac{1}{2ik} \sum_{l=0}^{\infty} \exp(2i\sigma_l)[(2l + 1)(\eta_l - 1)P_l(\hat{\mathbf{n}}_0 \cdot \hat{\mathbf{n}})]. \tag{20}$$

Except for the addition of the Coulomb amplitude f_c and the introduction of the Coulomb phase shifts σ_l, the scattering amplitude f is seen to be formally the same as for the neutral particle case, and all expressions for cross sections and polarization (as we shall note later) are unaltered in form. We note that the latter is properly recovered if η is set equal to zero since f_c and the σ_l all then vanish. In the evaluation of these cross sections, interference between the Coulomb and nuclear contribution typically appears. However, it turns out that the total cross section for absorption σ_r contains no such terms and is given in terms of the η_l appropriate to charged particles by Eq. (19), Section 3.1, without modification. This latter result can be obtained by calculating the net flux N_a into a large sphere surrounding the scattering center using Eq. (16), Eq. (18), and the Wronskian relation between the regular and the irregular Coulomb functions, $\mathscr{G}_l(d\mathscr{F}_l/dr) - \mathscr{F}_l(d\mathscr{G}_l/dr) = k$.

3.3   Scattering of Spin $\frac{1}{2}$ Particles

3.3a   Generalization of the Partial Wave Treatment

The particular solution of Schroedinger's equation appropriate to the scattering of a beam of particles with spin $\frac{1}{2}$ incident from infinity along the direction $\hat{\mathbf{n}}_0$, by an optical model potential with a spin orbit term

$$V = V_1 + V_2(\boldsymbol{\sigma} \cdot \mathbf{L}), \tag{1}$$

is characterized by the requirement that the field at large distances have the form

$$\psi = \exp(ik\hat{\mathbf{n}}_0 \cdot \mathbf{r})\chi_{\text{inc}} + F(\hat{\mathbf{n}}_0, \hat{\mathbf{n}})(e^{ikr}/r)\chi_{\text{inc}} \tag{2}$$

where the first term gives the incident field, the second the purely outgoing scattered field. The quantity χ_{inc} is the incident spin wave function which we write in the form

$$\chi_{inc} = a^+ \chi_+ + a^- \chi_- = \begin{pmatrix} a^+ \\ a^- \end{pmatrix} \qquad (3)$$

where χ_+ and χ_- are normalized spin eigenfunctions with respect to some arbitrarily oriented direction and where a^+ and a^- are the corresponding amplitudes normalized so that $|a^+|^2 + |a^-|^2 = 1$. The quantity $F(\hat{n}_0, \hat{n})$ is the 2×2 scattering matrix in the direction $\hat{n}$. Let us consider now the generalization of the partial wave analysis for neutral particles with spin $\frac{1}{2}$.

The incident plane wave term

$$\psi_{inc} = \exp(ik\hat{n}_0 \cdot \mathbf{r})\chi_{inc} = \exp(ikr\hat{n}_0 \cdot \hat{n}) \begin{pmatrix} a^+ \\ a^- \end{pmatrix} \qquad (4)$$

when expanded in spherical harmonics, yields the familiar result

$$\psi_{inc} = \sum_l (2l + 1)i^l j_l(kr)P_l(\cos \theta)\chi_{inc} \qquad (5)$$

where θ is the angle between $\hat{n}_0$ and $\hat{n}$, $j_l(kr)$ is the regular spherical Bessel function of order l and where the $P_l(\cos \theta)$ are the Legendre polynomials.

The product functions $P_l(\cos \theta)\chi_+$ which appear in Eq. (5) are simultaneous eigenfunctions of the operators $\mathbf{L}^2$, L_z, $\mathbf{S}^2$, and S_z but not of the operator $\mathbf{L} \cdot \mathbf{S}$ which appears in the spin orbit interaction. This may be remedied by projecting out simultaneous eigenfunctions of $\mathbf{L}^2$, $\mathbf{S}^2$, $\mathbf{J}^2$, and J_z and thus of $\mathbf{L} \cdot \mathbf{S}$ from the functions $P_l(\cos \theta)\chi_+$, where $\mathbf{J} = \mathbf{L} + \frac{1}{2}\boldsymbol{\sigma}$ is the total angular momentum. (In this section, all angular momenta are given in units of $\hbar$.)

It is convenient to define operators which, acting on states of given l, project out the two possible states of j (Lepore, 1950). These projection operators, which we denote by $\mathscr{P}_l^+$ and $\mathscr{P}_l^-$ for the $l + \frac{1}{2}$ and $l - \frac{1}{2}$ states, respectively, are easily seen to be

$$\mathscr{P}_l^+ - \frac{l + 1 + \boldsymbol{\sigma} \cdot \mathbf{L}}{2l + 1}, \qquad (6)$$

$$\mathscr{P}_l^- = \frac{l - \boldsymbol{\sigma} \cdot \mathbf{L}}{2l + 1}, \qquad (7)$$

since the eigenvalues of $(\boldsymbol{\sigma} \cdot \mathbf{L})$ are l and $-(l + 1)$ for $j = l + \frac{1}{2}$ and $l - \frac{1}{2}$, respectively. Their normalization gives them the properties

$$(\mathscr{P}_l^\pm)^2 = \mathscr{P}_l^\pm \qquad (8)$$

and

$$\mathscr{P}_l^+ + \mathscr{P}_l^- = 1. \qquad (9)$$

Furthermore, they satisfy

$$\mathscr{P}_l^+\mathscr{P}_l^- = \mathscr{P}_l^-\mathscr{P}_l^+ = 0. \tag{10}$$

The projection operators have the property that if φ_l is a product of a spin function χ and any eigenfunction of orbital angular momentum corresponding to the eigenvalue l, then $\mathscr{P}_l^\pm\varphi_l$ is a simultaneous eigenfunction of $\mathbf{J}^2$, $\mathbf{L}^2$, and $\mathbf{S}^2$ with the eigenvalue of J equal to $j = l \pm \tfrac{1}{2}$.

In particular, we have

$$(\boldsymbol{\sigma} \cdot \mathbf{L})\mathscr{P}_l^\pm P_l(\cos\theta)\chi_{\text{inc}} = \left\{\begin{matrix} l \\ -l-1 \end{matrix}\right\}\mathscr{P}_l^\pm P_l(\cos\theta)\chi_{\text{inc}}. \tag{11}$$

Using Eq. (9), ψ_{inc} given by Eq. (5) can be rewritten as

$$\psi_{\text{inc}} = \tfrac{1}{2}\sum_l (2l+1)i^l[h_l^{(2)}(kr) + h_l^{(1)}(kr)]\{\mathscr{P}_l^+ + \mathscr{P}_l^-\}P_l(\cos\theta)\chi_{\text{inc}} \tag{12}$$

which is just an identity since the factor in curly brackets is unity. We have also reexpressed the radial waves in terms of incoming and outgoing parts using Eq. (2), Section 3.1.

This expression for ψ_{inc} then represents a free particle solution of Schroedinger's equation for a particular direction of incidence and a particular incident spin state, and is represented by a superposition of incoming and outgoing eigenstates of $\mathbf{J}^2$ and $\mathbf{L}^2$.

The solution of the optical model Schroedinger's equation for a spherical complex potential corresponding to such an incident wave must have the same angular form but altered radial dependence, and we therefore write

$$\psi = \tfrac{1}{2}\sum (2l+1)i^l\left[\frac{G_l^+(r)}{kr}\mathscr{P}_l^+ + \frac{G_l^-(r)}{kr}\mathscr{P}_l^-\right]P_l(\cos\theta)\chi_{\text{inc}}. \tag{13}$$

The terms in this expansion have been constructed so as not to be coupled by the spin orbit interaction. Using the orthogonality of the angular momentum eigenfunctions, substitution into Schroedinger's equation yields the radial equations

$$\frac{d^2G_l^\pm}{dr^2} + \left\{k^2 - \frac{l(l+1)}{r^2} - \frac{2m}{\hbar^2}\left[V_1 + \left(\begin{matrix} l \\ -l-1 \end{matrix}\right)V_2\right]\right\}G_l^\pm = 0 \tag{14}$$

where we have used Eq. (11) and the orthogonality of $\mathscr{P}_l^\pm P_l(\cos\theta)\chi_{\text{inc}}$. Here the factor l appears in the equation for G_l^+, and $-l-1$ appears for G_l^-. With the boundary condition that $G_l^\pm$ be zero at the origin, these equations then serve for the determination of these radial functions apart from the normalization constant. These equations may be solved exactly as in the spinless case.

The remaining formalism follows from relatively simple generalizations of the spinless case. Thus the wave function at large distances is seen to be

$$\psi = \psi_{\text{inc}} + \tfrac{1}{2} \sum (2l+1) i^l h_l^{(1)}(kr)$$
$$\times [(\eta_l^+ - 1)\mathscr{P}_l^+ + (\eta_l^- - 1)\mathscr{P}_l^-] P_l(\cos\theta)\chi_{\text{inc}} . \tag{15}$$

Introducing the asymptotic representation

$$h_l^{(1)}(kr) \simeq (1/ikr)\exp[i(kr - l\pi/2)] \tag{16}$$

we obtain, in conformity with the original requirement on the asymptotic form of ψ,

$$\psi = \psi_{\text{inc}} + F(e^{ikr}/r)\chi_{\text{inc}} \tag{17}$$

where F is the operator

$$F = (1/2ik) \sum (2l+1)[(\eta_l^+ - 1)\mathscr{P}_l^+ + (\eta_l^- - 1)\mathscr{P}_l^-]P_l(\cos\theta) \tag{18}$$

or, introducing the explicit forms of $\mathscr{P}_l^\pm$,

$$F = (1/2ik) \sum [(l+1)(\eta_l^+ - 1) + l(\eta_l^- - 1)P_l(\cos\theta)]$$
$$+ (1/2ik) \sum (\eta_l^+ - \eta_l^-)\boldsymbol{\sigma} \cdot \mathbf{L}P_l(\cos\theta). \tag{19}$$

We also have

$$\mathbf{L}P_l(\cos\theta) = (r/i)\hat{\mathbf{n}} \times \nabla P_l(\cos\theta) = -(1/i)\hat{\mathbf{n}}_p P_l^1(\cos\theta) \tag{20}$$

where P_l^1 is the first associated Legendre polynomial, $\hat{\mathbf{n}}_p$ is a unit vector given by

$$\hat{\mathbf{n}}_p = \frac{\hat{\mathbf{n}}_0 \times \hat{\mathbf{n}}}{|\hat{\mathbf{n}}_0 \times \hat{\mathbf{n}}|} = \frac{\hat{\mathbf{n}}_0 \times \hat{\mathbf{n}}}{\sin\theta} \tag{21}$$

and θ is the angle of scattering. The vector $\hat{\mathbf{n}}_p$ is thus perpendicular to the plane of scattering. The scattering amplitude now takes the form

$$F(\hat{\mathbf{n}}_0, \hat{\mathbf{n}}) = f(\hat{\mathbf{n}}_0, \hat{\mathbf{n}}) + \boldsymbol{\sigma} \cdot \hat{\mathbf{n}}_p g(\hat{\mathbf{n}}_0, \hat{\mathbf{n}}) \tag{22}$$

where

$$f(\hat{\mathbf{n}}_0, \hat{\mathbf{n}}) = (1/2ik) \sum [(l+1)(\eta_l^+ - 1) + l(\eta_l^- - 1)]P_l(\hat{\mathbf{n}}_0 \cdot \hat{\mathbf{n}}) \tag{23}$$

and

$$g(\hat{\mathbf{n}}_0, \hat{\mathbf{n}}) = + (1/2k) \sum (\eta_l^+ - \eta_l^-)P_l^1(\hat{\mathbf{n}}_0 \cdot \hat{\mathbf{n}}). \tag{24}$$

In the absence of a spin orbit force, $V_2 = 0$, we note that $\eta_l^+ = \eta_l^- = \eta_l$ since $G_l^\pm$ then both satisfy the same differential equation. Hence g vanishes and f reduces to the familiar form given by Eq. (10), Section 3.1.

Our discussion thus far has leaned heavily upon the partial wave expansion. However, a number of the results can be obtained from more general arguments. For example the form of the scattering amplitude in the presence of spin [(Eq. (22)] is easily determined from the assumptions $V_1 = V_1(r)$ and $V_2 = V_2(r)$ and from the consequent requirement that F be a scalar quantity, that is, invariant, under combined rotations in ordinary and spin space. Regarded as a function of the Pauli operator $\boldsymbol{\sigma}$, F can always be expressed as a superposition of a spin independent term, which we call $f(\hat{\mathbf{n}}_0, \hat{\mathbf{n}})$, and a term linear in $\boldsymbol{\sigma}$. This follows because higher powers of $\boldsymbol{\sigma}$ can always be reduced using the commutation rules. Now $\boldsymbol{\sigma}$ is a pseudovector and to generate a scalar we must construct a second pseudovector from the other vectors which define the scattering. These are only the polar vectors $\hat{\mathbf{n}}_0$ and $\hat{\mathbf{n}}$ which can be combined to yield the axial unit vector $\hat{\mathbf{n}}_p$ defined by Eq. (21). The quantity $\boldsymbol{\sigma} \cdot \hat{\mathbf{n}}_p$ is now a scalar and it is the only independent scalar which can be found. Hence F is expressible in the form given by Eq. (22) where f and g are scalar functions of the scattering angles. The first term involves no change in the spin state of the incident particle, the second does involve a change, and it is, therefore, frequently called the spin flip part of the scattering amplitude.

3.3b   The Cross Sections

Using Eq. (52), Section 1.4, the flux of particles in the incoming beam is seen to be $J = \hbar k/m$ particles/cm^2/sec and the number of particles scattered per second in the direction $\hat{\mathbf{n}}$ into the solid angle $d\Omega_{\hat{\mathbf{n}}}$ is seen to be, in Dirac notation,

$$N = d\Omega_{\hat{\mathbf{n}}}(\hbar k/m)\langle F(\hat{\mathbf{n}}, \hat{\mathbf{n}}_0)\chi_{\text{inc}}, F(\hat{\mathbf{n}}, \hat{\mathbf{n}}_0)\chi_{\text{inc}}\rangle$$
$$= d\Omega_{\hat{\mathbf{n}}}(\hbar k/m)\{|f|^2 + |g|^2 + (f^*g + g^*f)\hat{\mathbf{n}}_p \cdot \mathbf{P}_0\} \qquad (25)$$

where the relation $(\boldsymbol{\sigma} \cdot \hat{\mathbf{n}}_p)^2 = 1$ has been used, and where the incident polarization vector $\mathbf{P}_0$ is given by

$$\mathbf{P}_0 = \langle \chi_{\text{inc}}|\boldsymbol{\sigma}|\chi_{\text{inc}}\rangle. \qquad (26)$$

The differential cross section for elastic scattering is defined by Eq. (10), Section 1.4, so that

$$\sigma(\hat{\mathbf{n}}_0, \hat{\mathbf{n}}) = |f|^2 + |g|^2 + (f^*g + g^*f)\hat{\mathbf{n}}_p \cdot \mathbf{P}_0. \qquad (27)$$

The total elastic scattering cross section σ_e is given by

$$\sigma_e = \int (|f|^2 + |g|^2)\, d\Omega_{\hat{\mathbf{n}}} \qquad (28)$$

and is independent of the initial polarization since the term in $\hat{\mathbf{n}}_p \cdot \mathbf{P}_0$ integrates to zero. Inserting the partial wave expansions this becomes

$$\sigma_e = \frac{\pi}{k^2} \sum_l \left[\frac{|(l+1)(\eta_l^+ - 1) + l(\eta_l^- - 1)|^2 + l(l+1)|\eta_l^+ - \eta_l^-|^2}{2l+1} \right] \quad (29)$$

or

$$\sigma_e = \sum_l \sigma_e^{(l)} \quad (30)$$

where $\sigma_e^{(l)}$, the elastic scattering cross section for the lth partial wave, is given by

$$\sigma_e^{(l)} = \frac{\pi}{k^2} \left[(l+1)|\eta_l^+ - 1|^2 + l|\eta_l^- - 1|^2 \right] \leq \frac{4\pi}{k^2}(2l+1). \quad (31)$$

It remains to express the absorption cross section σ_r in terms of the outgoing amplitudes $\eta_l^\pm$. Asymptotically, we can write

$$\psi = \frac{i}{2k} \sum_l \left\{ (2l+1) \frac{e^{-ikr}}{r} - [(l+1)\eta_l^+ + l\eta_l^-] \frac{e^{ikr}}{r} \right\} P_l(\cos\theta)\chi_{\text{inc}}$$

$$+ \frac{1}{2k} \sum_l (\eta_l^+ - \eta_l^-) \frac{e^{ikr}}{r} P_l^1(\cos\theta)\boldsymbol{\sigma} \cdot \hat{\mathbf{n}}_p \chi_{\text{inc}}. \quad (32)$$

The number of particles with orbital angular momentum l coming in per second is thus seen to be $(2l+1)\pi\hbar/mk$, while the number going out per second is

$$\frac{\pi\hbar}{mk} \left\{ \frac{|(l+1)\eta_l^+ + l\eta_l^-|^2}{2l+1} + \frac{l(l+1)|\eta_l^+ - \eta_l^-|^2}{2l+1} \right\}$$

$$= \frac{\pi\hbar}{mk} \left\{ (l+1)|\eta_l^+|^2 + l|\eta_l^-|^2 \right\}. \quad (33)$$

The total number N_a of particles absorbed per second is then

$$N_a = \frac{\pi\hbar}{mk} \sum_l \left[(2l+1) - (l+1)|\eta_l^+|^2 - l|\eta_l^-|^2 \right]. \quad (34)$$

Since the incident flux is $\hbar k/m$, we have

$$\sigma_r = \sum_l \sigma_r^{(l)} \quad (35)$$

where, $\sigma_r^{(l)}$, the absorption cross section for particles of angular momentum l, is given by

$$\sigma_r^{(l)} = \frac{\pi}{k^2} \left[(l+1)(1 - |\eta_l^+|^2) + l(1 - |\eta_l^-|^2) \right] \leq (2l+1)\frac{\pi}{k^2}. \quad (36)$$

For spinless particles, or in the absence of spin orbit forces, $\eta_l^+ = \eta_l^- = \eta_l$ as we have shown, and these results reduces to their familiar forms.

3.3c   Charged Particles

The extension of the results to charged particles is straightforward. The radial equation is now

$$\frac{d^2 G_l^{\pm}}{dr^2} + \left\{ k^2 - \frac{l(l+1)}{r^2} - \frac{2m}{\hbar^2} \left[V_{\text{coul}} + V_1 + \begin{pmatrix} l \\ -l-1 \end{pmatrix} V_2 \right] \right\} G_l^{\pm} = 0. \quad (37)$$

Thus two scattering amplitudes, $\eta_l^{\pm}$, may be extracted from the asymptotic form. The subsequent analysis now proceeds exactly as in the neutral particle case and leads to the result, that, as $r \to \infty$,

$$\psi \simeq \left(1 - \frac{\eta^2}{lk(r - \hat{\mathbf{n}}_0 \cdot \mathbf{r})} \right) \exp\{i[k\hat{\mathbf{n}}_0 \cdot \mathbf{r} - \eta \ln k(r - \hat{\mathbf{n}}_0 \cdot \mathbf{r})]\} \chi_{\text{inc}}$$

$$+ (f + \boldsymbol{\sigma} \cdot \hat{\mathbf{n}}_p g) \frac{\exp[i(kr - \eta \ln 2kr)]}{r} \chi_{\text{inc}} \quad (38)$$

where, with f_c given by Eq. (8), Section 3.2,

$$f(\hat{\mathbf{n}}_0, \hat{\mathbf{n}}) = f_c + (1/2ik) \sum_{l=0}^{\infty} \exp(2i\sigma_l)[(l+1)(\eta_l^+ - 1) + l(\eta_l^- - 1)]P_l(\hat{\mathbf{n}}_0 \cdot \hat{\mathbf{n}}) \quad (39)$$

and

$$g(\hat{\mathbf{n}}_0, \hat{\mathbf{n}}) = (1/2k) \sum_{l=0}^{\infty} \exp(2i\sigma_l)[\eta_l^+ - \eta_l^-]P_l^1(\hat{\mathbf{n}}_0 \cdot \hat{\mathbf{n}}). \quad (40)$$

Except for the addition of the Coulomb amplitude f_c and the introduction of the Coulomb phase shifts σ_l, the scattering amplitude f and g are formally the same as for the neutral particle case. All expressions for cross sections and polarization (as we shall see) in terms of the scattering amplitudes are unaltered in form. Furthermore, all of the neutral particle expressions are recovered if z is set to zero.

3.3d   Polarization

The polarization of particles scattered in the direction $\hat{\mathbf{n}}$ is expressed in terms of the polarization vector $\mathbf{P}$ defined by

$$\mathbf{P} = \frac{\langle F\chi_{\text{inc}} | \boldsymbol{\sigma} | F\chi_{\text{inc}} \rangle}{\langle F\chi_{\text{inc}} | F\chi_{\text{inc}} \rangle}. \quad (41)$$

We substitute Eq. (22) for F in Eq. (41), and make use of the relations

$$(\boldsymbol{\sigma} \cdot \hat{\mathbf{n}}_p)\boldsymbol{\sigma} = \hat{\mathbf{n}}_p + i\boldsymbol{\sigma} \times \hat{\mathbf{n}}_p \tag{42}$$

$$\boldsymbol{\sigma}(\boldsymbol{\sigma} \cdot \hat{\mathbf{n}}_p) = \hat{\mathbf{n}}_p - i\boldsymbol{\sigma} \times \hat{\mathbf{n}}_p \tag{43}$$

and

$$(\boldsymbol{\sigma} \cdot \hat{\mathbf{n}}_p)\boldsymbol{\sigma}(\boldsymbol{\sigma} \cdot \hat{\mathbf{n}}_p) = 2\hat{\mathbf{n}}_p(\boldsymbol{\sigma} \cdot \hat{\mathbf{n}}_p) - \boldsymbol{\sigma}. \tag{44}$$

Equations (42), (43), and (44) may readily be established by expressing $\hat{\mathbf{n}}_p$ in rectangular coordinates with z axis along $\hat{\mathbf{n}}_0$

$$\hat{\mathbf{n}}_p = -\sin \varphi \hat{\mathbf{i}} + \cos \varphi \hat{\mathbf{j}} \tag{45}$$

where φ is the angle of the plane of scattering relative to an arbitrarily chosen x axis. Then we find, from Eq. (41),

$$\mathbf{P} = \frac{(|f|^2 - |g|^2)\mathbf{P}_0 + (f^*g + fg^* + 2|g|^2 \mathbf{P}_0 \cdot \hat{\mathbf{n}}_p)\hat{\mathbf{n}}_p + i(f^*g - fg^*)\hat{\mathbf{n}}_p \times \mathbf{P}_0}{|f|^2 + |g|^2 + (f^*g + g^*f)\hat{\mathbf{n}}_p \cdot \mathbf{P}_0}. \tag{46}$$

If the incident beam is unpolarized ($\mathbf{P}_0 = 0$), then the scattered beam is polarized along $\hat{\mathbf{n}}_p$, perpendicular to the scattering plane, and we have

$$\sigma(\hat{\mathbf{n}}_0, \hat{\mathbf{n}}) = |f|^2 + |g|^2 \tag{47}$$

and

$$\mathbf{P}(\hat{\mathbf{n}}_0, \hat{\mathbf{n}}) = \hat{\mathbf{n}}_p \frac{fg^* + f^*g}{|f|^2 + |g|^2} \equiv \hat{\mathbf{n}}_p P(\hat{\mathbf{n}}_0, \hat{\mathbf{n}}). \tag{48}$$

To understand physically the fact that scattering produces polarization in an originally unpolarized beam, let us examine the classical trajectories in a given scattering plane. Let us choose the axis of spin quantization to be perpendicular to that plane. Then consider a beam which is completely polarized upward, say, as shown in Fig. 1. The angular momentum vector of the particles incident along trajectories initially lying to the right of the scattering center has its component $\mathbf{L}_p$ perpendicular to the scattering plane oppositely directed to that for particles incident along trajectories lying to the left, as also shown in the figure. Hence the spin orbit contribution to the potential has opposite sign in the two cases, and since the forces differ, the number of particles scattered through a given angle of deflection to the right and to the left will be different. The polarization, however, still remains up. Suppose, for example, that more particles are scattered to the right than to the left. Then conversely, for a beam polarized with spin down, more particles will be scattered to the left than to the right and the polarization of these will be down. An unpolarized beam can be regarded as a superposition of spin up and spin down beams of equal intensities and hence, for this example, the beam scattered to the right will have net upward polarization, that scattered to the left will have net

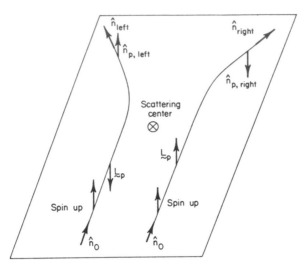

Fig. 1. Classical trajectories of a beam completely polarized upward undergoing a single scattering to the left and to the right in a given scattering plane, in relation with the angular momentum and the normal to the plane.

downward polarization. Of course, the total number of particles scattered to right and left are the same; the differential cross section is a function only of the scattering angle for an unpolarized beam.

To express this more quantitatively, for a spin up beam we have $\hat{\mathbf{n}}_{p,\text{right}}$ antiparallel to the spin and $\hat{\mathbf{n}}_{p,\text{left}}$ parallel to the spin. Hence from Eq. (27)

$$\sigma_{\text{up}}(\hat{\mathbf{n}}_0, \hat{\mathbf{n}}_{\text{right}}) = |f - g|^2 \tag{49}$$

and

$$\sigma_{\text{up}}(\hat{\mathbf{n}}_0, \hat{\mathbf{n}}_{\text{left}}) = |f + g|^2. \tag{50}$$

Conversely,

$$\sigma_{\text{down}}(\hat{\mathbf{n}}_0, \hat{\mathbf{n}}_{\text{right}}) = |f + g|^2 \tag{51}$$

and

$$\sigma_{\text{down}}(\hat{\mathbf{n}}_0, \hat{\mathbf{n}}_{\text{left}}) = |f - g|^2 \tag{52}$$

whence, for an unpolarized beam, either to the right or left

$$\sigma = \tfrac{1}{2}(\sigma_{\text{up}} + \sigma_{\text{down}}) = |f|^2 + |g|^2 \tag{53}$$

and

$$\mathbf{P}(\hat{\mathbf{n}}_0, \hat{\mathbf{n}}_{\text{right}}) = \frac{\tfrac{1}{2}[\hat{\mathbf{n}}_p |f + g|^2 - \hat{\mathbf{n}}_p |f - g|^2]}{|f|^2 + |g|^2}$$

$$= \hat{\mathbf{n}}_p \frac{fg^* + f^*g}{|f|^2 + |g|^2} \tag{54}$$

which is in agreement with our previous results.

The sign of polarization is determined according to the Basel convention, i.e., plus if **P** is parallel to $\hat{\mathbf{n}}_p$, where $\hat{\mathbf{n}}_p$ is defined by Eq. (21).

Experimentally, polarizations are determined by double scattering experiments. For example, if in the first scattering the beam is 100% polarized up, say, then a second scattering in the plane of the first, as shown in Fig. 2, yields cross sections for right and left scattering which are given by Eqs. (49) and (50).

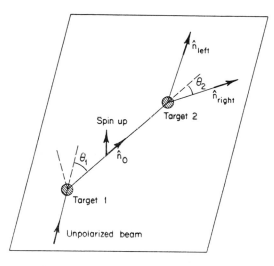

Fig. 2. Geometry for a double scattering of an originally unpolarized beam.

Noting that

$$\sigma_{\text{up}}(\hat{\mathbf{n}}_0, \hat{\mathbf{n}}_{\text{right}}) + \sigma_{\text{up}}(\hat{\mathbf{n}}_0, \hat{\mathbf{n}}_{\text{left}}) = 2(|f|^2 + |g|^2) \tag{55}$$

and

$$\sigma_{\text{up}}(\hat{\mathbf{n}}_0, \hat{\mathbf{n}}_{\text{right}}) - \sigma_{\text{up}}(\hat{\mathbf{n}}_0, \hat{\mathbf{n}}_{\text{left}}) = -2(fg^* + f^*g) \tag{56}$$

we have, compressing the notation,

$$\frac{\sigma_{\text{right}} - \sigma_{\text{left}}}{\sigma_{\text{right}} + \sigma_{\text{left}}} = -\frac{fg^* + f^*g}{|f|^2 + |g|^2} = -P \tag{57}$$

where P is the magnitude of the polarization which would be produced by single scattering of an unpolarized beam to the right. If P is positive the polarization is downward; if negative, it is upward. More generally, if the polarization in the first scattering is $P_1 = (\mathbf{P}_1 \cdot \hat{\mathbf{n}}_{\text{right}})$ instead of unity, then from Eq. (27) we find

$$\sigma_{\text{right}}(\theta_2) = |f(\theta_2)|^2 + |g(\theta_2)|^2 + (fg^* + fg^*)_{\theta_2} P_1(\theta_1) \tag{58}$$

and

$$\sigma_{\text{left}}(\theta_2) = |f(\theta_2)|^2 - |g(\theta_2)|^2 - (fg^* + fg^*)_{\theta_2} P_1(\theta_1) \tag{59}$$

and, therefore,

$$\frac{\sigma_{\text{right}} - \sigma_{\text{left}}}{\sigma_{\text{right}} + \sigma_{\text{left}}}\bigg|_{\theta_2} = \frac{f^*g + fg^*}{|f|^2 + |g|^2}\bigg|_{\theta_2} P_1(\theta_1) = P(\theta_2)P_1(\theta_1) \qquad (60)$$

or,

$$P(\theta_2) = \frac{1}{P_1(\theta_1)} \frac{\sigma_{\text{right}} - \sigma_{\text{left}}}{\sigma_{\text{right}} + \sigma_{\text{left}}}\bigg|_{\theta_2}. \qquad (61)$$

Equation (57) is the special case of Eq. (61) with $P_1(\theta_1) = (\mathbf{P}_1 \cdot \hat{\mathbf{n}}_{\text{right}}) = -1$.

3.3e   Method of Solution

The scattering cross sections and polarizations have been expressed in the last section in terms of the amplitudes $\eta_l^{\pm}$ of the outgoing radial waves of given orbital and total angular momenta. These amplitudes are, in turn, defined in terms of the asymptotic form of the regular solutions of the radial wave equations (Eq. (14) or (37)). For any but square well potentials, these solutions must be obtained by numerical integration and several programs for high speed digital computers are available. These programs typically provide a complete set of cross sections and polarizations for a given energy, target, incident particle, and optical model potential in times which are of the order of a few seconds. In this section we give a very brief description of the actual method of solution. The reader is referred to the article by Melkanoff et al. (1966), for example, for the details.

Since the optical model potential has an imaginary part, the solution $G_l(r)$ becomes complex. Writing $G_l(r) = x_l(r) + iy_l(r)$ (we suppress the $\pm$ superscripts), and expressing the term in the curly bracket appearing in Eq. (14) or (37), by $p_l(r) + iq_l(r)$, the radial equation becomes

$$\frac{d^2x}{dr^2} = px - qy$$

$$\frac{d^2y}{dr^2} = qx + py. \qquad (62)$$

This couplet set of equations for x_l and y_l is integrated numerically using standard techniques. Starting from the initial condition

$$G_l(r) \underset{r \to 0}{\to} \text{const} \times r^{l+1} \qquad (63)$$

the integration is performed outwardly to a sufficiently far distance r_m so that the nuclear interaction and the nuclear charge distribution become negligible. The quantity η_l is obtained by matching the logarithmic derivative of the numerical solution $G_l(r_m)$ to that of the asymptotic expression Eq. (18), Section 3.2, at $r = r_m$,

$$\left.\frac{dG_l/dr}{G_l}\right|_{r=r_m} = \left.\frac{dM_l^{(2)}/dr - \eta_l\,dM_l^{(1)}/dr}{M_l^{(2)} - \eta_l\,M_l^{(1)}}\right|_{r=r_m}. \tag{64}$$

This equation is then solved for η_l in terms of the known numerical solutions and the known Coulomb (or spherical Bessel) functions.

For a potential with a standard shape factor $\{1 + \exp[(r - R)/a]\}^{-1}$, the matching point r_m may typically be determined by $r_m = R + 8a$ so that the value of the potential becomes $\sim e^{-8}$ times its central depth.

For sufficiently large l values, the amplitudes η_l tend rapidly to unity and no longer contribute to the scattering. The number of partial waves required is determined by the fact that, if R is the range of the (non-Coulomb) interaction, then for $l \gg kR$, the η_l become indistinguishable from unity. In practice the maximum l values required might be of the order of $2kR$. In any case, the programs are normally written to cutoff when the contribution from successive η_l's is less than some preassigned small value.

Having obtained the η_l for each j, the scattering amplitudes $f(\hat{\mathbf{n}}_0, \hat{\mathbf{n}})$ and $g(\hat{\mathbf{n}}_0, \hat{\mathbf{n}})$ are calculated using Eqs. (39) and (40). Then the differential cross sections and polarizations are obtained using Eqs. (47) and (48) for the incident unpolarized beam. The total elastic and reaction cross sections are calculated directly from the η_l's using Eqs. (31) and (36).

Although the normalization factor of wave functions is immaterial to the determination of the η_l's, and hence to the determinations of the cross sections and polarizations of elastic scattering, for the application to inelastic scattering and reactions using distorted wave Born approximation (DWBA) type calculations, the numerical solution has to be properly normalized. Thus, if we denote the numerical solution by $u_l(r)$, the solution which has the asymptotic form (Eq. (18), Section 3.2) is given by

$$G_l(r) = \alpha_l u_l(r) \tag{65}$$

where

$$\alpha_l = \frac{M_l^{(2)}(r_m) - \eta_l\,M_l^{(1)}(r_m)}{u_l(r_m)}. \tag{66}$$

3.4   Early Quantitative Results for Nucleons

3.4a   *Parametrization of the Optical Model Potential*

In this section and in Chapter VI we discuss in some detail the earlier optical model analysis of the elastic scattering of nucleons.

Before going into the discussion of individual surveys, we must discuss the parametrization of the optical model potential in some detail.

The most commonly used form of a spherical optical model potential for either spin $\frac{1}{2}$ or spin 1 particles is

$$V(r) = V_{\text{coul}}(r) - U_0\xi_1(r) - i[W\xi_2(r) + W'\xi_3(r)]$$
$$- [U_{\text{so}}\,\xi_4(r) + iW_{\text{so}}\,\xi_5(r)](\mathbf{L}\cdot\boldsymbol{\sigma}). \tag{1}$$

The first term represents the Coulomb interaction. In principle it is determined by the Stanford experimental nuclear charge distribution, but in practice it is calculated from an equivalent uniform charge distribution of radius $R_c = r_c A^{1/3}\ F$ (Eqs. (1) and (2), Section 3.2). The second term in Eq. (1) represents the real central potential with shape factor $\xi_1(r)$,

$$\xi_1(r) = \frac{1}{1 + \exp(x_1)}, \qquad x_1 = \frac{r - R_0}{a}, \qquad R_0 = r_0 A^{1/3}. \tag{2}$$

The third term represents the imaginary central potential, for which either one of the following two shape factors is used:

volume absorption form

$$\xi_2(r) = \frac{1}{1 + \exp(x_2)}, \qquad x_2 = \frac{r - R_{\text{I}}}{a_{\text{I}}}, \qquad R_{\text{I}} = r_{\text{I}} A^{1/3} \tag{3}$$

surface absorption form

$$\xi_3(r) = \exp(-x_G^2), \qquad x_G = (r - R_G)/b, \qquad R_G = r_G A^{1/3} \tag{4a}$$
$$\text{(Gaussian form)}$$

or

$$\xi_3(r) = 4\left|\frac{d}{dx_3}\frac{1}{1 + \exp(x_3)}\right|, \qquad x_3 = (r - R_{\text{I}}')/a_{\text{I}}', \qquad R_{\text{I}}' = r_{\text{I}}'A^{1/3}. \tag{4b}$$
$$\text{(derivative form)}$$

Also, a mixture of volume and surface absorption is used. The factor 4 for the derivative form is chosen to make the maximum value of $\xi_3(r)$ unity. The last term of Eq. (1) is the complex spin orbit potential with still different shape factors $\xi_4(r)$ and $\xi_5(r)$

$$\xi_4(r) = \left(\frac{\hbar}{m_\pi c}\right)^2 \frac{1}{r}\left|\frac{d}{dr}\frac{1}{1 + \exp(x_4)}\right|, \qquad x_4 = \frac{r - R_{\text{so}}}{a_{\text{so}}}, \qquad R_{\text{so}} = r_{\text{so}} A^{1/3} \tag{5a}$$

and

$$\xi_5(r) = \left(\frac{\hbar}{m_\pi c}\right)^2 \frac{1}{r}\left|\frac{d}{dr}\frac{1}{1 + \exp(x_5)}\right|, \qquad x_5 = \frac{r - R_{\text{so}}'}{a_{\text{so}}'}, \qquad R_{\text{so}}' = r_{\text{so}}' A^{1/3}. \tag{5b}$$

The quantity $(\hbar/m_\pi c)$, the π-meson reduced Compton wavelength, provides a convenient, if arbitrary, unit of length, and it is customary to take it as $\sqrt{2}$ F exactly. To compare Eqs. (1) and (5a) with Eq. (16), Section 2.2, we must identify $(\hbar/m_\pi c)^2 U_{so}$ with $a_{so}^2 V_0/2$. The operator σ is defined by

$$\begin{aligned}\boldsymbol{\sigma} &= 2\mathbf{S} \qquad \text{for spin } \tfrac{1}{2} \text{ particles} \\ \boldsymbol{\sigma} &= \mathbf{S} \qquad \text{for spin 1 particles}\end{aligned} \qquad (6)$$

where $\mathbf{S}$ is the spin angular momentum of the incident particle in units of $\hbar$. A spherical optical model potential for a spin 0 particle is also commonly given by Eq. (1) with $\mathbf{S} = 0$.

For heavy ions the factor $A^{1/3}$ is replaced by $A_1^{1/3} + A_2^{1/3}$ where A_1 and A_2 are the mass numbers of the incident and target particles.

The algebraic signs of the well depth parameters are given in such a manner in Eq. (1) that positive signs of U_0, and W or W' correspond to attractive and absorptive potentials, respectively. A positive value of U_{so} increases the attraction for the $j = l + s$ wave.

The particular shape factors given above are the ones used most commonly, and known to work quite well. However, the question of whether that is the appropriate parametrization or not is difficult to answer phenomenologically. For example, for nucleons at high energies, there is some indication that a real central shape factor other than that assumed here may be needed to give satisfactory fits to the data. Since a minimum of two parameters is required for each shape factor, if each is regarded as independently adjustable, then a minimum of ten geometrical parameters is involved. In addition, the strengths of the five potentials must be specified, so that 15 parameters enter. At the other extreme, if the shape factors are all describable in terms of a single function, the number of parameters can be reduced to six. One expects, on both intuitive and theoretical grounds, that these shape factors are indeed interrelated so that a natural starting point is customarily to use the smallest possible number of parameters.[1]

3.4b   Early Phenomenological Results for Nucleons

The rest of this section is devoted to the discussion of early nuclear optical model analyses. The earliest quantitatively successful analyses (Woods and Saxon, 1954; Chase and Rohrlich, 1954; Melkanoff *et al.*, 1957; Glassgold

---

[1] Throughout this section and Chapter VI, the symbol W', etc., also serves to identify the shape factor used. Those shape factors with no entries for the depths have not actually been used in making analyses. The radius parameters other than r_0 will be given only if they are different from r_0. Similarly, the diffuseness parameters other than a will be given olny if they are different from a. In other words, if not given they assume the same values as r_0 and a.

et al., 1957) were carried out with the most simplified description, in which the shape factors are given by a single function for both real and imaginary central potentials, and in which the spin orbit terms were omitted. However, without the spin orbit terms, difficulties were encountered at large angles and, of course, no polarization effects were included. To rectify the situation, a spin orbit term, of the Thomas type, was soon added, with $\xi_4 = \xi_5 = \xi_1$.

In addition to the four potential strengths, U_0, W, U_{so}, and W_{so}, the parameters of the model are the potential radius R_0, the distance at which $\xi_1 = \frac{1}{2}$ (the potential here is very close to half its central value), and a, which measures the surface region over which the potential decreases smoothly to zero.

An early modification of the volume absorption model was introduced following its application to the analysis of medium energy neutron scattering. Beyster *et al.* (1956) showed that, to fit the data with the volume absorption model, it was necessary for W to decrease uniformly with mass number. The change required was more than a factor of two in going from light to heavy elements. They then suggested that for a model in which the absorption was confined to the surface region, W' could be expected to be more nearly independent of mass number. (In view of the more recent developments, at least part of this decrement of the strength W for the neutron potential with mass number could be attributed to a dependence on the symmetry parameter $(N - Z)/A$.) Following their suggestion, the *surface absorption model* was introduced by Fernbach (1958), Bjorklund and Fernbach (1958), and Bjorklund (1959) who wrote the absorptive central potential in the form of a Gaussian centered in the nuclear surface. Specifically, they used the form of Eq. (4a) for the central imaginary part, while ξ_1, ξ_4, and ξ_5 were left unchanged. In the above, R_0 has the same meaning as before, but a seventh parameter b, giving the width of the surface absorption region, has been added.

At low and medium energies, a peaking of the absorption at the nuclear surface is to be expected on theoretical grounds. The inhibiting effect of the exclusion principle is less significant in the low density surface region of the nucleus. For nuclei with collective degrees of freedom, those degrees of freedom such as the vibration and rotation of the nuclear surface may be predominantly excited by the incoming nucleon when it is near the surface. As the energy increases, however, these effects become less important and at higher energies the volume absorption model appears to be more realistic as well as simpler.

With these points in mind, Bjorklund and Fernbach (1958) carried out their survey using the surface form for energies up to about 50 MeV, the volume form at higher energies. The transition energy at 50 MeV was chosen rather arbitrarily, but since the absorption is rather large in this energy region, both models give similar values of W and W'. Thus one obtains a reasonably smooth connection of W' and W as well as of the other parameters through the transition region.

Their results can be briefly summarized as follows. The nucleon–nucleus scattering data can be satisfactorily fit with geometrical parameters having the values

$$R_0 = r_0 A^{1/3} \qquad r_0 = 1.25 \quad \text{F} \qquad a = 0.65 \quad \text{F}$$

$$b = \begin{cases} 0.98 & \text{F} \quad \text{(neutrons)} \\ 1.2 & \text{F} \quad \text{(protons)} \end{cases} \qquad E \le 50 \quad \text{MeV.} \tag{7}$$

The strengths of the four potentials as a function of energy for the case of neutrons are shown in Fig. 1. The behavior of the potential strengths for the protons is also found to be quite similar to that for the neutrons, except that the real central part for the protons is deeper than that for the neutrons.

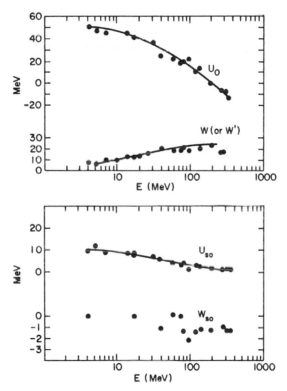

Fig. 1. General characteristics of the optical potential parameters as a function of energy (Bjorklund and Fernbach, 1958).

(The curves drawn through the points are computed using Riesenfeld and Watson's theory (Riesenfeld and Watson, 1956) and the case B Feshbach–Lommon (1956) phase shifts.)

Bjorklund and Fernbach reported that this difference goes as $Z/A^{1/3}$ [or $(N - Z)/A$, see Chapter II, Section 2.3].

Except for the change of the shape of the imaginary part of the potential from surface to volume absorption form, the geometrical parameters are energy independent. On the other hand, the dynamical parameters U_0, W, (or W'), U_{so}, and W_{so} are found to be energy dependent as seen from Fig. 1. The nuclear medium is dispersive.

An approximate characterization of the energy dependence of the Bjorklund–Fernbach parameters is given by the empirical formulas (Green, 1959).

$$U_0 = 52.5 - 0.6E_n \tag{8}$$

$$W = 2.5 + 0.3E_n \tag{9}$$

$$U_{so} = 10 - 0.15E_n. \tag{10}$$

The implications of the energy dependence or velocity dependence of the optical model potential have been the subject of many studies during the past decade. These features of the optical model potential relate closely to the energy dependence, velocity dependence or nonlocality of the shell model. It would, of course, be desirable to have a model whose potential parameters do not vary explicitly with energy. Such models will be discussed in detail in Chapter V. For the present we may regard the Bjorklund–Fernbach model, whose parameters depend upon energy, as providing an equivalent local potential (ELP) to what appears to be an intrinsically nonlocal or velocity dependent potential whose parameters are independent of energy.

The Bjorklund–Fernbach parameters fit the data on which they are based reasonably well. The neutron total cross sections and elastic differential cross sections, and the proton elastic differential cross sections and polarizations, are reasonably well predicted over most of the periodic table and over the energy region from a few to a few hundred MeV. Typical results in relation to the experimental data are illustrated by the dot-dash curves in Fig. 2. Also shown (solid curves) are the results of the study of Wyatt, et al. (1960) using an energy independent nonlocal optical potential which will be discussed in Chapter V.

It should be noted that the Bjorklund–Fernbach parameters are not at all reliable for light nuclei, and they fail to reproduce large angle scatterings in many cases. Furthermore, proton reaction cross sections are in general predicted to be too small. At low energies, these parameters are consistent with those obtained from the scattering lengths and the strength functions in an overall way, but they do not account for the detailed structure.

Since the time of the survey of Bjorklund and Fernbach, a large amount of new data has become available with better accuracy and wider angular coverage, as well as information on the proton reaction cross sections.

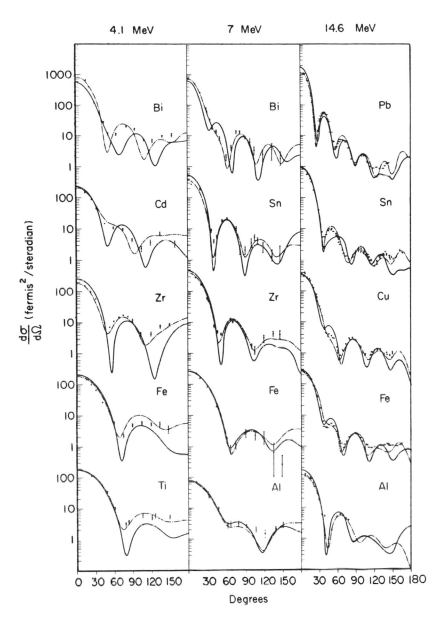

Fig. 2. Representative neutron differential scattering cross sections at 4.1, 7, and 14.6 MeV.

(The dashed curves represent the fits of Bjorklund and Fernbach using a local optical model whose parameters depend upon energy. The solid curves represent the fits of the Wyatt–Wills–Green nonlocal potential using energy independent parameters (see Chapter V, Section 5.4.)

Consequently, the analyses of these new data have presented a more severe test of the nuclear optical model.

We shall discuss the implications of these recent analyses in Chapter VI after we have developed some of the more recent theoretical and numerical methodologies used in connection with the optical model. Before doing so let us first examine several aspects of the optical model in the low and high energy limits.

IV

The Optical Model at Low and High Energies

4.1   Resonances and the Compound Nucleus

In the study of nuclear reactions, it is helpful to characterize the internal influence of the nucleus by the logarithmic derivative of the nuclear wave function at a radius outside the range of the nuclear interaction. Thus, we introduce a complex quantity

$$f_l = R\left[\frac{dG_l/dr}{G_l}\right]_{r=R} \tag{1}$$

where R refers to a radius outside (external to) the range of nuclear interaction. For s waves it is simple to relate f_0 to the quantity η_0 which we use to characterize the scattering. Thus, the asymptotic form of the $l = 0$ partial wave is (we shall drop all subscripts in the remainder of this section)

$$G = e^{-ikr} - \eta e^{ikr}. \tag{2}$$

Accordingly, we may obtain f from η with

$$f = -ikR\left[\frac{e^{-ikR} + \eta e^{ikR}}{e^{-ikR} - \eta e^{ikR}}\right]. \tag{3}$$

On the other hand, we may invert this to determine η in terms of f to obtain

$$\eta = \frac{f + ikR}{f - ikR}\exp[-2ikR]. \tag{4}$$

The s wave total, differential, and reaction cross section may now be related to f by using the $l = 0$ expressions for the cross sections. It is customary in resonance theory to write the scattering cross section in the form

$$\sigma_e = (\pi/k^2)|A_{pot} + A_{res}|^2 \tag{5}$$

where

$$A_{pot} = \exp(2ikR) - 1 \tag{6}$$

and

$$A_{res} = -\frac{2ikR}{f - ikR}. \tag{7}$$

If f is infinite as occurs in hard sphere scattering ($G(R) = 0$) then A_{res} vanishes and the A_{pot} accounts entirely for the scattering, On the other hand, near a so-called Breit–Wigner resonance, f becomes very small, in which case the resonant component contributes predominantly to the cross sections. Using Eq. (22), Section 3.1, the reaction cross section for s waves may be expressed in terms of f by

$$\sigma_r = \frac{\pi}{k^2} \frac{-4kR \operatorname{Im} f}{(\operatorname{Re} f)^2 + (\operatorname{Im} f - kR)^2}. \tag{8}$$

Similar but somewhat more complicated expressions may be obtained for the higher partial waves. From the involvement of f in Eq. (8) it should be clear that $\operatorname{Im} f$ must be a negative quantity.

Our discussion thus far has merely served to shift the wave description from the use of η, as the parameter which characterizes the influence of the nucleus towards s waves, to f. We could now pursue the implications of the optical model to arrive at values of f and indeed f_l for all the higher partial waves, by integrating from the origin to a point outside the nucleus and evaluating the logarithmic derivative there. If now we proceeded to do this as a function of energy or as a function of mass number, we would find that all f_l's undergo variations of an oscillatory nature. The minima of these f's thus correspond to maxima in both the scattering and reaction cross section, and lead to what is referred to as single particle resonances. Now the scattering analysis suggests that these resonances characteristically are very broad, having widths of the order of a few MeV in the low energy region and separations of the order of

$$\Delta E \sim \pi^2 \hbar^2 / mR^2. \tag{9}$$

We recall from our studies of bound states that the quantity $\hbar^2/2mR^2$ arises in a potential well description as a natural energy unit and that energy levels in a nuclear well are separated by energies of this order of magnitude. Since 1950, the existence of this independent particle structure has been established in bound states beyond doubt. In the initial interpretations of the optical model, the broad maxima observed in the differential and total cross sections were thought to be resonant positive energy states associated with particular partial waves. However, currently, these broad maxima are viewed to represent the interference effects of many partial waves as will be discussed at the end of Section 4.4. Much earlier, however, experimentalists had observed the very sharp resonances in low energy neutron scattering and Breit and Wigner (1936) found a simple way of parametrizing such resonances using a wave description which contains much of the formalism used in Chapter III. Let us indicate in a simple way how such a wave description may be used to arrive at the Breit–Wigner resonances (Blatt and Weisskopf, 1952).

To arrive at sharp resonances we assume that in the region inside the nucleus a large change occurs in the propagation constant. We also assume that the nuclear interaction is cut off sharply at the so-called channel radius R. We further assume that near the nuclear surface, the actual many particle nuclear wave function is approximated by an ad hoc oscillatory wave function $G_l(r)$. We simply point out that the more elegant and rigorous formulation of compound nuclear resonance formulas is free from these approximations (Kapur and Peierls, 1938). Again, restricting ourselves to an incident s wave neutron, the nuclear wave function just inside the nuclear boundary ($r < R$) is approximated by

$$G(r) = e^{iKr} - \eta e^{iKr} \tag{10}$$

which expresses the fact that the incident particle possesses an average wave number K, and that it has a finite chance to return into the entrance channel. We use Eq. (10) merely to calculate the logarithmic derivative of the internal wave function at R

$$f = KR \cot(KR - \Delta) \tag{11}$$

where Δ is defined by

$$\eta = e^{-2i\Delta}. \tag{12}$$

Now the main physical result of resonance theory can be shown to follow simply from the additional assumption that the argument of the cotangent factor varies smoothly with energy. Let us assume that

$$Z(E) = KR - \Delta = X(E) + iY(E) \tag{13}$$

where $Y(E)$ is a small imaginary term which measures the loss of flux to other processes (such as nuclear reactions). A small Y indicates that there is only a small probability that the incident particle is diverted into other processes during the time it needs to return again toward the nuclear surface in the incident channel, and it is a necessary condition for the existence of well-defined states in the compound nucleus. Were it not for the presence of this term, f would vanish whenever

$$X(E^{(s)}) = (n + \tfrac{1}{2})\pi. \tag{14}$$

We denote these energy values by $E^{(s)}$. Now in the neighborhood of $E^{(s)}$ we may expand

$$f(E) \cong (E - E^{(s)})(\partial f/\partial E)_s - i Y K R \tag{15}$$

where $(\partial f/\partial E)$ is evaluated at $E = E^{(s)}$ and $Y = 0$. If now we insert the internal f into Eq. (22), Section 3.1, we arrive at

$$\sigma_r^{(s)} = \frac{\pi}{k^2} \frac{(-4kR)(-YKR)}{(\partial f/\partial E)^2(E - E^{(s)})^2 + (-YKR - kR)^2}. \tag{16}$$

If we define the incident particle width

$$\Gamma_n^{(s)} = 2KR\gamma_n{}^s \tag{17}$$

where

$$\gamma_n{}^s = -(\partial f/\partial E)_s^{-1} \tag{18}$$

is called the reduced width, the reaction width

$$\Gamma_r^{(s)} = 2 Y K R \gamma_n{}^s \tag{19}$$

and the total width

$$\Gamma^{(s)} = \Gamma_n^{(s)} + \Gamma_r^{(s)} \tag{20}$$

it follows that the reaction cross section for the sth resonance is

$$\sigma_r^{(s)} = \frac{\pi}{k^2} \frac{\Gamma_n^{(s)}\Gamma_r^{(s)}}{(E - E^{(s)})^2 + \Gamma^{(s)2}/4}. \tag{21}$$

This is the well known Breit–Wigner formula for s wave resonance reaction cross sections.

In view of these defining equations, let us rewrite f, in the neighborhood of a resonance, in the form

$$f^{(s)} = -(E - E^{(s)})(2kR/\Gamma_n^{(s)}) - ikR(\Gamma_r^{(s)}/\Gamma_n^{(s)}). \tag{22}$$

It follows from Eq. (4) that

$$\eta^{(s)} = \left[\frac{(E - E^{(s)}) + i[\tfrac{1}{2}(\Gamma_r^{(s)} - \Gamma_n^{(s)})]}{(E - E^{(s)}) + i[\tfrac{1}{2}(\Gamma_r^{(s)} + \Gamma_n^{(s)})]}\right] e^{-2ikR} \tag{23}$$

which may be rewritten as

$$\eta^{(s)} = e^{2i\delta}\left[1 - \frac{i\Gamma_n^{(s)}}{(E - E^{(s)}) + i\Gamma^{(s)}/2}\right] \tag{24}$$

where the phase δ here is inserted to represent effects which are slowly varying on the scale of resonance widths. If we insert the resonant part of Eq. (24) into the formula for the elastic scattering cross section, we find that

$$\sigma_e^{(s)} = \frac{\pi}{k^2} \frac{\Gamma_n^{(s)2}}{(E - E^{(s)})^2 + (\Gamma^{(s)}/2)^2}. \tag{25}$$

The sum of the reaction and scattering cross sections leads to the total cross section for the resonance interaction

$$\sigma_c^{(s)} = \frac{\pi}{k^2} \frac{\Gamma_n^{(s)}\Gamma^{(s)}}{(E - E^s)^2 + (\Gamma^s/2)^2}. \tag{26}$$

It is left to evaluate the width $\Gamma_n^{(s)}$. A rough estimate of the reduced width $\gamma_n{}^s$ defined by Eq. (18) is given as follows. From Eq. (11) we obtain for a small $Y(E)$

$$-(df/dE)_s \simeq (KR\, dZ/dE)_s. \tag{27}$$

We now use the assumption that $Z(E)$ is a smooth function of energy. $Z(E)$ changes by π in going from one resonance ε_s to the next resonance ε_{s+1}. Hence, very roughly, $(dZ/dE)_s$ is of the order of

$$(dZ/dE)_s = \pi/D^* \tag{28}$$

where D^* is an average spacing of the compound nuclear resonance with the same spin and parity. Inserting Eqs. (27) and (28) into Eqs. (18) and (19) we find

$$\Gamma_n{}^s \simeq (2k/\pi K)D^* \qquad \text{and} \qquad \gamma_n{}^s = (D^*/\pi KR). \tag{29}$$

The smallness of the resonance width is thus the consequence of the smallness of the average spacing D^*. For lighter elements, the levels become sparse and the corresponding widths become much larger.

We recall now the Heisenberg energy time uncertainty principle $\Delta E\, \Delta t \sim \hbar$, which implies that states sharp in energy may be assigned a long lifetime. Thus, the sharp resonant structure described by Eqs. (21), (25), and (26) suggests that a state of the nucleon–nuclear system exists with a relatively long lifetime, compared to the natural time of a nuclear encounter which might be taken as the time required to traverse a nuclear radius ($\sim R/v$). Such considerations led Bohr and Breit and Wigner in 1936 originally to the concept of the compound nucleus which has played a useful role in nuclear reaction theory. Here the incident nucleon interacts so strongly with nucleons in the nucleus, that a composite system is formed which lasts long compared to the traversal time. Then the composite system forgets its mode of formation, and its subsequent decay depends purely upon transition probabilities to the various modes of decay which are energetically allowed. These transition probabilities are characterized by the widths. If, for example, we wish to determine the resonance elastic cross section, we would multiply the total cross section $\sigma_c^{(s)}$ by the branching ratio $\Gamma_n^{(s)}/\Gamma^{(s)}$ to the ground state. Thus

$$\sigma_e^{(s)} = (\Gamma_n^{(s)}/\Gamma^{(s)})\sigma_c^{(s)} \tag{30}$$

which indeed follows from Eqs. (25) and (26). Similarly

$$\sigma_r^{(s)} = \frac{\Gamma^{(s)} - \Gamma_n^{(s)}}{\Gamma^{(s)}} \, \sigma_c^{(s)} = \frac{\Gamma_r^{(s)}}{\Gamma^{(s)}} \, \sigma_c^{(s)} \tag{31}$$

which also follows from Eqs. (21) and (26).

4.2   The Compound Nucleus and the Optical Model at Low Energies

We now discuss the optical model in a relatively simple limit, namely that of the low energies. Here, we have specifically in mind the scattering of a nucleon, rather than an arbitrary incoming particle, by a complex nucleus. In the very low energy region, the cross sections exhibit the resonance structure, characteristic of the strongly interacting many body system, which led in the first place to the concept of the compound nucleus. On the other hand, as we have mentioned, the success of the shell model shows that the independent particle description also has a claim to validity. Our objective, following Feshbach *et al.* (1954), is to show how these opposing concepts can be reconciled by means of the optical model, and further, to actually relate the parameters of the optical potential to those characterizing the resonance levels, at least implicitly.

Consider the scattering of nucleons of energy E by a complex nucleus. For the present, we restrict our attention to neutrons and to states of zero orbital angular momentum (s waves) to avoid the algebraic complications associated with Coulomb effects and nonzero orbital angular momentum. For the same reason, we also neglect the spin of the neutron. With this restriction, the asymptotic form of the neutron wave function and the s wave elastic and absorption cross sections are, as shown in Chapter III, given by the following formulas:

$$\psi \sim (A/r)(e^{-ikr} - \eta e^{ikr}) \tag{1}$$

$$\sigma_e = (\pi/k^2) \, |1 - \eta|^2 \tag{2}$$

and

$$\sigma_r = (\pi/k^2)(1 - |\eta|^2). \tag{3}$$

The total cross section σ_t then follows from

$$\sigma_t = \sigma_r + \sigma_e = (2\pi/k^2)(1 - \text{Re } \eta) \tag{4}$$

where Re η means the real part of η. The amplitude η completely defines the asymptotic behavior of the neutron wave function, and therefore, completely defines the cross sections.

In the resonance region, η varies extremely sharply with energy, changing completely as the energy passes through a resonance. This rapid variation is superposed on a relatively small and relatively energy independent background which is called the potential or shape elastic scattering. These resonances are interpreted as the formation of states of the compound system which eventually decay by any of the modes energetically available to them. Among the possible modes of decay, reemission of the incident particle with its original energy is always possible. The elastic scattering cross section, therefore, contains to some degree a contribution arising from this decay mode of the compound nucleus. This contribution to the elastic scattering is called *compound elastic scattering* and its cross section is denoted by σ_{ce}. The remaining component of the elastic scattering is called the *shape elastic scattering*, and we thus have

$$\sigma_e = \sigma_{se} + \sigma_{ce}. \tag{5}$$

According to this picture, it is also natural to introduce the capture cross section, defined by

$$\sigma_c = \sigma_r + \sigma_{ce}. \tag{6}$$

and which is thus seen to be expressed in terms of the cross section for decay of the compound state by reactions and by reemission of the incident particle with unaltered energy. We mean by σ_c, the cross section for removal of the incoming particle from its entrance channel by any process. It includes not only compound nucleus formation in the strict sense, but also, for example, direct interactions. The relations among all these cross sections are summarized by

$$\sigma_t = \sigma_r + \sigma_e = \sigma_r + \sigma_{ce} + \sigma_{se} = \sigma_c + \sigma_{se}. \tag{7}$$

As we have already shown, the cross sections σ_r and σ_c and therefore also σ_t, can be expressed with complete generality in terms of η, independently of specific models. The cross sections σ_c, or equivalently, σ_{ce} cannot be so expressed; their definition explicitly involves the compound nucleus picture, and we must make use of the theory of resonances in order to exhibit them. According to that theory, in the neighborhood of an isolated resonance at the energy E_s, say, these cross sections are given by Breit–Wigner formulas, which, for s wave resonances, can be written in the form

$$\sigma_c = \frac{\pi}{k^2} \frac{\Gamma_n^{(s)} \Gamma^{(s)}}{(E - E_s)^2 + (\Gamma^{(s)}/2)^2} \tag{8}$$

and

$$\sigma_{ce} = (\Gamma_n^{(s)}/\Gamma^{(s)})\sigma_c \tag{9}$$

where $\Gamma^{(s)}$, the width of the resonance level, is inversely proportional to the life time of the compound state. The quantity $\Gamma_n^{(s)}$ is called the partial width for reemission of a neutron in the incident channel and, of course,

$$\Gamma^{(s)} \geq \Gamma_n^{(s)}. \tag{10}$$

The reaction cross section σ_r is then

$$\sigma_r = \sigma_c - \sigma_{ce} = \frac{\Gamma^{(s)} - \Gamma_n^{(s)}}{\Gamma^{(s)}} \sigma_c \tag{11}$$

and $(\Gamma^{(s)} - \Gamma_n^{(s)})$ is the width for all other modes of decay.

To a satisfactory approximation, in the neighborhood of such an isolated resonance, the amplitude η can be expressed in the form

$$\eta_{\mathrm{res}}^{(s)} = e^{2i\delta}\left(1 - \frac{i\Gamma_n^{(s)}}{(E - E^{(s)}) + i\Gamma^{(s)}/2}\right) \tag{12}$$

where the phase δ is to be regarded as slowly varying on the scale of the resonance behavior. It is easily verified that upon substitution into Eq. (3), this expression for η_{res} leads to Eq. (11). In the same way, from Eq. (2) we can obtain the elastic scattering cross sections σ_e and σ_{se}, where the latter follows from Eqs. (5) and (9).[1]

The shapes of many hundreds of resonance levels for various nuclear species have been experimentally measured, and the parameters of their Breit–Wigner representations have thereby been determined. The results are chaotic in the extreme and no general rule is yet available for predicting the energies, widths, spins, etc. of individual resonances.

For the present, we shall not be concerned with the fine details of the resonance structure, but instead we shall focus our attention on average cross sections which do exhibit systematic features as might be expected. It is these features which can be interpreted in terms of the optical model. Of course average cross sections are directly accessible to experimental observation using neutron beams which are not highly resolved in energy. Such poor resolution experiments, as they are called, have complemented the data obtained from the study of individual resonances in a very essential way. The results of Barschall (1952), in particular, played a major role in the development of the optical model because of their striking delineation of the systematic features.

---

[1] We remark that according to our definition, the shape elastic scattering includes the so-called interference term between the "potential" scattering amplitude and the "resonance" scattering amplitude.

We must now define more precisely what is meant by the average cross sections. As a first step, we define the average of the complex amplitude by

$$\langle \eta(E) \rangle = (1/I) \int_I \eta(E')\, dE \qquad (13)$$

where the integral extends over an energy interval I centered about E. We assume that I, while small compared to E, nevertheless contains many resonances and that $\langle \eta \rangle$ is a smooth function of E. Defining the energy averages of the cross sections in the same way, we obtain

$$\langle \sigma_r \rangle = (\pi/k^2)(1 - \langle |\eta|^2 \rangle) \qquad (14)$$

and

$$\langle \sigma_e \rangle = (\pi/k^2)\langle |1 - \eta|^2 \rangle = (\pi/k^2)|1 - \langle \eta \rangle|^2 + (\pi/k^2)[\langle |\eta|^2 \rangle - |\langle \eta \rangle|^2] \qquad (15)$$

while

$$\langle \sigma_t \rangle = (2\pi/k^2)(1 - \mathrm{Re}\langle \eta \rangle). \qquad (16)$$

These are the cross sections observed in a poor resolution experiment.

We note that $\langle \sigma_e \rangle$ contains two parts, the first arising from the smoothly varying averaged amplitude, the second from its mean square fluctuation over the energy interval I. Denoting this contribution by σ_{fl} we have

$$\sigma_{fl} \equiv (\pi/k^2)(\langle |\eta|^2 \rangle - |\langle \eta \rangle|^2) \qquad (17)$$

and hence

$$\langle \sigma_e \rangle = (\pi/k^2)\,|1 - \langle \eta \rangle|^2 + \sigma_{fl} \qquad (18)$$

while also

$$\langle \sigma_r \rangle = (\pi/k^2)(1 - |\langle \eta \rangle|^2) - \sigma_{fl}. \qquad (19)$$

As we have remarked, these average cross sections are just those which are experimentally observed, and there is nothing in principle to prevent us from defining the optical potential by requiring that it yield these directly observable quantities. On the other hand, it is conceptually simple and more reasonable physically, as we shall see, to relate the optical potential directly to the average amplitude $\langle \eta \rangle$, that is, to write

$$\eta_{\mathrm{opt}} \equiv \langle \eta \rangle. \qquad (20)$$

It is this procedure which is followed. Accepting this definition, we have

$$\sigma_{t,\,\mathrm{opt}} \equiv (2\pi/k^2)(1 - \mathrm{Re}\langle \eta \rangle) = \langle \sigma_{\mathrm{tot}} \rangle \qquad (21)$$

$$\sigma_{r,\,\mathrm{opt}} \equiv (\pi/k^2)(1 - |\langle \eta \rangle|^2) = \langle \sigma_r \rangle + \sigma_{fl} \qquad (22)$$

and

$$\sigma_{e,\,\mathrm{opt}} \equiv (\pi/k^2)|1 - \langle \eta \rangle|^2 = \langle \sigma_e \rangle - \sigma_{fl}. \qquad (23)$$

Introducing the cross sections from resonance theory, these last two can be rewritten as

$$\sigma_{r,\,\text{opt}} = \langle \sigma_c \rangle - [\langle \sigma_{ce} \rangle - \sigma_f]_1 \qquad (24)$$

and

$$\sigma_{e,\,\text{opt}} = \langle \sigma_{se} \rangle + [\langle \sigma_{ce} \rangle - \sigma_{fl}]. \qquad (25)$$

As we show in a moment, the quantity in brackets is negligible and we thus have

$$\sigma_{r,\,\text{opt}} \simeq \langle \sigma_c \rangle \qquad (26)$$

and

$$\sigma_{e,\,\text{opt}} \simeq \langle \sigma_{se} \rangle. \qquad (27)$$

This procedure thus leads to the intuitively reasonable identification of absorption in the optical model potential with the formation of a compound state (including direct interactions), and of the elastic scattering in the optical model with the shape elastic scattering of resonance theory.

At higher energies, the validity of this result follows from the fact that both σ_{fl} and σ_{ce} tend to zero. At these energies, the widths of the levels become large and the resonance structure is washed out. Thus η becomes smooth and σ_{fl} is negligible. At the same time, σ_{ce} becomes vanishingly small because the number of alternative modes of decay is so enormous. At lower energies both quantities increase, but at least in the extreme low energy limit, where the levels are narrow and well separated, they are approximately equal and the result remains valid. This last follows using the resonance theory expression for η of Eq. (12). We have

$$\langle \eta_{\text{res}} \rangle = (1/N) \sum_s \langle \eta_{\text{res}}^{(s)} \rangle \qquad (28)$$

where the summation extends over all levels in the energy interval I and where

$$\begin{aligned}
\langle \eta_{\text{res}}^{(s)} \rangle &= \frac{1}{D} \int_D \eta_{\text{res}}^{(s)} \, dE \\
&= \frac{1}{D} \int_{E_s - D/2}^{E_s + D/2} e^{2i\delta} \left(1 - \frac{i\Gamma_n^{(s)}}{(E - E_s) + i\Gamma^{(s)}/2} \right) dE
\end{aligned} \qquad (29)$$

Here, $D = I/N$ is the mean distance between levels. Taking δ as varying slowly, and recalling that $\Gamma/D \ll 1$ since we are discussing the limit of narrow, well separated resonances, we obtain, neglecting higher order terms

$$\langle \eta_{\text{res}}^{(s)} \rangle \simeq e^{2i\delta}(1 - \pi\Gamma_n^{(s)}/D) \qquad (30)$$

and

$$\langle \eta_{\text{res}} \rangle \simeq e^{2i\delta}(1 - \pi\bar{\Gamma}_n/D) \qquad (31)$$

where $\bar{\Gamma}_n = (1/N)\sum\Gamma_n^{(s)}$ is the mean neutron width. In the same way we could calculate $\langle |\eta_{\text{res}}^2| \rangle$ and thus obtain σ_{fl}, while $\langle \sigma_{ce} \rangle$ could be calculated from the Breit–Wigner formula, Eq. (8), and the equality could thereby be verified. Instead, it is simpler to proceed indirectly as follows. We have

$$\sigma_{r,\,\text{opt}} \equiv \frac{\pi}{k^2}\,(1 - |\langle\eta\rangle|^2) \simeq \frac{\pi}{k^2}\,\frac{2\pi\overline{\Gamma}_n}{D}\left(1 - \frac{\pi\overline{\Gamma}n}{D}\right) \tag{32}$$

or since $\overline{\Gamma}_n/D \ll 1$, and since we have already neglected terms of this order,

$$\sigma_{r,\,\text{opt}} \simeq \frac{\pi}{k^2}\,\frac{2\pi\overline{\Gamma}_n}{D}. \tag{33}$$

On the other hand, from the Breit–Wigner formula for σ_c, we find at once upon averaging in the same way

$$\langle\sigma_c\rangle = \frac{\pi}{k^2}\,\frac{2\pi\overline{\Gamma}_n}{D}. \tag{34}$$

We thus have shown that in this limit

$$\sigma_{r,\,\text{opt}} \simeq \langle\sigma_c\rangle \tag{35}$$

and hence, by Eq. (24), we have, as claimed,

$$\langle\sigma_{\text{ce}}\rangle \simeq \sigma_{\text{fl}}. \tag{36}$$

We have established that at both extremes of energy, the identification of η_{opt} with $\langle\eta\rangle$ leads to the intuitively reasonable result that formation of a compound state (even if it eventually decays into the elastic scattering channel) is to be regarded as absorption in the optical model, and it is reasonable to assume that this is so at intermediate energies as well. Of course, at higher energies, η is smooth and there is no real distinction between $\langle\eta\rangle$ and η itself. At low energies, on the other hand, the averaging is essential and the interpretation depends crucially on the equality of σ_{fl} and σ_{ce}.

The physical basis underlying the low energy optical model can be understood by examining the time development of a neutron wave packet. As shown by Friedman and Weisskopf (1955), that portion of the packet corresonding to $\langle\eta\rangle$ which gives $\langle\sigma_{\text{sc}}\rangle$, emerges immediately as the incident pulse sweeps over the nucleus, while the fluctuation scattering pulse is delayed by the decay time $\hbar/\Gamma$ of the compound state. Since this time is so large for narrow resonances, it has no influence on the original scattered pulse. It has been pointed out by Eisberg *et al.* (1960) that this time delay has physical consequences in the case of proton scattering. They have shown that there is a difference in the bremsstrahlung radiation of shape and compound elastically scattered protons which, though small, may be measurable under favorable circumstances.

We now return to the relation between the optical model absorption cross section and $\overline{\Gamma}_n/D$ of Eq. (33). It should be emphasized that this already implies striking consequences, which are quite independent of the parameter values of the optical model potential and of the numerical complexities. If the model is to maintain its intuitive basis, then we expect and even demand that the potentials describing differing nuclear species differ essentially only in their geometrical or spatial extent. This necessarily implies a systematic variation of $\bar{\Gamma}_n/D$ as one moves through the table of nuclei. Since the widths Γ_n and level spacings D, vary by orders of magnitude from one nuclear species to another, this is a strong requirement. It is one of the triumphs of the model that this requirement is met. Moreover, if the absorption of the well is not too great, we can expect to obtain large scale, or giant, resonances of just the kind observed by Barschall, when the nuclear size is such that an integral number of half-wavelengths can "fit" into the nucleus. This indeed proves to be the case.

The quantity $\bar{\Gamma}_n/D$ plays such an important role in the description of nuclear properties that it is given a special name, the *strength function*. Since $\bar{\Gamma}_n$ and, therefore, $\bar{\Gamma}_n/D$ is proportional to the incident neutron velocity, or wave number, it is usually expressed in terms of its value at an arbitrarily chosen energy, 1 eV, and it is then written $\bar{\Gamma}_n^{(0)}/D$. The low energy data are conveniently summarized in terms of this strength function, i.e., the average of the widths of nuclear states of a given spin and parity over a small energy interval, divided by the mean spacing between levels of the given spin and parity. Thus, in place of Eq. (34), we now have

$$\frac{2\pi^2}{k^2}(E_{ev})^{1/2}\frac{\bar{\Gamma}^{(0)}}{D} = \frac{\pi}{k^2}(1 - |\langle\eta_0\rangle|^2) = \frac{\pi}{k^2}(1 - |\eta_{0,\,opt}|^2). \tag{37}$$

For p wave neutrons, a similar definition can be introduced (Saplakoglu *et al.*, 1958) for the strength function $\bar{\Gamma}^{(1)}/D$:

$$\frac{2\pi^2}{k^2}(E_{ev})^{1/2}\frac{k^2R^2}{1 + k^2R^2}\frac{\bar{\Gamma}^{(1)}}{D} = \frac{\pi}{k^2}(1 - |\langle\eta_1\rangle|^2) = \frac{\pi}{k^2}(1 - |\eta_{1,\,opt}|^2). \tag{38}$$

In Eqs. (37) and (38), E_{ev} is the incident energy in electron volts. The strength function can be directly determined, either by averaging over the experimentally observed resonances or by a poor resolution experiment in which the average is observed directly. By either or both methods, the s wave strength function, and to a lesser extent, that for p waves have been determined for a large number of elements throughout the periodic table.

A second quantity of interest is the scattering length, which is defined as the radius of an impenetrable sphere which would give the same shape elastic scattering, observed as a smooth background scattering upon which the sharp resonances are superposed. Explicitly,

$$R' = -\lim_{k\to 0}(\delta_0/k) \tag{39}$$

where δ_0 is the phase of $\langle \eta_0 \rangle \equiv \eta_{0,\text{opt}} = |\eta_{0,\text{opt}}|e^{2i\delta}$. More familiarly, the magnitude of R' is defined by

$$4\pi R'^2 = \sigma_{se}(E = 0) = \lim_{k \to 0} [(\pi/k^2)|1 - \eta_{0,\text{opt}}|^2]. \tag{40}$$

The magnitude of this quantity is thus also observable, and in favorable cases, when the interference between shape and resonant elastic scattering can be observed, so is its sign.

The strength functions and scattering length alone are not sufficient to determine the multiparameter optical potential uniquely at low energies. Nevertheless, as we shall see, certain interesting features of the optical potential at low energies can be found directly by fitting this low energy data. The potential, however, can also be determined by extrapolation from the potentials found by fitting differential and total cross section data at higher energies, since the energy dependence of optical model potentials is smooth and relatively slow. There is no *a priori* reason why these two determinations must yield results which are in detailed correspondence. The former involves state by state analysis and thus gives information on the state dependence of the interaction. The latter, since a complete phase shift analysis is impossible, gives information about an inseparable mixture of many states, and it is only simplicity which dictates an optical potential, already containing many parameters, which is state independent except for the spin orbit term. In actual fact, it turns out that the extrapolated state independent potential accounts for the over all features of the great bulk of the low energy data, but that there are some striking discrepancies. As we shall see, for *s* waves these carry an implication about the shape of the optical potential, for *p* waves these discrepancies seem to imply at least some state dependence.

We look first at the *s* wave strength function and scattering length. The experimental data are shown in Figs. 1 and 2 for $\overline{\Gamma}^{(0)}/D$ and R', respectively. Both data clearly exhibit giant 3*s* resonance at $A \sim 55$ and 4*s* resonance at $A \sim 160$. The results of early optical model calculations using a standard volume absorption potential with parameters which are reasonably consistent with higher energy data give an over all fit to both $\overline{\Gamma}^{(0)}/D$ and R'. Both the scattering length and strength function show giant (*s* waves) resonances at $A \simeq 50$ and $A \simeq 160$. The scattering length fits the data quite well but the calculated strength function does not reproduce the experimental splitting of the $A = 160$ resonance and the apparent structure near $A \simeq 70$ (Good *et al.*, 1966). Secondly, it does not give the correct magnitude of the strength function in the region $A \simeq 100$ to 120 between resonances, being too large by a factor of about two and occasionally as much as ten. We first consider the question of the disagreement between resonances. It has long been recognized that this disagreement would be decreased by a surface peaked absorption. This follows since the strength function is proportional to the optical model

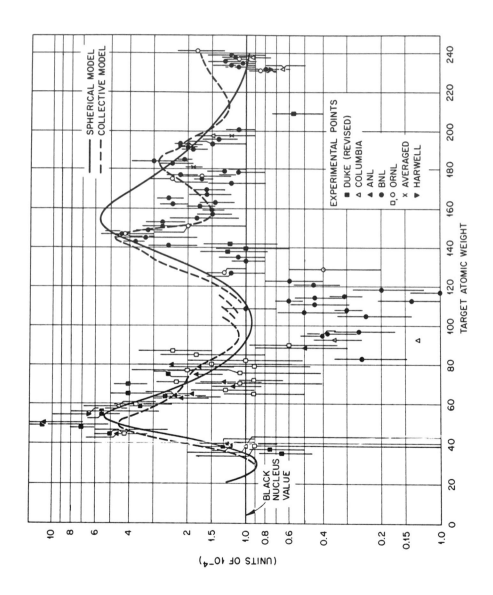

Fig. 1.

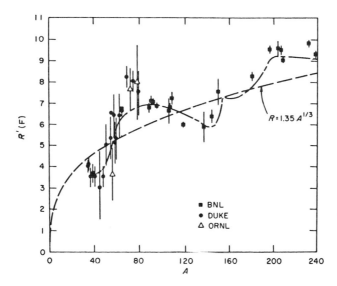

Fig. 2. The potential scattering radius (R') data as a function of atomic weight and the vibrational rotational optical model calculations with parameters $U_0 = 49$ MeV, $W' = 10$ MeV, $a = 0.52$ F, $a_I = 0.40$ F, $U_{so} = 8$ MeV, $r_0 = 1.35$ F (derivative absorption form). Also shown is the curve R, based on the relation $R = 1.35 A^{1/3}$ F (Jain, 1963).

absorption cross section which is in turn proportional to the volume integral of the imaginary part of the potential times the absolute square of the wave function. The absorbing potential is quite small at low energies so changes in it produce only second order changes in the wave function. Hence, a decrease in W is mirrored by a corresponding decrease in strength function. In addition, there is the possibility that there is a genuine scarcity of levels for elements in this mass region so that W should be smaller than normal for such elements, as emphasized by Lane *et al.* (1959). However, it now appears that surface peaking of absorption alone is not sufficient; the absorption in a fringe area is required also, as established by Fiedeldey and Frahn (1961), and by Krueger and Margolis (1961), and as explained by Moldauer (1962, 1963).

Fiedeldey and Frahn used a potential which permits an exact analytic solution of the *s* wave Schroedinger equation and which thus leads to closed form expressions for the *s* wave scattering length and strength functions, so

---

Fig. 1. The *s* wave neutron strength functions for even-even nuclei and the optical model calculations using the equivalent local parameters of the Perey and Buck nonlocal potential.

(The solid curve is obtained with the spherical potential, and the dashed curve is obtained with the coupled-channel calculation using the axially symmetric rotator model for the permanently deformed nuclei, and the pure quadrupole vibration model for the dynamically deformable nuclei (Buck and Perey, 1962).)

that their dependence on all potential parameters can be studied explicitly. The shape of their potential is shown in Fig. 3. Its real part is seen to be very similar to the standard form. Its imaginary part peaks at R_0 and turns out to be very similar to the shape of the absorption potential predicted theoretically by Gomes (1959).

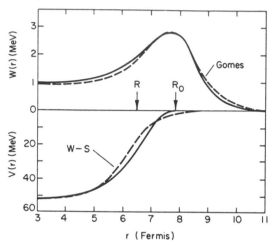

Fig. 3. The shape of the potential used by Fiedeldey and Frahn (1961) (solid curves), compared with the real potential of the $W-S$ form and the imaginary potential calculated by Gomes (1959) (dashed curves).

Upon studying the effect of parameter variations on the strength function, these authors then concluded that with the ratio of surface to volume absorption strengths approximately equal to 3, in agreement with the predictions of Gomes, the strength function between resonances could be reduced by about 50%, while the values near the resonances could be left unaltered. Experimentally, there appears to be an overall reduction of just about this amount, upon which is superposed individual fluctuations to still lower values near the neutron and proton magic number 50, and which, presumably, do represent genuine shell effects (Block and Feshbach, 1963; Shakin, 1963). Later, Fiedeldey and Frahn (1961) actually obtained an excellent overall agreement with the data as a function of A in the region between the $3s$ and $4s$ resonances.

We next turn to the work of Krueger and Margolis who examined both s and p wave strength functions using a spin orbit optical model potential with surface peaked absorption. The potential they used was qualitatively similar to that used by Fiedeldey and Frahn. Krueger and Margolis first fit the p wave data which is shown in Fig. 4, and then used the same parameters to fit the s wave data.

The p wave data shows $3p$ resonance near $A \simeq 100$ with asymmetric structure. These authors reproduced the splitting by introducing a strong spin orbit coupling which divides the peak into a $p_{3/2}$–$p_{1/2}$ doublet.

The most striking feature of their result is that the spin orbit strength required to fit the p wave strength function is about twice as strong as that required for shell model calculations and for optical model fits at higher energies. The "normal" spin orbit value fails completely to give the observed splitting of the $A \simeq 100$ resonance. The fit of the s wave data was found to be improved considerably by changing the parameters of the real potential from the values for the p wave. This implies a state dependence of the optical model potential but the analysis has not yet been carried out in a sufficiently systematic and extensive way to permit any definite conclusions. As is discussed later, the $3p$ resonance splitting is also explained by dynamical deformation effects with a "normal" spin orbit strength (Buck and Perey, 1962). We should mention that the Krueger and Margolis result has a large discrepancy between the calculated and observed p wave strength function for the isolated points in the neighborhood of Pb. Data from regions of A where nuclei are highly deformed were not fitted either since these regions require special consideration, as we shall see.

Moldauer (1963) has obtained a good agreement, not only with the $\overline{\Gamma}^{(0)}/D$, $\overline{\Gamma}^{(1)}/D$, and R', but also with the available data for the total and elastic cross sections, and polarizations below inelastic thresholds (i.e., below 600 or 800 keV) for nuclei with mass number $40 < A < 140$, explicitly taking into account the compound elastic contributions. He used a potential of the form of Eq. (1), Section 3.4, with the real potential radius $R_0 = r_0 A^{1/3} + r_1$ and with either a pure volume absorption potential $R_I = R_0$ or a pure Gaussian surface absorption potential $R_G = R_0 + c$. It was first ascertained that a satisfactory fit could not be obtained with a pure volume absorption potential. Best agreement with all the data considered was found with a potential having a thin surface absorption whose parameters are

$$U_0 = 46, \qquad W' - 14, \qquad U_{so} = 7,$$
$$r_0 = 1.16, \qquad r_1 = 0.6, \qquad a = 0.62, \qquad (41)$$
$$b = 0.5, \qquad c = 0.5.$$

It should be mentioned that he found that the effect of doubling the spin orbit coupling strength on the p wave strength function was small, not enough to produce the $p_{1/2}$–$p_{3/2}$ splitting.

We next turn to the question of the disagreement near the size resonances. First we consider the splitting of the $4s$ resonance which has two peaks at $A \sim 140$ and ~ 180. Since this is the mass number region where nuclei are known to be deformed, it was suggested by Bohr and Mottelson (1953) that

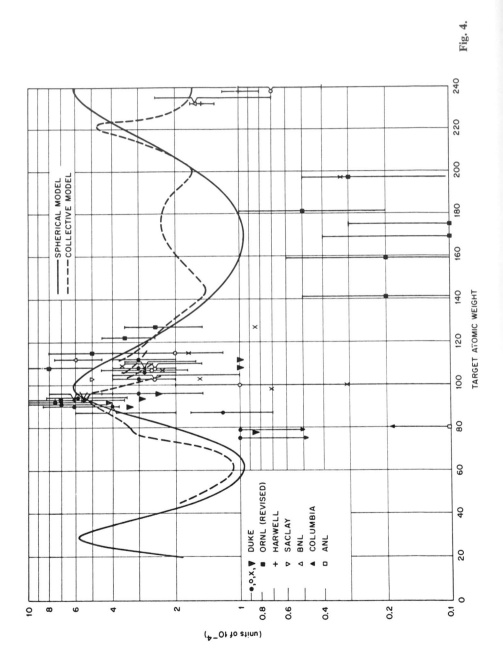

Fig. 4.

they might be accounted for if the asphericity of the target nuclei were taken into account. This indeed turns out to be the case as shown by Margolis and Troubetskoy (1957) and by Chase *et al.* (1958). These latter authors used the so-called axially symmetric rotator model.

Thus we assume that the nucleus has a well-defined axially symmetric equilibrium shape whose rotational motion is slow compared to the single particle frequencies of the internal motion, so that the intrinsic motion and the rotational motion are well uncoupled. That it is possible to separate the motion of the deformed nucleus into these two components is clearly indicated by the great regularities seen in the rotational band spectra of deformed nuclei. Restricting ourselves to the neutron scattering which induces rotational transitions connecting lowest states within the ground state rotational band (that is, the sequence of states which have the same intrinsic wave function as the ground state and differ only in their rotational wave functions), the nuclear Hamiltonian is simply given by the Bohr–Mottelson rotation Hamiltonian, H_{rot}. A conventional deformation coordinate β is introduced by choosing the nuclear surface of the following cylindrical symmetry:

$$R(\Theta) = R_0[1 + \beta Y_2{}^0(\Theta)] \qquad (42)$$

where Θ is the angle between the neutron position vector and the symmetry axis of the nucleus.

Since we may expect the optical potential to follow the shape of the nucleus, this leads naturally to an extension of the optical model to include non-spherical shape. This is most simply done by considering the potential to depend only on the distance $(r - R)$ from the surface,

$$V(r, \Theta) - V[r \quad R(\Theta)]. \qquad (43)$$

The total Hamiltonian of the system describing the scattering of neutrons from deformed nuclei is now given by

$$H = -(\hbar^2/2m)\,\nabla^2 + V(r, \Theta) + H_{rot}. \qquad (44)$$

Expansion of $V(r, \Theta)$ in terms of the deformation coordinate β yields

$$V(r, \Theta) = V(r) - R_0\,\beta\,dV(r)/dr\;Y_2{}^0(\Theta) \qquad (45)$$

where higher order terms have been neglected. The first term $V(r)$ is the usual (spherical) optical potential, and the second term is the coupling interaction which couples the target spin and the neutron angular momentum. In other words, neutron total angular momentum is not conserved, being taken up by the target nucleus, and thus we obtain a coupled set of radial equations. At

---

Fig. 4. The p wave neutron strength functions and the optical model calculations. (See the legend for Fig. 1 (Buck and Perey, 1962).)

low energies, only a few low lying collective states have to be considered explicitly by coupling to the ground state, thus restricting the number of coupled channels significantly. The imaginary potential simulates the effects of all eliminated channels, but does not include the effect of the states explicitly coupled to the ground state. Thus, the imaginary part of the potential is expected to be considerably weaker than that obtained by the elastic scattering alone for strongly collective nuclei.

Chase *et al.* (1958) carried out the calculation for even-even nuclei, explicitly taking into account the coupling between the ground ($I = 0^+$) and the first excited ($I = 2^+$) state. The deformation was introduced only for the real part of the potential. To simplify this calculation, a trapezoidal potential was used in which the falloff distance was taken to be equivalent to that using a standard volume absorption potential. Using experimental values of the deformation parameter, they obtained results in excellent agreement with the experiment. The splitting of the $A = 160$ resonance, as pointed out by Margolis and Troubetskoy (1957), is a consequence of the existence of a nearby d state resonance which is strongly coupled to the s state resonance by the deformation. The effects on the scattering length are less striking and do not particularly improve the agreement with experiment.

The discrepancies near the $3s$ and $3p$ resonances occur at those mass numbers where the nuclei are known to be spherical but susceptible to collective vibrations around the equilibrium shape. Coupling to the low lying vibrational states can be explicitly taken into account in the following manner. As in the case of any small oscillations near equilibrium, the vibrations of the nuclear shape around its spherical mean can be described by a sum of harmonic oscillators with the Hamiltonian H_{vib}, by introducing the collective vibrational coordinates $\alpha_{\lambda\mu}$ and their canonical conjugates. A quantized vibration of eigenfrequency ω_λ is called a 2^λ pole phonon, and $\alpha_{\lambda\mu}$ and the nuclear vibrational states are expressed in terms of the creation and annihilation operators of these phonons. Thus, for a pure quadrupole vibration, for example, the nuclear surface is given in a way similar to Eq. (42) but with $\alpha_{2\mu}$ instead of β and the angles θ, φ referring to the space fixed coordinate axes

$$R(\theta, \varphi) = R_0 \left[1 + \sum_\mu \alpha_{2\mu}^* Y_2^\mu(\theta, \varphi) \right]. \tag{46}$$

The optical potential is again considered to follow the nuclear shape and is a function of $(r - R)$ alone. Thus, instead of Eq. (45) we have

$$V(r; \theta\varphi) = V(r) - R_0 \frac{dV(r)}{dr} \sum_\mu \alpha_{2\mu}^* Y_2^\mu(\theta, \varphi) \tag{47}$$

and the total Hamiltonian is given by

$$H = -(\hbar^2/2m) \nabla^2 + V(r; \theta\varphi) + H_{\text{vib}}. \tag{48}$$

The second term of Eq. (47) is the coupling interaction. Restricting coupling to a few low lying vibrational states, one again finds a set of coupled channel equations. It is customary to define a " dynamical deformation parameter " β as the square root of the expectation value of $\sum_\mu |\alpha_{2\mu}|^2$ with respect to the nuclear ground state. Then the coupling strength can be given by the product of β, R_0 and the strength of the optical potential, quite similarly to the rotator model.

Buck and Perey (1962) and Jain (1963) have investigated the data for a large number of even–even nuclei using the axially symmetric rotator model for the permanently deformed nuclei, and the pure quadrupole vibration model for the dynamically deformable nuclei along with the method described above. The results for the s wave and p wave strength functions obtained by Buck and Perey are shown in Figs. 1 and 4. These authors used equivalent local parameters of their nonlocal potential, which produces a good account of a wide range of neutron scattering data (Perey and Buck, 1962), together with the value of β obtained from Coulomb excitation; thus, no free parameters were introduced. The results with the spherical potential are shown by the solid curves, and those with a quadrupole deformation by the dashed curves in Figs. 1 and 4. Jain also obtained similar fits to the data. A typical example of his results with a derivative surface absorption is shown for the scattering length R' in Fig. 2, where the parameters he used were

$$U_0 = 49, \qquad W' = 10, \qquad U_{so} = 8,$$
$$a = 0.52, \qquad a_I = 0.40, \qquad R_0 = 1.35A^{1/3}.$$

Besides the splitting of $4s$ resonance by the rotational model, the asymmetry near the $3s$ resonance and the splitting of the $3p$ resonance are seen to be reproduced fairly well by the vibrational model. Also, the strong rotational splitting of the $4p$ resonance yielded low values in the neighborhood of uranium in agreement with the data.

There still remains the disagreement for the $\overline{\Gamma}^{(0)}/D$ near $A \approx 100$ (which was removed by the absorption in a fringe area), and for the $\overline{\Gamma}^{(1)}/D$ between the $3p$ and $4p$ resonances. This may indicate state dependent optical absorption potentials in some mass regions.

Recent measurements by Divadeenam (1967) indicate two giant resonance peaks for d wave strength functions at $A = 60$ and $A = 160$. The second peak at $A = 160$ seems to split into two peaks. This can be understood as due to the deformation of the rare earth nuclei in analogy with the splitting of the $4s$ resonance peak.

Coupled channel calculation was originated in the studies of low energy neutron scattering as we have indicated in this section, and such calculation has been developed a great deal since then and has become a very powerful tool in analyzing various scattering data and in extracting spectroscopic information. A comprehensive review of the subject has been presented by Tamura (1965).

4.3   The Optical Model at High Energies

4.3a   The Born Approximation

The necessarily numerical nature of the solution of the optical model Schroedinger's equation tends to obscure even its simplest qualitative features. Therefore, as a guide to these features, we now discuss some approximate treatments of that equation, for simplicity, restricting our attention to neutral particles. As a starting point, we write the well-known exact expression for the scattering amplitude

$$F(\hat{\mathbf{n}}_0, \hat{\mathbf{n}}) = -(m/2\pi\hbar^2) \int \exp(-ik\hat{\mathbf{n}} \cdot \mathbf{r})V(r)\psi_{\hat{\mathbf{n}}0}(\mathbf{r}) \, d^3r \tag{1}$$

where $\psi_{\hat{\mathbf{n}}0}$ is the (unknown) solution of Schroedinger's equation for particles incident in the direction $\hat{\mathbf{n}}_0$.

The simplest (and quantitatively least reliable) treatment is based on the Born approximation to the scattering amplitude. This approximation follows from the argument that at sufficiently high energies, when $V(r) \ll E$, the scattering is weak and that, therefore, in the exact expression above, $\psi_{\hat{\mathbf{n}}0}$ can be replaced by the incident field. We thus obtain

$$F_B(\hat{\mathbf{n}}_0, \hat{\mathbf{n}}) \simeq -(m/2\pi\hbar^2) \int \exp(-ik\hat{\mathbf{n}} \cdot \mathbf{r})V(r) \exp(ik\hat{\mathbf{n}}_0 \cdot \mathbf{r}) \, d^3r \tag{2}$$

or, writing $V(r) = V_1 + V_2\boldsymbol{\sigma} \cdot \mathbf{L}$, and using

$$\mathbf{L} \exp(ik\hat{\mathbf{n}}_0 \cdot \mathbf{r}) = k(\mathbf{r} \times \hat{\mathbf{n}}_0) \exp(ik\hat{\mathbf{n}}_0 \cdot \mathbf{r}) \tag{3}$$

we find

$$F_B \simeq -(m/2\pi\hbar^2) \int V_1 \exp(i\mathbf{K} \cdot \mathbf{r}) \, d^3r$$

$$+ (mk/2\pi\hbar^2)\boldsymbol{\sigma} \cdot \left(\hat{\mathbf{n}}_0 \times \int \mathbf{r}V_2 \exp(i\mathbf{K} \cdot \mathbf{r}) \, d^3r\right) \tag{4}$$

where $\mathbf{K}$, the momentum transfer wave vector, is given by

$$\mathbf{K} = k(\hat{\mathbf{n}}_0 - \hat{\mathbf{n}}), \qquad |\mathbf{K}| = K = 2k \sin \theta/2 \tag{5}$$

and θ is the scattering angle. For spherically symmetric V_1 and V_2 these expressions can be simplified by introducing $\mathbf{K}$ as the polar axis, giving the expected form

$$F_B = f_B(\hat{\mathbf{n}}_0, \hat{\mathbf{n}}) + \boldsymbol{\sigma} \cdot \hat{\mathbf{n}}_p g_B(\hat{\mathbf{n}}_0, \hat{\mathbf{n}}) \tag{6}$$

where

$$f_B(\hat{\mathbf{n}}_0, \hat{\mathbf{n}}) = -(m/2\pi\hbar^2) \int V_1 \exp(iKr \cos \vartheta) 2\pi r^2 \sin \vartheta \, d\vartheta \, dr$$

$$= -(2m/\hbar^2 K) \int_0^\infty r V_1(r) \sin (Kr) \, dr \tag{7}$$

and

$$g_B(\hat{\mathbf{n}}_0, \hat{\mathbf{n}}) = -(mk/2\pi\hbar^2) \cos(\theta/2) \int r \cos \vartheta \, V_2 \exp(iKr \cos \vartheta) 2\pi r^2 \sin \vartheta \, d\vartheta \, dr$$

$$= (im/\hbar^2) \cot (\theta/2) \int_0^\infty r^2 [\cos (Kr) - (\sin Kr)/(Kr)] V_2(r) \, dr. \tag{8}$$

The latter is obtained by noting that the terms involving components of **r** perpendicular to **K** integrate to zero.

The differential cross sections predicted by these expressions are qualitatively reasonable, having the appearance of typical diffraction patterns but they tend to oscillate more strongly than is observed. In exact calculations, the imaginary part of the potential tends to damp such oscillations, but there is no such effect in the Born approximation. At lower energies, particularly, the spin orbit terms also tend to damp the oscillations since the maxima and minima of f and g do not coincide in general and this feature also is not adequately accounted for in the Born approximation. Indeed, for a spin orbit force of the Thomas type, g_B turns out to be proportional to f_B. As a particular example, if we write

$$V = (1 + i\beta)U + \alpha \frac{1}{r} \frac{\partial V}{\partial r} \boldsymbol{\sigma} \cdot \mathbf{L} \tag{9}$$

then it turns out that in the Born approximation

$$g_B = -\frac{ik^2\alpha \sin \theta}{1 + i\beta} f_B. \tag{10}$$

The polarization P is then just

$$P_B = -\frac{2\alpha\beta k^2 \sin \theta}{1 + \beta^2 + \alpha^2 k^4 \sin^2 \theta} \tag{11}$$

which is independent of the shape of the potential. However, as shown by Köhler (1956, 1958), at energies above 100 MeV, and for scattering at not too large angles, this represents a good approximation for the polarization. In fact, the relative insensitivity of the polarization to the details of the potential shape factor, as predicted by this result, is actually observed even at energies well below those at which the calculation is expected to be valid.

An interesting feature of this treatment follows from the fact that if V_1 and V_2 are both purely real, then f_B is seen to be real and g_B imaginary. As a consequence, it follows from Eq. (48), Section 3.3, that the scattering of an unpolarized beam produces no polarization in this approximation. For real potentials, polarization is a second order effect. On the other hand, if V_1 is complex, as in practice, then there is a first order polarization proportional to the imaginary part of V_1, and to V_2 in agreement with the special case treated above. Except at high energies these conclusions have only qualitative validity.

A similarly crude estimate can be given for the total absorption cross section σ_r. From Eq. (58), Section 1.4, we obtain, on replacing the actual field by the incident field, the result

$$\sigma_r \simeq -(2m/\hbar^2 k) \int W(r)\, d^3 r. \tag{12}$$

To first order, the reaction cross section is simply proportional to the volume integral of the imaginary part of the optical potential. Again, this is at best a qualitative guide to the actual behavior.

The inadequacy of the Born approximation even for energies in the hundreds of MeV region is a consequence of the fact that the field in the interior of the nucleus has a substantial effect upon the nuclear wave function. We may embody this effect approximately by the use of the so-called physical optics approximation.

4.3b   Physical Optical Approximation

A systematic development of high energy scattering theory using the physical optical approximation has been formulated by Saxon (1957) and Schiff (1956). For small angle scattering which predominates at high energies, this formulation takes a particularly simple form as had been previously emphasized and elegantly exploited by Glauber (1955). If we consider a ray, incident parallel to the z axis and entering the nucleus at a distance $\mathbf{b}$ from the axis, and neglect refraction, then the complex phase of such a ray can be written in the form $kz + \varphi(\mathbf{b}, z)$ where

$$\varphi(\mathbf{b}, z) = \int_{-\infty}^{z} \{(k^2 - (2m/\hbar^2)V(\mathbf{b}, z))^{1/2} - k\}\, dz. \tag{13}$$

The optical phase shift function $\varphi(\mathbf{b})$ is therefore given by

$$\varphi(\mathbf{b}) = \varphi(\mathbf{b}, z = \infty) = \int_{-\infty}^{\infty} \{(k^2 - (2m/\hbar^2)V(\mathbf{b}, z))^{1/2} - k\}\, dz \tag{14}$$

or in the limit of high energies under consideration,

$$\varphi(\mathbf{b}, z) = -(m/\hbar^2 k) \int_{-\infty}^{z} V(\mathbf{b}, z)\, dz, \tag{15}$$

$$\varphi(\mathbf{b}) = \varphi(\mathbf{b}, z = \infty) = -(m/\hbar^2 k) \int_{-\infty}^{\infty} V(\mathbf{b}, z)\, dz \tag{16}$$

and

$$\Psi_{\hat{n}_0} \simeq \exp[i\varphi(\mathbf{b}, z)] \exp[ikz] = \exp\left[-(im/\hbar^2 k) \int_{-\infty}^{z} (U + iW)\, dz \right] e^{ik}. \tag{17}$$

For simplicity, consider first the case in which no spin orbit term is present. It then turns out that, in the small angle approximation, by sub-stituting Eq. (17) into Eq. (1) the scattering amplitude can be expressed in the form

$$f(\hat{n}_0, \hat{n}) = (k/2\pi i) \int \exp(i\mathbf{K} \cdot \mathbf{b})[\exp(i\varphi(\mathbf{b})) - 1]\, d^2 b \tag{18}$$

where $\varphi(\mathbf{b})$ is given by Eq. (16).

If $V(r)$ is spherically symmetric, the angular integration is easily performed and

$$f(\hat{n}_0, \hat{n}) = (k/i) \int_{0}^{\infty} J_0(Kb)[\exp(i\varphi(b)) - 1]b\, db \tag{19}$$

where J_0 is the zero order Bessel function.

Even for a square well potential, no general convenient expression can be given for f. However, if the absorption is large enough [$\exp(i\varphi(b))$ is essen-tially zero over the nuclear radius and unity outside], the result for such an opaque sphere is the familiar physical optical expression

$$f = ikR^2 J_1(KR)/KR. \tag{20}$$

Actually, the result gives a qualitatively reasonable description of the scat-tering, even for nonopaque nuclei, provided the radius is replaced by an effective radius, smaller than the true one. In any case, the cross section for elastic scattering is seen to be similar to the Fraunhofer pattern for optical scattering.

The absorption cross section, given by Eq. (58), Section 1.4, can be expressed in the form

$$\sigma_r = \int (1 - |e^{i\varphi}|^2)\, d^2 b \tag{21}$$

which yields for a square well potential, for example,

$$\sigma_r = \pi R^2 \left\{ 1 - \frac{2}{\alpha^2} [1 - (1 + \alpha)e^{-\alpha}] \right\} \tag{22}$$

where

$$\alpha = -\frac{2mW(r)}{\hbar^2 k} \ 2R = \frac{2R}{\Lambda} \tag{23}$$

and Λ is the mean free path. We note that, as is to be expected, σ_r approaches πR^2 for large enough value of k, when the nucleus is opaque. However, σ_r can be appreciably smaller than this limiting value when the nucleus is small enough to be transparent, in agreement with observations.

We now turn to the question of the spin dependent part of the potential. If the potential contains a spin orbit term, then it turns out that the scattering amplitude can be written in the form

$$F = (k/2\pi i) \int \exp[i\mathbf{K} \cdot \mathbf{b}] \{ \exp[i\varphi_1(\mathbf{b})] \cos[kb\varphi_2(\mathbf{b})] - 1$$
$$+ \ i\boldsymbol{\sigma} \cdot (\mathbf{b}/b \times \hat{\mathbf{n}}_0) \exp[i\varphi_1(\mathbf{b})] \sin[kb\varphi_2(\mathbf{b})] \} \ d^2 b \tag{24}$$

where φ_1 and φ_2 are the phase shift functions arising from V_1 and V_2, respectively. Assuming spherical symmetry, F reduces to the standard form with

$$f = (k/i) \int_0^\infty J_0(Kb) \{ \exp(i\varphi_1) \cos(kb\varphi_2) - 1 \} b \ db \tag{25}$$

and

$$g = -(k/i) \int_0^\infty J_1(Kb) \exp(i\varphi_1) \sin(kb\varphi_2) b \ db. \tag{26}$$

These expressions provide a relatively reliable guide to the qualitative features of the scattering even at intermediate energies. They contain, for example, the damping effects of the imaginary part of the potential and of the spin orbit forces referred to earlier. Unfortunately, no simple closed forms can be given, even for the simplest potential, and therefore, it is not possible to exhibit these features explicitly.

4.4 Semiclassical Description of Scattering

The semiclassical analysis or the JWKB approximation (Ford and Wheeler, 1959a,b) not only illuminates the correspondence principle, but also is of practical value in the analysis of some atomic and nuclear scattering processes. In particular, the semiclassical description points to a number of interesting characteristic features of scattering which may be related to the classical deflection function $\Theta(b)$ where b is the impact parameter. For example, when the classical deflection function possesses more than one branch at a given angle, we observe a wave phenomenon of interference. When the deflection function has a relative maximum or minimum, we observe the wave phenomenon of rainbow scattering. When the deflection function passes smoothly through zero degrees, or an integral multiple of $\pm\pi$, we observe glory scattering; and, when the deflection function possesses a singularity, we observe the phenomena of orbiting. The JWKB approximation requires for its validity the condition of a slowly varying potential, i.e.,

$$|(\lambda/V)\, dV/dr| \ll 1.$$

According to the JWKB approximation, when applied to the radial wave equation, the solutions have the form

$$G(r) \sim k(r)^{-1/2}\, \exp\left[\pm i \int^r k(r)\, dr\right] \tag{1}$$

where

$$k(r) = \left\{\frac{2m}{\hbar^2}\,[E - V(r)] - \frac{(l+\tfrac{1}{2})^2}{r^2}\right\}^{1/2} \tag{2}$$

corresponds to the classical radial momentum. The presence of $(l+\tfrac{1}{2})^2$ instead of $l(l+1)$ is a refinement which follows from an accurate handling of the boundary conditions. Thus the classical impact parameter is replaced by

$$b = (l+\tfrac{1}{2})\hbar/mv = (l+\tfrac{1}{2})/k. \tag{3}$$

We require the combination of the two radial solutions that is finite at the origin. We note that k vanishes at the classical turning point r_0. For $r < r_0$, $k(r)$ is imaginary. For $r > r_0$, $k(r)$ is real. Accordingly, the JWKB solution will have an oscillating character to the right of r_0, and an exponential character to the left. To the left we choose the solution that decreases exponentially as r approaches 0. Then it can be shown that this solution goes over at large values of r to the form (Landau and Lifshitz, 1956)

$$G(r) = \sin\left\{\tfrac{1}{4}\pi + \int_{r_0}^{\infty} [k(r) - k]\, dr + k(r - r_0)\right\} \quad (r \to \infty). \tag{4}$$

Comparing this with the usual asymptotic formula in terms of the phase shift δ_l,

$$G_l \sim \sin(kr - \tfrac{1}{2}\pi l + \delta_l). \tag{5}$$

We see that according to the JWKB approximation the phase shift is given by

$$\delta_l = \tfrac{1}{4}\pi + \tfrac{1}{2}l\pi - kr_0 + \int_{r_0}^{\infty} [k(r) - k]\, dr. \tag{6}$$

The semiclassical approximation may now be defined by a set of mathematical approximations. The minimum set of such approximations may be taken as the following:

i. The phase shift δ_l is replaced by its JWKB approximate value (Eq. (6)). It can be shown using Eqs. (6) and (3) that the JWKB phase shift has a simple relationship to the classical deflection function in that

$$\Theta(l) = 2 \, d\delta_l/dl. \tag{7}$$

ii. In the semiclassical approximation, the Legendre polynomial is replaced by

$$P_l(\cos \theta) \cong [\tfrac{1}{2}(l + \tfrac{1}{2})\pi \sin \theta]^{-1/2}\sin[(l + \tfrac{1}{2})\theta + \tfrac{1}{4}\pi] \qquad (\sin \theta \geq 1/l) \quad (8a)$$

and

$$P_l(\cos \theta) \cong (\cos \theta)^l J_0[(l + \tfrac{1}{2})\theta] \qquad (\sin \theta \leq 1/l). \quad (8b)$$

These formulas overlap slightly so that all angles are effectively covered. While Eqs. (8a) and (8b) are good approximations even at small l values, the semiclassical approximation requires for its validity that many l values contribute to the scattering at a given angle or that the major contributions come from large l values.

iii. The third approximation in the semiclassical approach is to replace the summation on l by integration over l. Here again, the validity of this approximation requires that many partial waves contribute to this scattering and that the phase shift δ_l and P_l may be treated as smooth continuous functions of l.

If we now exclude angles very close to 0 or π, the approximations above permit us to convert the scattering amplitude given by Eq. (10), Section 3.1, with $\eta_l = \exp(2i\delta_l)$ into the semiclassical form

$$f_{\rm sc} = -\lambdabar(2\pi \sin \theta)^{-1/2} \int_0^\infty (l + \tfrac{1}{2})^{1/2}[\exp(i\varphi_+) - \exp(i\varphi_-)] \, dl \tag{9}$$

where the phases φ_+ and φ_- are defined by the formula

$$\varphi_\pm = 2\delta_l \pm (l + \tfrac{1}{2})\theta \pm \tfrac{1}{4}\pi \tag{10}$$

and we have set

$$\int (2l + 1)P_l \, dl = 0. \tag{11}$$

iv. The integral for the scattering amplitude is evaluated by an approximate method such as the method of stationary phase, the method of steepest descent, or some other approximation method. Using these methods and evaluating the scattering amplitude integral by the method of stationary phase, Mott and Massey (1965) obtained the result

$$\sigma_{\rm sc} = |f_{\rm sc}(\theta)|^2 = \sigma_{\rm cl} \tag{12}$$

where σ_{cl}, the classical differential scattering cross section, is given by

$$\sigma_{cl} = \frac{\lambdabar^2(l_\theta + \tfrac{1}{2})}{\sin \theta \, |d\Theta/dl|_{\Theta=\theta}}$$

$$= \frac{\lambdabar^2(l_\theta + \tfrac{1}{2})}{2 \sin \theta \, |d^2\delta_l/dl^2|_{\Theta=\theta}}. \tag{13}$$

Here we distinguish explicitly between the angle of observation θ and the classical function $\Theta(l)$ (positive for net repulsion and negative for net attraction). The positive quantity l_θ is defined by the relation

$$\Theta(l_\theta) = \pm\theta. \tag{14}$$

Referring to Eq. (9), constructive interference occurs only near the l value of stationary phase $l = l_\theta$ where one of the exponents has an extremum, i.e.,

$$2(d\delta_l/dl)_{l_\theta} = \Theta(l_\theta) = \theta \quad \text{or} \quad -\theta. \tag{15}$$

Destructive interference begins with those l values where the curve δ_l differs from the line which is tangent by an amount significantly more than one radian (see Fig. 1). Where constructive interference occurs we replace the curve δ_l by its osculating parabola. Under these circumstances Eq. (9) becomes a Gauss–Fresnel integral of classical optics. In this approximation the scattering amplitude is found to have the value

$$f_{sc}(\theta) = \lambdabar[(l + \tfrac{1}{2})/(2 \sin \theta \, |\delta_l''|]^{1/2}_{l=l_\theta} e^{i\beta} \tag{16}$$

where

$$\beta = 2\alpha_\theta - \tfrac{1}{4}\pi\left(2 - \frac{\delta''}{|\delta''|} - \frac{\delta'}{|\delta'|}\right)_{l=l_\theta} \tag{17}$$

and

$$\alpha_\theta = [\delta_l - (l + \tfrac{1}{2})(d\delta_l/dl)]_{l=l_\theta}. \tag{18}$$

Although the squared absolute value of f_{sc} is equal to the classical cross section, nevertheless, the phase angle β is, in principle, measurable through interference with the wave scattered by the same center out of another part of the incident wave front. The result $\sigma_{sc} = \sigma_{cl}$ depends upon two conditions not inherent in the semiclassical approximation itself, (a) that the angle of scattering is not too close to 0 or π, and (b) that there must be one and only one point of stationary phase. This latter condition will be met for all deflection angles only if the classical deflection function varies monotonically between 0 and $\pm\pi$. Such a variation is special and cannot be expected to occur often in practice. In particular, the Coulomb potential is almost the only simple attractive potential with this property.

Classically, it is possible that several incident angular momenta may, at a given energy, lead to the same scattering angle. The total cross section is, in general, the sum of the contributions from the different branches.

When these branches are sufficiently separated, each will give a separate contribution to the quantum scattering amplitude, which may be evaluated by the method of stationary phase. Under these circumstances, the total semiclassical amplitude is given by the sum of contributions to Eq. (16) from each branch.

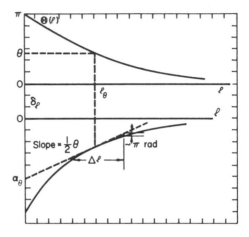

Fig. 1. Classical deflection function and phase shifts for simple case of one to one relation between deflection and impact parameter.

($\Theta(l) =$ deflection function; $\delta_l =$ phase shift; $l =$ angular momentum; $\theta =$ angle of observation; $l_\theta =$ angular momentum for classical deflection to angle of observation, i.e., $\Theta(l_\theta) = \pm \theta$. A range of l values centered about l_θ contributes to the quantum cross section at θ, those l values being important for which the curve δ_l and the line tangent to the curve at l_θ differ by less than a few radians. The semiclassical result, that the quantum and classical cross sections are equal, requires that l_θ and Δl be large compared to unity, and that the curve δ_l is well represented by a parabola over the interval Δl. The phase of the quantum scattering amplitude is simply related to the intercept, α_θ, of the tangent line (Eq. (18)). In the case illustrated in the diagram, α is negative (Ford and Wheeler, 1959a).)

If the classical deflection function passes smoothly through 0 or through $\pm \pi$, an effect occurs which is called the glory effect. The vanishing of $\sin \Theta$ when $d\Theta/dl$ and l are finite leads to a singularity in the forward or backward scattering cross section. In this case, let us for definiteness, consider a backward glory. The deflection function near π may be approximated by the expression

$$\Theta(l) = \pi + a(l - l_g). \tag{19}$$

Then the two equal contributions from $\theta > \pi$ and $\theta < \pi$ add up to the classical cross section

$$\sigma_{cl} = 2\lambda^2 l_g / |a| (\pi - \theta). \qquad (20)$$

For angles sufficiently far from π, the semiclassical cross section in the presence of the glory may be calculated by the interference method. The two contributing amplitudes at $\Theta(l) = \theta$ and $\Theta(l) = 2\pi - \theta$ are evaluated by the method of stationary phase, and combined with the approximate phase. Near π, the Legendre function must be replaced by the Bessel function approximation. Then we may integrate Eq. (19) to obtain a suitable approximate expression for the phase shift for those values of l that contribute to glory,

$$\delta_l = \tfrac{1}{2}\pi(l - l_g) + \tfrac{1}{4}a(l - l_g)^2 + \delta_g. \qquad (21)$$

The scattering amplitude becomes

$$f_{sc} = (\lambda/2i) \exp(2i\delta_g - \pi i l_g) \int_0^\infty (2l + 1)\{\exp[\tfrac{1}{2}ia(l - l_g)^2]\}J_0(l \sin \theta)\, dl. \qquad (22)$$

This integral may be evaluated using the integral representation

$$J_0(x) = (1/2\pi) \int_0^{2\pi} \exp(ix \cos \varphi)\, d\varphi. \qquad (23)$$

The result is

$$f_{sc}(\theta) = \lambda(l_g + \tfrac{1}{2})(2\pi/a)^{1/2} e^{i\zeta} J_0(l_g \sin \theta) \qquad (24)$$

for a backward glory where the phase constant ζ is given by

$$\zeta = 2\delta_g - \pi l_g - \pi/4. \qquad (25)$$

For a forward glory the πl_g term is missing. The glory cross section is given finally by the formula

$$\sigma_{sc} = \lambda^2(l_g + \tfrac{1}{2})^2(2\pi/|a|)J_0^2(l_g \sin \theta). \qquad (26)$$

Here the singularity in the classical cross section is replaced by a finite peak whose magnitude is

$$\sigma_{sc}(\text{peak}) = \lambda^2(l_g + \tfrac{1}{2})^2(2\pi/|a|). \qquad (27)$$

The Bessel function oscillations may be said to arise from interference of the contributions from the two branches of the deflection function found near a glory. The phenomenon of glory has been observed in the backward peaking of alpha particles scattered from complex nuclei (Bryant and Jarmie, 1967).

Studies of strongly absorbed particles indicate that the elastic scattering cross sections are essentially independent of the form of the potential at small internuclear distances. Figure 2 illustrates in classical terms the semitransparent nuclear model for high energy nuclear scattering. Fig. 2a shows the real part of an idealized nuclear potential in which the repulsive field zZe^2/r gives way in some surface transition to an attractive field within the nucleus. The geometry of the classical orbits is illustrated in Fig. 2c and a qualitative graph of the classical deflection function $\Theta(l)$ is shown in Fig. 2b. At an

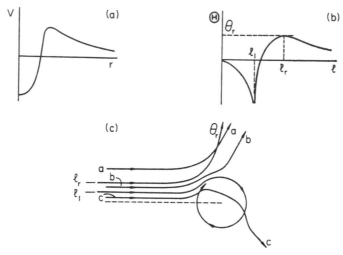

Fig. 2. Pictorial description of classical scattering of alpha particles by nuclei.
((a) Assumed form of real part of potential. (b) Classical deflection function versus angular momentum, l, ignoring absorption. Depicted are the characteristic features of rainbow angle and spiral scattering. If the actual nuclear absorption is large, the attenuation should fall from large to small values within the interval $l_1 \lesssim l \lesssim l_r$. (c) Geometry of classical orbits. In particular, three different orbits, a, b, and c, with the same scattering angle are shown. Quantum mechanically these must interfere. However, c should be strongly damped by absorption while the larger area associated with a will make its contribution to the scattering amplitude at this angle much greater than the contribution from b (Ford and Wheeler, 1959b).)

angular momentum l_r, close to that for a grazing collision, the deflection reaches a maximum giving rise to a rainbow angle θ_r. For somewhat smaller impact parameters θ passes rapidly through 0. At a somewhat smaller critical angular momentum l_1 the deflection angle approaches $-\infty$. This corresponds to an infinite spiraling of the trajectory.

It should be clear from Fig. 2c that the rainbow angle trajectory only grazes the nuclear surface, while trajectories leading to the anomolous behavior of $l < l_1$ at smaller angular momenta traverse at least one diameter of nuclear matter. Thus in the neighborhood of the rainbow angle we may ignore absorption. On the other hand, for appreciably smaller impact parameters scattering may be ignored since in effect such particles are completely absorbed (or broken up) upon impact. The scattering near the rainbow angle is described semiclassically by Ford and Wheeler (1959a) as follows.

When the classical deflection function is nonmonotonic, contributing two or more branches to the same deflection angle, then $\Theta(l)$ must possess either singularities or maxima or minima. At a maximum or minimum, i.e.,

$$d\Theta/dl = 0 \tag{28}$$

a phenomenon known as rainbow scattering occurs. The simplest potentials which give rise to such behavior are monotonic attractive potentials finite at the origin. Since the deflection vanishes for $l = 0$ and for $l = \infty$, and is negative in between, one or more minima must occur. By virtue of the factor $(d\Theta/dl)^{-1}$ in the classical cross section, a singularity occurs when $d\Theta/dl = 0$. The corresponding phenomenon in optics is responsible for rainbows and hence the name rainbow angle is applied to such an extremum of the deflection function. Further, the scattering in the neighborhood of the rainbow angle is referred to as rainbow scattering.

Using quadratic expansion for the deflection function in the neighborhood of the rainbow angle θ_r we have

$$\Theta(l) = \theta_r + q(l - l_r)^2 \tag{29}$$

Deflection angles greater than θ_r correspond to the dark side whereas angles less than θ_r correspond to the bright side. On the bright side of the rainbow angle the classical intensity will be

$$\sigma_{cl} = \frac{\lambda^2 (l_r + \tfrac{1}{2})}{2 \sin \theta_r |q(\theta - \theta_r)|^{1/2}} . \tag{30}$$

On the dark side the classical intensity vanishes. The same results follow from geometrical optics from the scattering of light from water droplets near the rainbow angle.

Far from the rainbow angle on its bright side, the semiclassical cross section may be found as previously mentioned by considering the interference between the two branches. However, near the rainbow angle, contributions from the two branches overlap and cannot be computed independently. Moreover, the phase shift cannot be approximated by a parabola since $d^2\delta/dl^2$ is approaching zero and the third derivative terms must be included.

Using the quadratic approximation Eq. (29), the deflection function near the rainbow angles leads to the phase shift

$$\delta_l = \delta_r \pm \tfrac{1}{2}\theta_r(l - l_r) + \tfrac{1}{6}q(l - l_r)^3 . \tag{31}$$

The dominant contribution to Eq. (9) for $\theta_r > 0$ comes from the second term. Substituting Eq. (31) into Eq. (9) we obtain the formula

$$f_{sc}(\theta) \simeq \frac{(l_r + \frac{1}{2})^{1/2}\lambda}{(2\pi \sin \theta)^{1/2}}$$

$$\times e^{i\phi} \int_{-\infty}^{\infty} \exp[i(\theta_r - \theta)(l - l_r) + i(q/3)(l - l_r)^3]\, d(l - l_r) \quad (32)$$

where the phase ϕ is given by

$$\phi = 2\alpha_r - \tfrac{1}{4}\pi + (l_r + \tfrac{1}{2})(\theta_r - \theta) \tag{33}$$

and α_r is defined by Eq. (18). The integral which must be evaluated is the same as that obtained by Airy (1839) in his famous work on the optical rainbow, and the scattering amplitude near the rainbow angle has the form

$$f_{sc}(\theta) = \lambda \left[\frac{2\pi(l_r + \frac{1}{2})}{\sin \theta}\right]^{1/2} q^{-1/3} e^{i\phi}\, \text{Ai}(x) \tag{34}$$

where for positive $\Theta(l_r)$, ϕ is given by Eq. (33) and by definition

$$x = q^{-1/3}(\theta_r - \theta) \tag{35}$$

and for negative Θ we replace $\theta_r - \theta$ by $\theta - \theta_r$ in both Eq. (33) and Eq. (35). The total phase of the rainbow amplitude will either be ϕ or $\phi + \pi$ according as the product $q^{-1/3}\, \text{Ai}(x)$ is positive or negative. In the absence of interference from other branches of the deflection function, the differential cross section near the rainbow angle is given by

$$\sigma_{sc} = \lambda^2 \frac{(l_r + \frac{1}{2})2\pi}{\sin \theta} |q^{-2/3}|\, \text{Ai}^2(x) \tag{36}$$

The Airy integral itself is defined by [see Table II of Ford and Wheeler (1959a)]

$$\text{Ai}(x) = (1/2\pi) \int_{-\infty}^{\infty} \exp[ixu + \tfrac{1}{3}iu^3]\, du. \tag{37}$$

This function has an oscillatory behavior on the bright side ($x < 0$) and a rapid falloff on the dark side ($x > 0$).

When other branches of the deflection contribute at the rainbow angle, these must be combined and the absolute square taken. This situation occurs in a number of physical situations. However, in the absence of other contributing amplitudes, the rainbow cross section can be identified by its characteristic shape and from this shape the parameters l_r, θ_r, and q can be deduced.

To illustrate the semiclassical approximation we show in Fig. 3 the scattering of 22 MeV alpha particles by silver. While this is a borderline case for the application of a semiclassical model, nevertheless a crude description of scattering beyond the rainbow angle leads to qualitative agreement with experiment. Thus the ratio of the cross section near the rainbow scattering to the Rutherford cross section is given by

$$\frac{\sigma}{\sigma_c} = \left(\frac{2\sin^2\frac{1}{2}\theta_r}{nq^{1/3}}\right)^2 \frac{(l_r + \frac{1}{2})}{\sin\theta} 2\pi \, \text{Ai}^2[q^{-1/3}(\theta - \theta_r)] \qquad (38)$$

where $n = 2Ze^2/\hbar v$. In view of nuclear absorption, which has been neglected, it is expected that this would be more nearly valid on the high angle side of θ_r than the low angle side. Equation (38) contains two adjustable parameters which can be adjusted to give the best fit to the experimental data. The fit is shown in Fig. 3 with the choice of parameters

$$\theta_r = 1.22 \,\, (70 \,\, \text{degrees}) \qquad q^{1/3} = 0.70. \qquad (39)$$

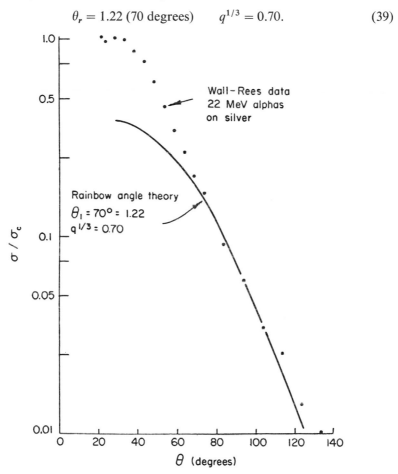

Fig. 3. Fit of the approximate rainbow angle cross section (Eq. (38)) to the observed cross section for 22 MeV alpha particles scattered by silver. Two parameters are adjusted (Ford and Wheeler, 1959b).

For this case the rainbow l_r is ~ 9 and the "thickness" of the nuclear surface in units of l is

$$\Delta l = [\theta_r/q]^{1/2} \cong 2. \tag{40}$$

While with two adjustable parameters the fit need not be too significant, it does appear significant that experimental and theoretical cross sections show a smooth falloff. Similar rainbow angle fits have been found for other substances. The influence of absorption on the semiclassical model has also been examined by Ford and Wheeler (1959b).

Austern (1961) has given particular consideration to the strong absorption case using the JWKB approximation to calculate scattering amplitudes. Now, if $\eta_l = 0$ in Eq. (7), Section 3.1, then reflection vanishes for the lth partial wave. We might say that nucleus is black for that wave. However, the situation is complicated in three dimensions in that, not only are waves absorbed or reflected, but they are also diffracted. This influence of diffraction is related to the fact that although $\eta_l = 0$ may hold for all low particle waves, yet as l goes to infinity η_l must eventually go to 1. Thus the phenomenon of diffraction complicates the discussion, and points to the fact that the concept of black cannot be incorporated exactly in any quantum mechanical treatment.

In the sharp cutoff model developed by Blair (1957) to account for alpha particle scattering, the transition from $\eta_l = 0$ to $\eta_l = 1$ is made abruptly at an angular momentum which corresponds to the classical impact parameter of the nuclear surface. The work of Austern improves upon this extreme model and handles intermediate situations.

In the lowest JWKB approximation the ingoing wave function

$$G_l^0 \approx e^{-ip(r)} \tag{41}$$

where

$$p(r) = kr + \int_\infty^r [k(r) - k] \, dr \tag{42}$$

may be viewed as representative of the partial wave. Because of the imaginary part of $V(r)$ this wave decreases towards small r. Inside the classical turning point, we would expect the wave function to damp rapidly to zero. Austern proposes as a zero order solution the simple approximate boundary condition in which the wave function is forced to vanish at the classical turning point r_0. Thus he chooses

$$G_l^0 = \exp[-ip(r)] - \exp[ip(r) - 2ip(r_0)]. \tag{43}$$

In this approximation

$$\eta_l = -\exp[-2ip(r_0)] \tag{44}$$

is a term which may be interpreted as the reflection from the centrifugal potential. Austern also gives a correction to this initial approximation

$$\Delta\eta_l = \tfrac{1}{2} \int_{r_0}^{\infty} \{\exp[-2ip(\xi)] - \exp[2ip(\xi) - 4ip(r_0)]\} \frac{k'(\xi)}{k(\xi)} \, d\xi \qquad (45)$$

which corresponds to reflection from the derivative of the optical potential $V(r)$ which occurs predominantly at the nuclear surface. If the reflection is weak, i.e., η_l is very small, then the once corrected solution is sufficient. These results permit us to distinguish several effects which cause η_l to be small. For the low partial waves the centrifugal reflection occurs deep inside the nucleus, and hence the absorptive part of the potential is able to cause strong attenuation of the radial waves of these cases, both as the wave proceeds toward r_0 and back again. Thus, the net reflected amplitude, which the centrifugal potential is able to cast outside the nucleus, is small. Furthermore, only weak reflection occurs in the nuclear surface region. Not only is $k'(\xi)/k$ usually rather small but it is averaged over products of oscillatory wave functions so that the integral tends to average to zero. This phase averaging is much more important than the damping of the wave function in minimizing reflection from the surface region. The reflected wave cast back at r_0 does not upset the phase averaging in the surface region so long as G is reasonably sinusoidal. Strong reflections can occur from the centrifugal barrier if absorption is weak as in the case of nucleons, or if the centrifugal barrier is moved out to large r for higher partial waves. Strong reflection can also occur from the nuclear surface if the phase averaging is upset. As l increases both of these effects take place and cause the eventual rise of η_l to 1.

For actual values of the nuclear surface thickness, phase averaging is probably rather effective for all alpha particle bombarding energies above 10 MeV. Thus, reflections at the surface are important only if the centrifugal barrier overlaps the surface region upsetting the phase averaging. Those partial waves for which $r_0(l)$ appears in the surface region may be thought of as sampling the structure of the nuclear surface. For these partial waves careful treatment of the surface boundary condition is needed. For other partial waves the detailed structure of the surface is not very important.

One interesting implication of the above discussion is that reflections by the optical potential are expected to be important only at low energies at which the projectile wave length becomes comparable with or greater than the surface thickness. Then phase averaging is upset. Thus, shape or size resonance should occur only at low energies.

Figure 4 illustrates several radial wave functions computed for 11 MeV alpha particles incident to Ar^{40}. It is seen that the low partial waves penetrate to small r with rather high probability. Thus the small η_l must largely be accounted for by phase averaging. Indeed, it is this phase averaging that causes the

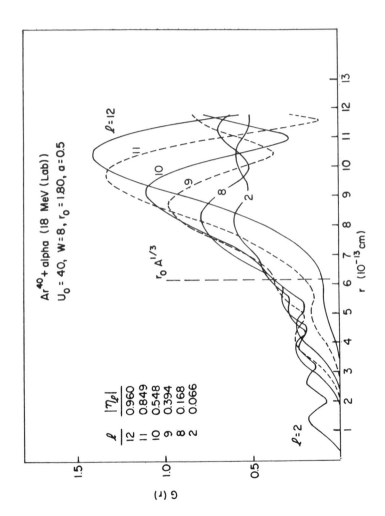

Fig. 4. Radial wave functions G_l for several values of l computed by numerical solution of the radial differential equation, for 18 MeV alpha particles incident on Ar^{40}. (The real and imaginary parts of the optical well have the depths shown, and the W–S shape as given by Igo (1959b) (Austern, 1961).)

optical model calculations to be so sensitive to the structure at the surface. Furthermore, a few partial waves experience centrifugal reflection in the surface region. Figure 5 shows the modulus and phase of η_l for scattering of alpha particles using Igo's parameters (Igo, 1959b). Note that η_l fluctuates somewhat with l. This corresponds to an interference between the reflections from the surface region and the interior region. Note, also, that at the region of the classical cutoff, the magnitude of η_l goes over rather abruptly from small values to values near 1.

The reflection from the centrifugal potential, i.e., Eq. (44), is seen to play an important role in the determination of discrete families of optical potentials found for the elastic scattering of composite particles such as deuterons, He^3, t, and alpha particles from complex nuclei (Drisko *et al.*, 1963), as we shall discuss in Chapter VI.

Finally, as a related topic of a stationary phase, the interference maxima seen in the energy averaged neutron total cross section $\sigma_t(E)$, as a function of energy, should be mentioned (Peterson, 1962; Franco, 1965; McVoy, 1965, 1967). In the data by Barschall (1952), as shown in Fig. 3, Section 1.4, broad maxima are seen to arrange themselves into a series of continuous "ridges" in the mass number versus energy contour plot of $\sigma_t(E)$ (Peterson, 1962). One of the most remarkable features is that the loci of the ridges in the A-E plane move to *higher* energies as A is increased, quite contrary to the expectation of the interpretation as a manifestation of giant resonances. These nonresonant peaks seen in single particle scattering cross sections were called a "nuclear Ramsauer effect" by Peterson. Alternatively, as the phase shifts go downward as a function of energy in this region, they are called "echoes." Physically, this phenomenon occurs due to constructive interference between that part of the incident beam which passes through the nucleus and that part which passes around it, as emphasized by Peterson and by Lawson (1953). If the incident momentum is high enough to justify the ray tracing JWKB approximation, and the refraction effects can be ignored, then one can easily see that the maxima as a function of E and R lie approximately on the curve

$$(K - k)R = (n - \tfrac{1}{2})\pi \qquad (n = 1, 2, \ldots) \tag{46}$$

in the E-R plane. In Eq. (46), K and k are the internal and external wave numbers, respectively. Thus, the loci of the ridges move to higher energies as R is increased. Including refractive bending of the rays at the nuclear surface, Peterson (1962) and Franco (1965) obtained good agreement between loci of the Eq. (46) type and the experimental maxima. The essential feature of the scattering is that a "stationary phase" $d\delta_l/dl = 0$ occurs at some value of l, so that many partial waves "pile up" and make an abnormally large contribution to $\sigma_t(E)$. This will occur for any potential $V(r)$ which has a minimum

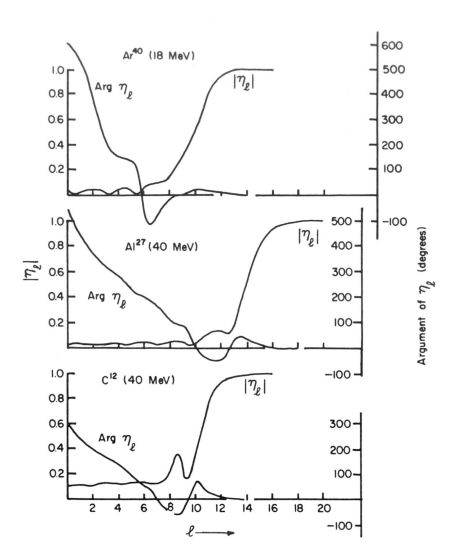

Fig. 5. Modulus and phase of η_l for the scattering of alpha particles from the indicated targets, computed by exact numerical integration of the radial differential equation, using Igo's parameters.

(Only the η_l values at integer values of l were computed, and are of physical interest; however, the radial differential equation has solutions for all values of l, so the smooth curves in this figure are meaningful. Interpolation between points was assisted by the use of graphs of real and imaginary parts of η_l (Austern, 1961).)

as a function of r, and is predicted also in the atom–atom scattering with the Lennard-Jones potential (Rothe *et al.*, 1962). In the above JWKB picture the shift δ_l, in the phase of the part of the incident wave which passes through the nuclear region relative to the part which goes around it, is proportional to the length of the chord intercepted by the potential sphere at impact parameter $b_l \sim l/k$, which is nearly $2R$ for all waves with $l \ll kR$. Hence, at the energy where one of these waves passes downward through $90°$, all of them will, and the resulting superposition of echoes is just the interference maximum in $\sigma_t(E)$. Thus, the ridge is not identifiable by a single l value as a giant resonance is, but rather by the radial quantum number n which appears in Eq. (46) and which is common to all contributing partial waves. McVoy (1967) has examined in detail whether Lane–Thomas–Wigner giant resonances [the " spreading " of a single particle neutron width over many compound nucleus levels via configuration interaction (Lane *et al.*, 1955)], ever cause corresponding maxima in the energy dependence of $\sigma_t(E)$, and has concluded that the maxima they produce in these nonelastic cross sections are so small compared to the interference ridges occurring in the shape elastic cross sections that they manifest themselves in the *total* cross section merely as minor irregularities in the ridge pattern. In other words, giant resonances play a very minor role in the energy dependence of the poor resolution total cross sections for N–$\mathcal{N}$ scattering.

V

Velocity Dependent and Nonlocal Potentials

5.1 General Features

5.1a Early History of Velocity Dependent Potentials

The concept of velocity dependent interactions has old roots in the literature of physics which reach back almost to the discovery (in 1785) by Coulomb (with the aid of work by Priestly and Cavendish) of the static interaction $V \sim r^{-1}$. The subsequent development of electrostatics proceeded rapidly thereafter with important theoretical contributions by Poisson, Laplace, Green, and Gauss; and, experimental contributions by Volta, Galvani, and others. Volta's work, particularly, paved the way for the development of electromagnetics, which as a science, might be assigned 1820 as a birth year, the year of the discovery by Oersted of the deflection of a compass needle by an electric current. Within little over a decade, a succession of discoveries by Arago, Gay-Lussac, Ampere, Biot and Savart, Henry, Faraday, Lenz, and Weber, had established most of the macroscopic laws relating electricity to magnetism. Furthermore, the interactions between magnetic dipoles, a magnetic dipole and a current element, and between current elements were established.

The first quantitative effort within the framework of classical mechanics to describe the magnetic interaction of isolated charged particles was made by Ampere, Neumann and Weber. Indeed, Weber in 1848, working within the framework of classical mechanics, proposed the (erroneous) velocity dependent potential $V(r, \dot{r}) \sim r^{-1}[1 + (\dot{r}/c)^2]$ as a generalized electrodynamic potential governing the motion of a particle relative to a fixed center of force. Further efforts to embody conservative velocity dependent forces in classical mechanics were made before the turn of the century by Schering, Helmholz, Mayer, and Hirsch.

The mainstream of the development of electricity and magnetism, however, proceeded via the development of the concept of the electromagnetic field by Faraday during the period 1837 to 1846, and by Maxwell during the period 1855 to 1862. Maxwell presented a self-consistent set of partial differential equations, which, in a vacuum, related the electromagnetic field vectors **E** and **H**. Subsequent studies by Lorentz, Poynting, Poincare, and others related the electromagnetic field vectors to a four vector potential $\phi_\alpha(\mathbf{r}, t)$ which is often taken as $[\mathbf{A}, i\phi_0]$ where $\phi_0(\mathbf{r}, t)$, in the language of relativity, is the timelike component of a four vector field, and $\mathbf{A}(\mathbf{r}, t)$ represents the spacelike components. The interaction of a particle with charge e with such a field is then characterized by the interaction Lagrangian $e\phi_0 - e(\mathbf{v} \cdot \mathbf{A})/c$. The second term represents the velocity dependent interaction between the particle and the field. When two particles interact one can look upon each particle as a source of the field and as acted upon by the field. Alternatively, one can eliminate the field and derive a direct interaction. The $\mathbf{v} \cdot \mathbf{A}$ term occasions the direct velocity dependent interactions between charged particles.

As the quantum theory of the atom developed during the early decades of the twentieth century, velocity dependent forces or potentials again manifested themselves. Thus the magnetic effects upon atomic spectra noted by Zeeman, Paschen, Back, and others, and the spin orbit effect noted by Thomas and Frenkel have their origin in the velocity dependent interaction of electrons with the vector potential.

The problem of the two interacting Dirac particles, which influence each other through their interactions with the electrodynamic field, was studied intensively in the 1929–1934 era of quantum electrodynamics by Heisenberg and Pauli (1929), Dirac (1932), Dirac *et al.* (1932), Fermi (1932), Fock and Podolsky (1932), Rosenfeld (1932), Breit (1929, 1932), Møller (1931), and others. These men developed what might be called the Diracian one photon exchange potential (DOPEP). To the order v^2/c^2 this leads to Breit's e–e interaction which has a number of velocity dependent terms of relativistic (or magnetic) origin.

5.1b Velocity Dependent Potentials (VDP) in Nuclear Physics

Velocity dependent potentials also have rather old roots in the nuclear literature, arising almost simultaneously with Yukawa's (1935) proposal of a scalar meson theory of the N–N interaction. The work of Proca (1936) and Kemmer (1938) which extended Yukawa's theory to coupling via vector, tensor, pseudovector and pseudoscalar fields, led to a variety of one boson exchange potentials (OBEP). While these works implied the existence of velocity dependent interactions among relativistic effects, the major terms, as in electrodynamics, were static in nature.

Velocity dependent potentials and nonlocal N-$\mathcal{N}$ potentials were first considered in 1936 by Fay and by Wheeler. Way and Wheeler (1936) suggested that nuclear saturation might be explained by assuming that the nucleon–nuclear force is velocity or momentum dependent, i.e., $V = V(\mathbf{r}, \mathbf{p})$. Then a difficulty arises because momentum enters the Schroedinger formalism as the differential operator. Accordingly, if $V(\mathbf{r})$ is replaced by a general form of $V(\mathbf{r}, \mathbf{p})$, one, in general, arrives at a nonlinear differential equation

$$[E - (p^2/2m_0)]\Psi = V(\mathbf{r}, \mathbf{p})\Psi. \tag{1}$$

Wheeler, however, identified a technique for dealing with velocity dependent potentials by the use of an equivalent integral operator representation. Thus, he showed that we may let

$$V(\mathbf{r}, \mathbf{p})\Psi(r) = \int \tilde{V}(\mathbf{r}, \mathbf{r}')\Psi(\mathbf{r}')\, d\tau' \tag{2}$$

where

$$\tilde{V}(\mathbf{r}, \mathbf{r}') = (1/2\pi\hbar)^3 \int V(\mathbf{r}, \mathbf{p}) \exp[(i/\hbar)(\mathbf{r} - \mathbf{r}') \cdot \mathbf{p}]\, d\tau_p. \tag{3}$$

At about the same time, Inglis (1936) noted that the apparent inversion of doublets in nuclei might be accounted for by a Thomas-like N–N interaction term such as arises from a Dirac equation. Breit (1937) gave detailed attention to two Diracian N–N interactions which, in their Pauli equivalents, lead to many velocity dependent terms. Further, Møller and Rosenfeld (1940) showed that nonstatic interaction terms, while usually small, might become of significance in mixed meson theory.

In the early postwar years relatively little attention was given to velocity dependent nucleon–nucleon or nucleon–nuclear potentials. Green (1948; 1949a,b), using "regulated" meson fields, derived OBEP's based upon nucleons coupled to a vector plus scalar field (a so-called five vector field) which led to purely relativistic Diracian interactions whose Pauli equivalents contained velocity dependent interactions. Because of cancellation of the major static terms, these VDP's became major residual effects. The pseudo-scalar–pseudoscalar interaction was also considered since it also represents a purely relativistic interaction (see Section 7.4).

Relatively little direct attention, however, was given to velocity dependent and nonlocal potentials in nuclear structure physics until about 1955–1957. Then the use of velocity dependent potentials and nonlocal equations received considerable stimulus from four separate directions.

i. The self-consistent field studies of Brueckner *et al.* (1954, 1958), which attempted to describe the many nucleon systems in terms of a phenomenological static nucleon–nucleon force, suggested that particle motion in the nucleus is highly correlated. This was partly due to the hard core nucleon–nucleon force which was assumed, and partly due to exchange effects. Because of this, the potential is nonlocal, as discussed particularly by Bethe (1956a).

ii. The work of Johnson and Teller (1955), using an explicitly velocity dependent meson theoretic N–$\mathcal{N}$ potential, and its extensions by Duerr (1956, 1958), and Ross *et al.* (1956b), displayed a number of reasonable saturation properties as well as shell structure.

iii. Detailed studies, using diffuse boundary phenomenological nucleon–nuclear potentials in bound state problems, pointed to the need for velocity dependent potentials to account for both total nuclear energies and single particle binding energies within the framework of a realistic IPM (Lee and Green, 1956a,b; Green, 1957, 1958a,b).

iv. Detailed "cloudy crystal ball" studies by Beyster *et al.* (1956), Bjorklund *et al.* (1956), Melkanoff *et al.* (1957), and others pointed to the need for energy dependent potential parameters in using the optical model. An attempt (Green, 1959; Wyatt *et al.*, 1960) to unify the bound state and scattering problem with a nonlocal complex optical model potential, using an extension of the effective mass approximation of Frahn and Lemmer (1957), was reasonably successful. Further, Lemmer and Green (1960) showed that the spherical nonlocal potential so obtained provided a good point of departure to treat spheroidal nuclei. Without availing themselves of any adjustable parameters, their work led directly to the energy level structures which Nilsson (1955) had obtained with static spheroidal potentials but with many adjustable constants.

Because of the vastness of the nuclear physics effort, it is difficult to present a comprehensive review of the involvement of nonlocal or velocity dependent interactions during the past decade. The literature is growing so rapidly that we shall concentrate on some of the systematic phenomenological attempts to develop velocity dependent or nonlocal IPM models.

Without doubt, the neglect of velocity dependent potentials has been due to the apparent complexity of the mathematical problem of treating such potentials within the framework of the Schroedinger equation. We should note, however, that a classical potential

$$V(\mathbf{r}, \mathbf{p}) = V(r) + \delta p^2/2m_0 \tag{4}$$

where δ is a constant, can be dealt with in a very simple way. Thus, we may write Schroedinger's equation in the form

$$(E - p^2/2m)\Psi = V\Psi \tag{5}$$

where $m = m_0(1 + \delta)^{-1}$ is the so-called effective mass; a reduced mass if δ is positive, an enhanced mass if δ is negative. We may also deal with the quantum mechanical problem if the classical potential has the form

$$V(r, p) = -V_0 \xi_0(r) + (\delta/2m_0)p^2\xi(r) \tag{6}$$

where $\xi_0(r)$ and $\xi(r)$ are positive form factors. We first construct a Hermitian counterpart of the classical term such as

$$V(\mathbf{r}, \mathbf{p}) = -V_0 \xi_0(r) - (\delta\hbar^2/2m_0) \, \mathbf{\nabla} \cdot \xi \, \mathbf{\nabla} \tag{7}$$

or

$$V(\mathbf{r}, \mathbf{p}) = -V_0 \xi_0(r) - (\delta\hbar^2/8m_0)[\nabla^2\xi + 2\,\mathbf{\nabla} \cdot \xi \, \mathbf{\nabla} + \xi \, \nabla^2] \tag{8}$$

or

$$V(\mathbf{r}, \mathbf{p}) = -V_0 \xi_0(r) - (\delta\hbar^2/4m_0)[\nabla^2\xi(r) + \xi(r) \, \nabla^2]. \tag{9}$$

We may now insert these potentials into Schroedinger's equation to obtain a differential equation which is not very much more complicated than the ordinary Schroedinger equation. We may rewrite Eqs. (7)–(9) in a common form

$$V(\mathbf{r}, \mathbf{p}) = V_s(r) - (\delta\hbar^2/2m_0)[\langle\mathbf{\nabla}\xi(r)\rangle \cdot \mathbf{\nabla} + \xi(r) \, \nabla^2] \tag{10}$$

where

$$V_s(r) = -V_0 \xi_0(r), \tag{11}$$

$$V_s(r) = -V_0 \xi_0(r) - (\delta\hbar^2/8m_0)\langle\nabla^2\xi(r)\rangle \tag{12}$$

and

$$V_s(r) = -V_0 \xi_0(r) - (\delta\hbar^2/4m_0)\langle\nabla^2\xi(r)\rangle. \tag{13}$$

for Eqs. (7), (8), and (9), respectively. Here the angular brackets define the limit of action of the differential operator. We note that $V(\mathbf{r}, \mathbf{p})$ should be quite sensitive to the form of $\xi(r)$ which is chosen, not only through the common $\langle\mathbf{\nabla}\xi\rangle$ term which appears in conjunction with the gradient operator, but also for Eqs. (8) and (9) due to the term involving $\langle\nabla^2\xi\rangle$ which is absorbed into the central interaction.

5.1c.   The Effective Mass Approximation

In many phenomenological studies it has been customary to start with a nonlocal interaction of the type given by Eq. (2). The direct solution of the integro-differential Schroedinger equation, of course, would represent the straightforward mathematical approach to such a problem if one knew precisely the kernel. However, in the absence of a detailed knowledge of the kernel we might assume

(i)   that the kernel must be Hermitian which means that $\tilde{V}(\mathbf{r}, \mathbf{r}')$ must be symmetric in its dependence on $\mathbf{r}$ and $\mathbf{r}'$ if it is real,

(ii)   that the approximate validity of calculations employing local potentials indicates that nonlocal effects should not be too large,

(iii)   that $\tilde{V}(\mathbf{r}, \mathbf{r}')$ must be translationally invariant in infinite nuclear matter.

As a starting point for our discussions we shall assume that

$$\tilde{V}(\mathbf{r}, \mathbf{r}') = V(\bar{\mathbf{r}})\delta_b(\mathbf{r} - \mathbf{r}') \tag{14}$$

where $\bar{\mathbf{r}} = \frac{1}{2}(\mathbf{r} \mid \mathbf{r}')$, and $\delta_b(\mathbf{r} - \mathbf{r}')$ is a sharply peaked even function of its argument with " range " b, whose integral properties are described by Eq. (19). In the limit of zero range, $\delta_b(\mathbf{r} - \mathbf{r}')$ becomes the usual Dirac delta function and Eqs. (1) and (2) immediately reduce to the usual Schroedinger equation. As an example, $\delta_b(\mathbf{r} - \mathbf{r}')$ is often chosen as a normalized Gaussian (Frahn and Lemmer, 1957)

$$\delta_b(\mathbf{r} - \mathbf{r}') = (\pi b^2)^{-3/2} \exp[-(\mathbf{r} - \mathbf{r}')^2/b^2]. \tag{15}$$

For the case of small nonlocality and $\tilde{V}$ real, we may proceed as follows: letting $\mathbf{r}' = \mathbf{r} + b\mathbf{s}$, the integral in Eq. (2) becomes

$$V(\mathbf{r}, \mathbf{p})\Psi(\mathbf{r}) = \int V(\mathbf{r} + \tfrac{1}{2}b\mathbf{s})\Psi(\mathbf{r} + b\mathbf{s})\delta_b(\mathbf{s})b^3 \, d\mathbf{s}, \tag{16}$$

expanding $V(\mathbf{r} + \frac{1}{2}b\mathbf{s})$ and $\Psi(\mathbf{r} + b\mathbf{s})$ in a Taylor's series about $b\mathbf{s} = 0$,

$$V(\mathbf{r} + \tfrac{1}{2}b\mathbf{s}) = V(\mathbf{r}) + \tfrac{1}{2}b\mathbf{s} \cdot \nabla\, V(\mathbf{r}) + \tfrac{1}{8}b^2(\mathbf{s} \cdot \nabla)^2 V(\mathbf{r}) + \cdots$$

and $\tag{17}$

$$\Psi(\mathbf{r} + b\mathbf{s}) = \Psi(\mathbf{r}) + b\mathbf{s} \cdot \nabla\Psi(\mathbf{r}) + \tfrac{1}{2}b^2(\mathbf{s} \cdot \nabla)^2\Psi(\mathbf{r}) + \cdots.$$

Collecting nonvanishing terms to order b^2, Eq. (16) reduces to

$$V(\mathbf{r}, \mathbf{p})\Psi(\mathbf{r}) = V(\mathbf{r})\Psi(\mathbf{r}) + \int \frac{b^2 s^2}{24} [\nabla^2 V + 2\, \nabla \cdot V\, \nabla + V\, \nabla^2]\Psi(\mathbf{r})\delta_b(\mathbf{s})b^3 \, d\mathbf{s}. \tag{18}$$

If the properties of $\delta_b(\mathbf{s})$ are defined as

$$\int \delta_b(\mathbf{s})b^3 \, d\mathbf{s} = 1 \quad \text{and} \quad \int s^2 \delta_b(\mathbf{s})b^3 \, d\mathbf{s} = 3/2 \tag{19}$$

Eq. (18) becomes

$$V(\mathbf{r}, \mathbf{p})\Psi(\mathbf{r}) = V(\mathbf{r})\Psi(\mathbf{r}) + \frac{b^2}{16} [\nabla^2 V(\mathbf{r}) + 2\, \nabla \cdot V(\mathbf{r})\, \nabla + V(\mathbf{r})\, \nabla^2]\Psi(\mathbf{r}). \tag{20}$$

For a central potential of the form $V(\mathbf{r}) = -V_0 \xi(r)$, the nonlocal Schroedinger equation may be placed in the form

$$-\frac{\hbar^2}{8}\left[\nabla^2 \frac{1}{m(r)} + 2\,\boldsymbol{\nabla}\,\frac{1}{m(r)}\,\boldsymbol{\nabla} + \frac{1}{m(r)}\,\nabla^2\right]\Psi - V_0\,\xi(r)\Psi(\mathbf{r}) = E\Psi(\mathbf{r}) \qquad (21)$$

where

$$m(r) = m_0/[1 + \delta\xi(r)], \qquad \delta = b^2 m_0 V_0/2\hbar^2. \qquad (22)$$

Note that the $m(r)$, the so-called effective mass, varies from $m_0/(1 + \delta)$ at the center to m_0 outside the nucleus. Separating variables in the usual way, the radial wave equation may now be placed in the form

$$G'' + \left[\frac{\gamma^2\xi(r)}{1+\delta\xi} - \frac{\beta_e{}^2}{1+\delta\xi} - \frac{l(l+1)}{r^2}\right]G + \frac{\delta}{1+\delta\xi}\left\{\left[\frac{\xi''}{4} - \frac{\xi'}{2r}\right]G + \xi'G'\right\} = 0$$
$$(23)$$

where

$$\gamma^2 = 2m_0\,V_0/\hbar^2 \qquad \text{and} \qquad \beta_e{}^2 = 2m_0\,|E|/\hbar^2. \qquad (24)$$

The influence of the three small terms on the right of Eq. (23) can be estimated qualitatively. For a smooth $\xi(r)$ of the WS or GW type, the function ξ' is zero in the uniform region, goes negative to a peak in the surface region, and then decays to zero. ξ'' is expected to go negative to a large peak, then cross over to a small positive peak, and then decay to zero. For states of binding G' starts out at long ranges at a negative value which can be estimated from the properties of spherical Bessel functions. It declines gradually in magnitude towards zero at the first peak of the wave function on going radially inward. Since this first peak is practically never in the surface region for the case of the bound states of importance, G' is on the average a negative quantity in the surface region. Therefore, the term $\xi''/4$ acts to weaken the effective well and hence move the energy levels upward, whereas the terms $-\xi'/2r$ and $\xi'G'$ tend to strengthen the effective well and move the energy levels downward (Green, 1957, 1958a). The effects are of the order of 1 MeV in magnitude for realistic well shapes, fluctuating somewhat from state to state.

It should be emphasized that the structure of the small terms in the radial equation depends upon the particular choice of the N–$\mathcal{N}$ VDP. Equation (23) corresponds to Eq. (20) or (8) with $\xi_0(r) = \xi(r)$. Equations (7) and (9) lead to a somewhat different set of ξ' and ξ'' terms. All of the radial equations, however, have a G' term which is not normally present when the N–$\mathcal{N}$ potential is static.

The radial equation solved by Brueckner et al. (1958, 1961) in their self-consistent field calculation for the finite nucleus may be written

$$G'' + \left[\gamma^2 f_{nlj}(r) - \beta^2 - \frac{l(l+1)}{r^2}\right]G_{nlj} + g_{nlj}\,G'_{nlj} = 0 \qquad (25)$$

where f_{nlj} and g_{nlj} are state dependent " pseudopotentials " which are expressed as integrals involving a nonlocal potential $V_{lj}(\mathbf{r}, \mathbf{r}')$ and the wave functions of the previous iteration. We should note that the more general phenomeno- logical forms of velocity dependence such as given by Eqs. (7)–(9), in which the forms $\xi_0(r)$ and $\xi(r)$ differ, lead to pseudopotentials of this form. In fundamental self-consistent field studies, these pseudopotentials are derived from the fundamental two body force. This approach, however, is still in an unsettled state (see Section 7.2).

It is noteworthy, however, that these BGW pseudopotentials differ markedly from state to state; the $f_{nlj}(r)$ terms appear to have a repulsive behavior at the center; the g_{nlj} terms are smaller in magnitude than the f_{nlj} terms.

The repulsive effect of the non-local potential is a rather significant effect which has been noted in many investigations. However its magnitude and origins are still not entirely clear. By combining this effective repulsion together with the centrifugal effect it is possible to use the repulsive core Morse poten- tial to obtain analytic solutions and eigenvalues for velocity dependent N–$\mathcal{N}$ potentials (Green *et al.*, 1967) (see Section 5.2).

5.1d   Equivalences

There have been many recent developments in the solution of scattering problems with nonlocal potentials. The study of Green (1959) and Wyatt *et al.* (1960), based upon the effective mass approximation, utilized straightforward numerical techniques for integrating the coupled differential equations and extracting the phase shifts. Perey and Buck (1962) attacked the integro- differential equation directly, but for a modified kernel. In the course of their study, they found a rather accurate prescription for the equivalent local potential (ELP) which has a greater range of applicability than the empirical forms of Green (see Eqs. (8)–(10), Chapter III, Section 3.4). The ELP concept has been developed further by Perey and Saxon (1964), Gersten (1967), and Fiedeldey (1967) who, within the context of a nonlocal N–$\mathcal{N}$ optical model, have established rather accurate procedures for obtaining the equivalent local potential (see Section 5.4). Among the most interesting general conclusions reached in these studies is the fact that the presence of the velocity dependent or nonlocal terms acts, in the case of N–$\mathcal{N}$ potentials, to "push" the radial wave function outward from the nuclear center.

Perhaps the most intensive studies of the equivalence between nonlocal and local potentials have been carried out within the context of the nucleon– nucleon problem. In large measure, the purpose of these phenomenological studies was to replace a static nucleon–nucleon potential with a hard core by an equivalent nonlocal potential (ENLP) having a less singular nature. The hope was that the VDP or NLP could be used in perturbation treatments of the many body problem (Moshinsky, 1957; Moszkowski and Scott, 1960; A. M. Green, 1962; Razavy et al., 1962; Rojo and Simmons, 1962; Herndon et al., 1963; Tabakin, 1964; Stocker, 1966; Mittelstaedt, 1965; Mittelstaedt and Ristig, 1966; Darewych and Green, 1967). In these studies the greatest concentration of effort has been related to the inner region of the potential. The net conclusion of all these studies is that it is indeed possible to replace a hard static core potential by an equivalent nonlocal or velocity dependent potential in a number of possible ways.

In many respects the N–N problem has a somewhat complementary aspect to the N–$\mathcal{N}$ problem. In the former problem, various investigators have found a coreless or soft core ENLP to replace the static hard core which first dominated the N–N scene (Jastrow, 1950). The motivation has been the hope that the many body problem would then be more tractable. In the N–$\mathcal{N}$ problem the conviction has developed that the potential is indeed nonlocal but the search for the ELP has been prompted by the belief that the ELP would be more tractable in practical optical model calculations. Mittelstaedt and Ristig (1966) have derived necessary and sufficient conditions which must be fulfilled by a unitary transformation to derive an ENLP from a static potential.

Darewych and Green (1967) examined N–N VDP's of the form

$$V(\mathbf{r}, \mathbf{p}) = V_c(r) + M^{-1}[p^2 w(r) + w(r)p^2]. \tag{26}$$

This can also be written in the equivalent potential form

$$V(r, p) = V_0(r) + a^2[\nabla V_\Delta \cdot \nabla + V_\Delta \nabla^2] \tag{27}$$

where a is a suitable unit of length, $E_0 = \hbar^2/Ma^2$,

$$V_0(r) = V_c(r) - E_0 a^2 \nabla^2 w(r) \quad\text{and}\quad V_\Delta = -2E_0 w(r) \tag{28}$$

or

$$V_c = V_0 - \tfrac{1}{2}a^2 \nabla^2 V_\Delta \quad\text{and}\quad w = -\tfrac{1}{2}V_\Delta/E_0. \tag{29}$$

The static component of the potential $V_0(r)$ may look quite different from $V_c(r)$. A third possible way of expressing the interaction potential given by Green and Sharma (1965) is

$$V_e(r, \Psi) = V_0(r) + a^2\Psi^{-1}(\nabla V_\Delta \cdot \nabla\Psi + V_\Delta \nabla^2\Psi) \tag{30}$$

where Ψ is the exact wave function. This "trivially equivalent potential" (Fiedeldey, 1967) is of course equivalent, in its action on the true wave function, to that of a static potential. The fourth possibility is to work with the energy dependent effective potential given by

$$V_{\text{eff}}(r, E) = (1 - V_\Delta/E_0)^{-1}\left[V_0(r) - \tfrac{1}{2}a^2 \nabla^2 V_\Delta - a^2 k^2 V_\Delta - \frac{a^2(\nabla V_\Delta)^2}{4(E_0 - V_\Delta)}\right]$$
$$+ l(l+1)E_0 a^2/r^2 \tag{31}$$

This potential is obtained by transforming to the "false" wave function $X_l(r)$ using (A. M. Green, 1962; Rojo and Simmons, 1962)

$$X_l(r) = (1 - V_\Delta/E_0)^{1/2} G_l(r). \tag{32}$$

One must distinguish carefully between these various representations of a velocity dependent potential. Figure 1 illustrates the varying views of the

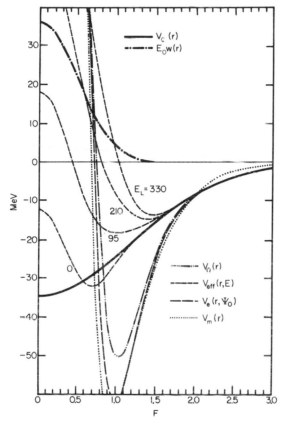

Fig. 1. Various representations of the coreless velocity dependent N–N potential of Herndon *et al.* (1963) for the $^1S_0$ state.

($V_c(r)$ and $E_0 w(r)$ represent the basic components of Eq. (26) given by Eqs. (33) and (34). $V_m(r)$ is a rather hard core ELP which yields the same S wave phase shifts. $V_0(r)$ is the static part of the alternative representation given by Eq. (27). Note the extra long range attraction and the short range repulsion due to $\nabla^2 w$. $V_e(r, \Psi_0)$ is the equivalent local potential at $E = 0$, based upon the zero energy wave function from effective range theory. V_{eff} are the effective potentials at various energies acting upon the "false" wave function X. Note that here X is softly repelled from the center. In addition, the transformation to $G(r)$ given by Eq. (32) reduces further the radial wave function at the center (Darewych and Green 1967).)

phenomenological velocity dependent N–N potential of Herndon *et al.* (1963). Here $V_c(r)$ and $w(r)$ are the coreless Gaussian functions

$$V_c(r) = -V_0 \exp(-r^2/a^2) \tag{33}$$

and

$$E_0 w(r) = V_v \exp(-r^2/b^2) \tag{34}$$

where $V_0 = 34.8$, $V_v = 37.3$ (in MeV), $a = 1.70$ and $b = 0.68$ (in F). On the other hand, the curve labeled $V_0(r)$ which embodies $\nabla^2 w(r)$ [Eq. (28)], has a more attractive exterior and a repulsive core by virtue of the curvature of the shorter ranged $w(r)$. The equivalent static Morse potential which has a similar effect on the S wave phase shifts is shown by the purely dotted curve. The varying effective potentials, as functions of energy, are shown in Fig. 1 by the dashed curves. Note how the effective potential varies explicitly as a function of energy, and how a core develops even though one starts with coreless, Gaussian type form factors. The effective potential at zero energy based upon the zero energy wave function

$$\Psi_0 = 1 - (r/a_s) - \exp(-3r/r_0), \tag{35}$$

where a_s is the scattering length and r_0 is the effective range, is shown by the dashed curves. Note that it also looks like a Morse function. Darewych and Green (1967) showed that a number of possible N–N interactions exist which fit the S wave data equally well including several interactions arising out of meson theory. We shall return to the detailed consideration of the N–N problem in Chapter VII. From the standpoint of the present discussion of the N–$\mathcal{N}$ interaction, we simply wish to point to the relative openness of the question of the ENLP to a specified static potential or of the ELP to a specified nonlocal potential. Thus far, for the N–$\mathcal{N}$ problem, the question has been pursued mostly in the rather narrow context in which, effectively, the form factors $\xi(r)$ and $\xi_0(r)$ are the same and flat at the center (such as the WS or GW forms). Let us now consider some of the results of these studies.

5.2 Bound States

5.2a The Nuclear Mass Formula

As we indicated in the previous section, the first consideration of velocity dependent potentials arose in connection with the problem of nuclear energy saturation as well as in connection with the problems of insufficient nuclear binding.

Let us first illustrate, in fairly elementary terms, what velocity dependence of the nucleon–nuclear potential might be expected to do to the independent particle model of the mass surface. We assume, for simplicity, that the nuclear potential is given by

$$V = -V^*\xi(r) + \beta T, \tag{1}$$

where β is a coefficient which is a measure of the degree of velocity dependence. Schroedinger's equation then becomes

$$[T - V^*\xi(r) + \beta T - E]\Psi = 0, \tag{2}$$

which may be rewritten as

$$\left[-\frac{\hbar^2}{2m}\nabla^2 - V^*\xi(r) - E\right]\Psi = 0 \tag{3}$$

where $m = m_0/(1 + \beta)$ is the effective mass. The radial equation is

$$G'' + \left[\frac{\gamma^2}{1+\beta}\xi(r) - \frac{\beta_e^2}{1+\beta} - \frac{l(l+1)}{r^2}\right]G = 0 \tag{4}$$

where $\gamma^2 = 2m_0 V^*/\hbar^2$ and $\beta_e^2 = 2m|E|/\hbar^2$.

Assuming the nucleon–nuclear potential arises strictly from two-body forces, the total energy of a system of identical nucleons (i.e., same spin and isotopic spin) is given by

$$E_T(\Lambda) = \sum_{i=1}^{\Lambda}(E_i - \tfrac{1}{2}\langle V_i\rangle) = -\tfrac{1}{2}\Lambda V^* + \frac{1+\tfrac{1}{2}\beta}{1+\beta}E_0\sum\varepsilon_i^2 - \frac{1}{2}\frac{V^*}{1+\beta}\sum f_i, \tag{5}$$

where ε_i^2 represents a dimensionless eigenvalue measured from the bottom of the well and f_i, the leakage factors, are defined by

$$\langle\xi(r)\rangle = 1 - f_i. \tag{6}$$

Now the static case discussed in Section 2.1 corresponds to the case in which $\beta = 0$. Here the choice $V^* = 40$ leads to the difficulty of insufficient binding energy which we mentioned earlier (Section 2.1). Then, the first term contributed -20 MeV per particle, the last term (the leakage factor) contributed ~ -2 MeV per particle, and the middle term (the "kinetic energy") contributed ~ 16 MeV. If, now, β is made of the order of 1, then the well depth must be increased substantially. Indeed, studies dealing with outermost neutron states (Green, 1957) indicated that, to maintain last particle binding energies at approximately the experimental values at the fixed radius parameters, we must relate V^* and β in a sharply restricted way. To a good approximation, this may be expressed by the relation

$$V^* = V_0 + V_1\beta = V_0(1 + k_v\beta), \tag{7}$$

where $k_v \approx 0.76$. Thus, if we go to $\beta \sim 1$, V^* must be made about 70 MeV. Looking again at the terms in Eq. (5), the first term now contributes -35

MeV, the last term ~ -2 MeV, and the average kinetic energy, when reduced by $(1 + \frac{1}{2}\beta)/(1 + \beta)$, ~ 25 for an energy of the order of -12 MeV.

Lee and Green(1956a) attempted to make quantitative estimates of nuclear energy based upon the IPM by studying the sums $\sum \varepsilon_i^2$, calculated from realistic potentials. The quantity ε_i^2 is a convenient one for forming eigenvalue sums since, being measured relative to the bottom of the well, it is rather insensitive to changes near the top. Furthermore, this quantity corresponds closely to the dimensionless kinetic energy of particles, and hence, we can use the statistical expressions based upon the Fermi gas model as a guide. Here we use the familiar expression

$$d\mathcal{N}(k) = \frac{k^2}{2\pi^2} \, dk \tag{8}$$

for the number of states per unit volume in the propagation interval k to $k + dk$. Denoting by Λ the number of particles of one type (up spin neutrons, say), it follows that

$$\Lambda = \frac{4}{3} \pi R^3 \int_0^{k_m} \frac{k^2}{2\pi^2} \, dk = \frac{2}{9\pi} R^3 k_m^{\ 3}. \tag{9}$$

The total kinetic energy is

$$T(\Lambda) = \frac{4}{3} \pi R^3 \int_0^{k_m} \frac{\hbar^2 k^2}{2m} \frac{k^2}{2\pi^2} \, dk = \frac{\hbar^2 g_0}{2mR^2} \Lambda^{5/3} \tag{10}$$

where $g_0 = (3/5)(9\pi/2)^{2/3} = 3.508$. Letting $R = r_0 A^{1/3}, E_0 = \hbar^2/2ma_f^{\ 2} = 20.73$, $\Lambda_1 = \Lambda_2 = \frac{1}{2}N = (A + D)/4$, $\Lambda_3 = \Lambda_4 = \frac{1}{2}Z = (A - D)/4$ and expanding to order D^2/A^2 it follows that

$$\sum T(\Lambda_i) = \frac{E_0}{r_0^{\ 2}} \frac{g_0}{4^{2/3}} A\left(1 + \frac{5}{9}\frac{D^2}{A^2}\right). \tag{11}$$

Lee and Green (1956a) arrived at corresponding $\sum \varepsilon_i^2$ by using the eigenvalues for diffuse potentials of the type described in Section 2.2. Recall that these were characterized by the well depth parameter $\varepsilon_0^{\ 2} = V^*/E_0$, the interior radius a, and a fixed diffuseness distance d. Their expression took on a form

$$\sum_{i=1} \varepsilon_i^{\ 2} = \Lambda^{5/3}(g_0 + g_1 \Lambda^{-1/3} - g_2 \varepsilon_0^{\ -1}) \equiv \Lambda^{5/3} G, \tag{12}$$

where $g_0 = 3.50$, $g_1 = 4.40$, and $g_2 = 12.60$. The fit of these expressions to the actual sums is shown in Fig. 1. The "leakage" factors f_i have also been evaluated. Their sums are fitted quite well by

$$\sum_i f_i = f_0 \Lambda^{5/3}/\varepsilon_0^{\ 2}, \tag{13}$$

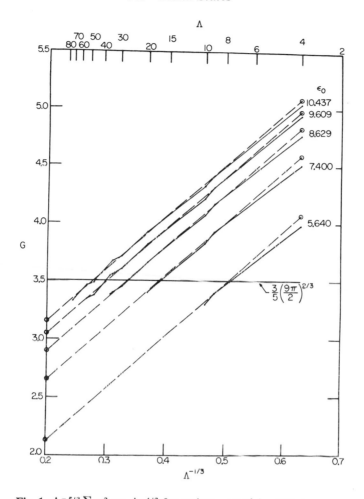

Fig. 1. $\Lambda^{-5/3} \sum \varepsilon_i{}^2$ vs. $\Lambda^{-1/3}$ for various potential parameters ε_0.
(The straight lines correspond to Eq. (28). The horizontal line corresponds to the constant g predicted for the kinetic energy on the Fermi gas model.)

where $f_0 = 0.87$. Using the foregoing expressions in Eq. (5) and letting $U_0 = E_0 a^2/(1 + \beta)$, the total energy of Λ identical particles in a velocity dependent well is

$$E_T(\Lambda) = -\tfrac{1}{2}\Lambda V^* + U_0 a^{-2}(1 + \tfrac{1}{2}\beta)$$

$$\times \Lambda^{5/3}(g_0 + g_1\Lambda^{-1/3} - g_2\varepsilon_0^{-1}) - \tfrac{1}{2}f_0 U_0 \Lambda^{5/3}a^{-2}. \quad (14)$$

Using this expression for both spins of neutrons and protons, and adding a Coulomb energy correction, we obtain a mass formula in terms of the potential parameters $V^*(\beta)$, a, and ε_0. A quantitative study shows that the mere increasing of β, i.e., turning on velocity dependence, is not sufficient to obtain a good mass formula. However, if V^* is given approximately (Green, 1958b) by

$$V^* \approx 40 + 30.5\beta + [5 \pm 28(N - Z)/A], \tag{15}$$

where the upper sign is for protons and the lower sign is for neutrons, then a good mass surface is secured for β in the neighborhood of unity ($m^*/m \approx 0.5$). Thus the need for a symmetry dependent term in the nucleon–nuclear potential manifests itself in the derivation of the nuclear mass surface from the independent particle model even when we use a velocity dependent potential.

5.2b   Neutron Energy Levels in a Nonlocal Potential

Here, let us consider the general effects of introducing nonlocality upon energy levels in a finite nucleus. Figure 2 illustrates the results of numerical

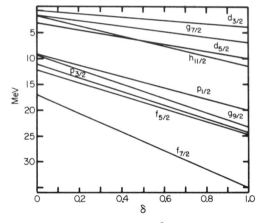

Fig. 2. Neutron energy levels as a function of δ, the velocity dependence parameter, for the nucleus $A = 89$ (Green, 1957).

calculations obtained with the aid of the Oak Ridge Oracle (Green, 1957). The eigenvalues are plotted as a function of the degree of velocity dependence for a typical nucleus, in this case with $A = 89$. Similar plots have been made for other nuclei, and the following conclusions can be made from these plots.

i. The variation of the eigenvalues with change in δ is very nearly linear, and the downward shift of levels results in an increase of particle binding energies rather systematically.

ii. Among the states of the same l, the up spin states (i.e., $j = l + \frac{1}{2}$) are shifted more than the down spin states ($j = l - \frac{1}{2}$), thus increasing the splitting of the two.

iii. Among the up spin (or the down spin) states the shift increases with the increasing (a) l value, and (b) binding energy.

iv. With slight readjustments, namely, a decrease of spin orbit coefficient, an increase of diffuseness parameter, and a change in constant well depth in accord with $V_0^* \approx 0.9V_0(1 + \delta)$, we can restore the satisfactory level sequence obtained from a static family of potentials. The magnitude of the changes depends primarily upon the value of the velocity dependence parameter δ or the effective mass ratio m/m_0.

Thus, from the standpoint of the essential characteristics of the shell model as revealed in the last particle separation energies, the problem of a velocity dependent potential may be reduced to an equivalent static case with a varying effective mass. The value of the effective mass at the center of the nucleus may thus be chosen in consideration of total energies or, possibly, scattering data.

A number of studies of the total energy problem have been made which suggest a variety of values of m/m_0 varying from 0.35 to 0.75. A specific model of velocity potential N–$\mathcal{N}$ IPM with $m/m_0 = 0.5$ was proposed by Ross *et al.* (1956b). Using an analog computer, they determined the nucleon energy levels in a N–$\mathcal{N}$ potential having a velocity dependent term of the form $\mathbf{p} \cdot V(r)\mathbf{p}$ (see also Moshinsky, 1954, 1957). Choosing the Woods–Saxon form, they achieved a reasonable neutron shell structure in a selected sample of nuclei with the parameters $V_0 = 69$ MeV, $R = 1.3A^{1/3}$ F, and $d = 0.88$ F, with spin orbit coupling 33 times the Thomas term. For protons using the same R, d, and V_{so} they found that a deeper well was needed for Pb^{208} to bind the correct number of protons. They examined the prescription of increasing the neutron well depth by the amount $(N + \frac{1}{2}Z)/(Z + \frac{1}{2}N)$ (see Section 2.3), but found that it was not possible to bind the proper number of protons. Green (1956c) and Green and Sood (1958), in their first efforts, used the Ed form with $m/m_0 = 0.6$, $V_0^* = 55.2$ MeV, $a = 1.30(A^{1/3} - 1)$, $d = 1.25$, and $a_{\text{so}}^2 = 0.77$. The neutron eigenvalues for this set of potential parameters appear very similar to those of a static potential (see Fig. 4, Section 2.2), except that they are stretched so that the lower states lie more deeply. The single particle energy levels obtained on the basis of this family of potentials reproduce all of the qualitative features of the observed single particle levels. No particular improvement in single particle levels, themselves, is obtained by going to a velocity dependent potential. Thus, the justification for the introduction of velocity dependence must rest on considerations of total nuclear energies, such as those discussed in the previous subsection, or on the scattering problem which will be discussed in Section 5.4.

For the precise determination of potential parameters which yield a desired set of energy levels, it is helpful to use the method of parameter derivatives (Green, 1956c). In essence, we use a routine which first determines the eigenvalue for a set of initially chosen parameters. Then, each parameter in turn is altered by a small fixed factor. Letting P_i denote the ith parameter, the effect of these operations is to give the partial derivatives of the eigenvalue with respect to each parameter. The usefulness of the tabulated eigenvalues is thus extended into a multispaced neighborhood surrounding each point, defined by the above parameter values, using the relations

$$E(P_i) = E(\bar{P}_i) + \sum_i \frac{\partial E}{\partial P_i}\bigg|_{P_i} \Delta P_i. \tag{16}$$

We shall consider the application of this technique later.

5.2c   The Energy Levels of Protons and the Proton Potential Anomaly

In several early articles on velocity dependent potentials, the difference between the potentials seen by a proton and a neutron was attributed largely to the velocity dependence of the nucleon–nuclear potential. In view of the importance of this effect, a rather detailed discussion may be appropriate.

The argument in favor of velocity dependence as the explanation for the proton potential anomaly went as follows (Lane, 1957). If for a neutron, $U_{0n} = U_{00} + \beta T$, then, using the total energy $E = T + U_0$, we may express the potential in terms of total energy by $U_{0n} = (U_{00} + \beta E)/(1 + \beta)$. On the other hand, for a proton, $U_{0p} = U_{00} + \beta T + V_c$. Hence, it follows in a similar way that apart from the Coulomb potential the proton is acted upon by

$$U_0(E) = \frac{U_{00}}{1 + \beta} + \frac{\beta}{1 + \beta} E - \frac{\beta}{1 + \beta} V_c. \tag{17}$$

If $\beta \approx 1$ it follows that the last term represents a subtractive correction which is one-half the Coulomb correction.

While this argument, based upon infinite nuclear matter, appears to give the right order of magnitude for the anomaly, detailed bound state calculations for finite nuclei lead to a somewhat different result. Let us examine these calculations.

Having found a reasonable family of parameters for neutrons in a nonlocal potential, we may now introduce the Coulomb potentials for the last proton. To avoid a major alteration of the calculative technique used for neutrons, we approximate the Coulomb potential by (Green, 1956c; Green and Sood, 1958)

$$\begin{aligned} V_c(r) &= (Z - 1)e^2(1 + k)/a, & r < a \\ &= (Z - 1)e^2[1 + k\xi(r)]/r, & a < r < c, \\ &= (Z - 1)e^2/c, & r > c, \end{aligned} \tag{18}$$

where a and $\xi(r)$ are the radial parameters and the form functions used with the neutron well.

The parameter $k(a)$ can be evaluated by matching well strength values within a region of radius c, which is chosen to be a point where the wave functions have effectively declined to zero. In this approximation the radial equation (Eq. (23), Section 5.1) for the Coulomb case contains an added term $V_c/(1 + \delta\xi)$.

It is seen that in the nonlocal equation, the Coulomb potential energy is decreased by the factor $(1 + \delta\xi)^{-1}$. The argument of Lane, in effect, suggests that this decrease is equivalent to the appearance of a subtractive term $-\delta\xi V_c/(1 + \delta\xi)$ which for $\delta\langle\xi\rangle \approx 1$ is approximately equal to half the Coulomb term. We must note, however, that the eigenvalue parameter β_e^2 in Eq. (23), Section 5.1, is also divided by the same factor and, accordingly, this effective reduction of the Coulomb potential does not influence the energy eigenvalues appreciably. Thus, contrary to a number of early explanations, we still have need for introducing an explicit proton potential anomaly even in the velocity dependent case. To determine the magnitude of the extra proton potential we may use the method of parameter derivatives to good avail.

The results of detailed calculations by Green and Sood, carried out for a wide range of even–even nuclei using $m/m_0 \approx 0.6$, are represented by the triangular points in Fig. 7, Section 2.3. The study concluded with the determination of the symmetry coefficients $V_1 = 25 \pm 3$ as compared to 28.5 ± 2 for the static case. When the symmetry term is included, Green and Sood found that the well depth V_0^* must be increased from 55.2 to 62.2 to maintain neutron separation energies at their experimental values.

The next systematic study of the velocity dependent shell model (Green, 1959; Wyatt et al., 1960) was made in connection with an attempt to find a unified IPM embodying both the shell model and the optical model. They used the effective mass approximation and the other essential features of the Green–Sood study for bound states. However, for positive energies, they embodied imaginary terms characterized by two additional free parameters ζ_0 and ζ_1. For computational simplicity and speed of convergence they used a 5th degree polynomial between a radius a (within which $\xi(r) = 1$) and a radius b (for which $\xi(r) = 0$) (see Eq. (3), Section 2.2). This form factor has the advantage that, within the radius a and outside the radius b, the various derivative terms in Eq. (23), Section 5.1, all vanish. Thus, the solutions in these regions are the familiar spherical Bessel functions, and numerical solutions have to be carried out in the transitional region only. The surface limits a and b may be expressed in terms of the more familiar constants, the surface thickness T, and the half-falloff radius R, by the simple relations $a = R - T$ and $b = R + T$. It should be noted that $\xi(r)$, $\xi'(r)$, and $\xi''(r)$ are continuous for all values of r subject to the above definitions. By letting $T = 2a_{WS}$, $\ln 9 = 4.4a_{WS}$ (i.e., equating the 0.1 and 0.9 points), an almost perfect match may be obtained to the Woods–Saxon form. The radius was taken as $R = r_0 A^{1/3}$. On the basis of the work of Green and Sood concerning the proton potential anomaly, as well as the work of Nemirovsky (1959), the central well depth was chosen to depend on the neutron excess, i.e., $V^* = -[V_0 \pm V_1(N - Z)/A]\xi(r)$.

The parameters V_0, V_1, r_0, T, a_{so}^2, and the nonlocality range b were first investigated using the parameter derivative technique in conjunction with a least squares fitting routine involving an overdetermined set of the particle separation energies of 14 nuclei. The scattering quantities, which were compared with experiment, consisted of the total, reaction, and differential elastic cross sections. These data were used primarily to determine ζ_0 and ζ_1, and to help fix b. If all the remaining parameters were taken as free, the usual ambiguity $Vr_0^2 \simeq$ constant arose. It was observed that for any r_0 an equivalently suitable set of parameters could be found. It was found also that near $r_0 = 1.25$, if b (the nonlocality) were allowed to vary, the least squares procedure favored $b = 0$, i.e., the local case. However, the scattering predictions were then very poor.

The final adjustment of the parameters was therefore accomplished as follows.

i. b was fixed to provide an effective mass at the nuclear center compatible with studies of the properties of infinite nuclear matter.

ii. r_0 was fixed at values between 1.15 and 1.30.

iii. The remaining parameters were adjusted via the least squares technique (both neutron and proton states were examined, but the scattering calculations were applied only to neutrons).

iv. With all the parameters now fixed, the scattering predictions were examined for a large range of ζ_0 and ζ_1. If the fits were poor, r_0 was adjusted to another value, and steps iii and iv repeated.

v. Once a set of fixed parameters V_0, V_1, r_0, a_{so}^2, T (and ζ_0 and ζ_1 for scattering) were established, the level structures of several isotopes were examined in detail. If the structures produced were in good agreement with the expected shell structure, then, subject to the previous bound state and scattering calculations, the set was considered to be consistent.

Table I shows the set of parameters arrived at as a best basis for the unification of the bound states and scattering within the framework of the effective mass formalism. The probable range of values (based on the analysis) is also indicated. Also shown are the corresponding parameters of the NLP of Perey and Buck (see Section 5.4). Table II shows a comparison of the eigenvalues with experimental data. Figure 3 illustrates the results for Ca^{41} and Hf^{177}. We will discuss the scattering aspects of the Wyatt et al. (1960) study in Section 5.4. Recently, Green et al. (1967a) have found approximate analytic solutions for bound states in a velocity dependent potential which reproduces the Wyatt et al. numerical solutions rather accurately. Let us

TABLE I

PARAMETERS CONSTITUTING THE BEST BASIS FOR UNIFICATION
OF BOUND STATES AND SCATTERING

Parameter	Best value	Probable variation	Perey and Buck (1962)
V_0 (MeV)	70	± 3	71
V_1 (MeV)	22	± 6	—
r_0 (fermi)	1.20	± 0.02	1.22
T (fermi)	2.85	± 0.40	2.82^a
a_{so}^2 (fermi^2)	2/3	± 0.05	0.41^b
b^2 (fermi^2)	2/3	± 0.03	0.71
ζ_0	0.2	± 0.1	$—^c$
ζ_1	-0.7	± 0.3	$—^c$

^{a} $T = 4.4a$.
^{b} $a_{so}^2 V_0 = U_{so}(\hbar^2/2M^2c^2)$.
^{c} Not strictly comparable to quantities used by Wyatt, Wills, and Green.

TABLE II

COMPARISON OF LAST PARTICLE EIGENVALUES^a
BASED ON PARAMETER VALUES OF TABLE I

Isotope	State	E_{expt}	E_{theory}
O^{17}	$d_{5/2}$	4.14	4.81
F^{17}	$d_{5/2}$	0.60	1.65
Si^{31}	$d_{3/2}$	6.60	6.21
Cl^{33}	$d_{3/2}$	2.50	1.12
Ca^{41}	$f_{7/2}$	8.37	7.64
Sc^{41}	$f_{7/2}$	1.83	0.95
Zn^{67}	$f_{5/2}$	7.00	8.16
Ge^{73}	$g_{9/2}$	6.64	6.58
Rb^{85}	$f_{5/2}$	6.83	7.09
Nb^{93}	$g_{9/2}$	6.24	3.97
Sn^{115}	$s_{1/2}$	7.91	8.01
Xe^{137}	$f_{7/2}$	3.57	2.94
Pb^{207}	$p_{1/2}$	6.73	7.07
Bi^{209}	$h_{9/2}$	3.72	0.31

^{a} In MeV.

consider the essence of their work, which again starts with the velocity dependent potential given by Eq. (18).

We let $x = r/a$ (where a is a convenient length) and $E_0 = \hbar^2/2ma^2$ (as the corresponding unit of energy), define the dimensionless energy parameters $\varepsilon^2 = -W/E_0$ and $\varepsilon_0^2 = V_0/E_0$, and introduce the effective radial wave function

$$X(x) = [1 + \delta\xi(x)]^{1/2}G(x) \qquad (19)$$

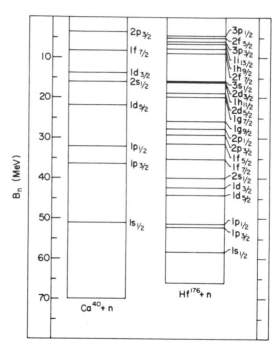

Fig. 3. Neutron levels in Ca^{41} and Hf^{177} based on Table II (Wyatt *et al.*, 1960).

where $G(x)$ is the usual radial wave function. Then the radial wave equation may be placed in the form

$$X'' - v_l(x, \varepsilon)X - [\varepsilon^2/1 + \delta]X = 0 \qquad (20)$$

where $v_l(x, \varepsilon) = v_l(x) + v_\varepsilon(x)$ with

$$v_l(x) = -\frac{\varepsilon_0^2\xi_0}{1 + \delta\xi} + \frac{1}{4}\frac{\delta\xi''}{(1 + \delta\xi)} - \frac{1}{4}\frac{\delta^2\xi'^2}{(1 + \delta\xi)^2} + \frac{\delta\xi'}{2(1 + \delta\xi)x} + \frac{l(l + 1)}{x^2} \qquad (21)$$

and

$$v_\varepsilon(x) = -\varepsilon^2\frac{\delta(\xi - 1)}{(1 + \delta)(1 + \delta\xi)}. \qquad (22)$$

For the sake of generality we allow here the possibility that $\xi_0(r) \neq \xi(r)$. For reasonable nuclear form factors, the complicated effective potential $v_l(x, \varepsilon)$ can usually be approximated by one of the analytically solvable potentials. Furthermore, $v_\varepsilon(x)$ usually represents a small effect because $(\xi - 1)$ is a small residual for deeply bound states and ε^2 is small for lightly bound states.

The technique, therefore, is to estimate from theory or experiment the value of ε^2, generate the function $v_l(x, \varepsilon)$ which is then replaced by an analytically solvable potential $v_a(x)$, which leads to an eigenvalue for ε^2. Using the corresponding $v_l(x, \varepsilon)$, the iterative procedure usually requires just two cycles. The addition of perturbations such as the spin orbit or Coulomb perturbations does not greatly complicate the problem, but simply alters the parameters of the approximating potential.

In treating Eq. (20) for neutron states of O^{17} or Ca^{41}, i.e., neutrons bound by O^{16} and Ca^{40} cores, Green *et al.* (1967a) made use of the repulsive core Morse function as an approximating effective potential which has analytic solutions and an eigenvalue formula. Here we approximate $v_l(x, \varepsilon)$ for each n, l, j state by

$$V_m(r) = V_0\{\exp[-2(r - R_e)/d] - 2\exp[-(r - R_e)/d]\} + B \qquad (23)$$

using V_0, R_e, d, and B as adjustable parameters. The eigenvalues in Mev then are computed from the formula

$$E - -(1 + \delta)\{[(A + 1)/A]20.73[\varepsilon_0 - (n - \tfrac{1}{2})/d]^2 + B\}. \qquad (24)$$

The eigenfunctions are given by

$$X = z^k e^{-z/2} L^{(2k)}_{n-1}(z) \frac{(n - 1)!}{(2k + 1)_{n-1}} \qquad (25)$$

where the L's are Laguerre polynomials $(r)_m = r(r + 1) \cdots (r + m - 1)$,

$$k = d[(B - E)/E_0(1 + \delta)]^{1/2} \qquad (26)$$

and

$$z = 2\varepsilon_0\, d \exp[-(r - R_e)/d]. \qquad (27)$$

When $n = 1$ and 2 the eigenfunctions are $z^k e^{-z/2}$ and $z^k[1 - z/(2k + 1)]e^{-z/2}$. Figure 4 illustrates their Morse eigenvalues, eigenfunctions, and potentials along with the corresponding WWG results for the neutron states in O^{17}. Table III gives the parameters determined by least square fits to the $v_l(x, \varepsilon)$. Also given in Table III are the WWG eigenvalues, the experimental eigenvalues, and the results of a recent self-consistent field study.

Recent studies (Darewych and Green, 1967; Gersten and Green, 1968; Green and Miller, 1968) suggest that the repulsive core Morse potential may

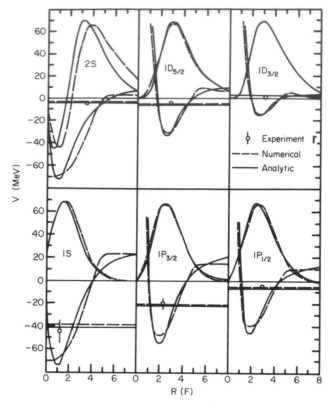

Fig. 4. Analytical and numerical effective potentials, wave functions, and energy levels for neutrons in O^{17}.

(The open circles with approximate error bars represent experimental separation energies from data in Tyren *et al.* (Green *et al.*, 1967a).)

TABLE III

MORSE PARAMETERS AND EIGENVALUES FOR NEUTRON STATES IN O^{17} (GDB)[a]

Neutron state	V_0 (MeV)	d (F)	R_e (F)	B (MeV)	Z_0	E (MeV)	WWG[c] (MeV)	KBD[d] (MeV)	Exper.[e] (MeV)	Ref.
$1S_{1/2}$	54.2	1.46	1.02	6.0	10.0	−41.5	−39.0	−46.6	−44 ± 9	A[f]
$1P_{3/2}$	48.8	1.32	1.91	13.0	17.0	−21.6	−20.9	−19.0	−19.0 ± 1	A[f]
$1P_{1/2}$	36.5	1.22	1.88	7.1	15.5	−14.6	−13.7	—	−12.4 ± 1	A[f]
$2S_{1/2}$	54.0	1.50	1.06	5.5	9.8	−2.4	−2.5	−0.9	−3.27	T[g]
$1D_{5/2}$	27.8	1.08	2.48	6.2	25.8	−5.4	−5.1	—	−4.14	E[b]
$1D_{3/2}$	13.0	0.90	2.50	2.2	23.2	1.86	—	—	0.94	T[g]

[a] GDB: Green *et al.* (1967a).
[b] E: Endt and van der Leun (1962).
[c] WWG: Wyatt *et al.* (1960).
[d] KBD: Krieger *et al.* (1967).
[e] Experimental.
[f] A: Amaldi *et al.* (1966).
[g] T: Tyren *et al.* (1966).

have a broader range of applicability in nuclear physics than might have been anticipated. There are at least three physical effects which may lead to a repulsive core N–$\mathcal{N}$ potential: (1) the centrifugal effect (not present for S waves), (2) repulsive velocity dependent components arising from $\xi'(r)$ and $\xi''(r)$ in Eqs. (21), and (3) the apparent repulsion at the center associated with the factor $(1 + \delta\xi)^{-1}$ in the "equivalent local potential" (ELP). For positive δ (i.e., a reduced mass) $G(x)$, the true radial wave function, is reduced at the center of the force field [see Eq. (19)] just as if a static repulsion acted upon it.

In the GDB study the Morse parameters are determined by fitting each $v_l(x, \varepsilon)$ by least squares. It is possible to deal more directly with the many terms represented in a realistic velocity dependent potential with spin orbit, symmetry, and Coulomb effect by adapting the centrifugal perturbation technique used by Pekeris (1934) for diatomic molecules. This leads to an explicit eigenvalue and eigenfunction formula for all states in terms of all the potential parameters. Within its domain of applicability it should provide a useful way of treating bound states of velocity dependent potentials.

5.3   Bound States in Nonlocal Spheroidal Potentials

In this section we outline the calculations made by Lemmer and Green (1960) of single particle bound states and wave functions in a realistic non-spherical, nonlocal force field that is appropriate for strongly deformed nuclei. As usual we assume that the adiabatic approximation holds, i.e., that the intrinsic motion is not appreciably altered by the rotation of the nucleus as a whole. The problem then reduces to a study of nucleon motion in the average nonspherical field $V(\mathbf{r})$ of the nucleus, which is regarded as fixed in space. As a further approximation we also ignore all residual interactions and assume that each nucleon moves independently of its neighbors in the collective nuclear field. We assume the effective mass approximation (Eq. (21), Section 5.1) to be the wave equation describing the single particle motion and proceed to study how this modification effects the motion of individual nuclei in a realistic nonspherical potential well. The solutions of a spherical wave equation have already been extensively studied for several forms of spherical potentials.

To pursue the case where $V(\mathbf{r})$ is nonspherical we confine ourselves to small deformations of a spheroidal nature only. Accordingly, we approximate the potential as

$$V(\mathbf{r}) = V(r) - \varepsilon(r\, \partial V/\partial r)P_2(\cos \theta) + \tfrac{1}{2}\varepsilon^2(r\, \partial V/\partial r) \tag{1}$$

where θ is the angle between the particle's radius vector and the nuclear symmetry axis, and ε is a measure of the deformation. Following the procedure used by Gottfried (1956), we treat all ε-dependent terms which arise when Eq. (1) is substituted into Eq. (21), Section 5.1, as perturbations, and expand the wave functions u in terms of the basic set of wave functions provided by the solutions of the spherically symmetric wave equation

$$[T_{sym} + V(r) + V_{so}(r)]\Psi(nlj\Omega) = E_0(nlj)\Psi(nlj\Omega) \qquad (2)$$

where T_{sym} is an abbreviation for the symmetrized kinetic energy operator appearing in Eq. (21), Section 5.1, and $nlj\Omega$ denote the usual set of radial and angular momentum quantum numbers required to describe a single nucleon state in a spherical potential well. Equation (2) is identical with Eq. (21), Section 5.1, for $\varepsilon = 0$ apart from an additional Thomas type spin orbit force V_{so} which is needed to obtain a reasonable set of spherical energy levels. We ignore here the influence of deformation and nonlocality on the spin orbit force since effects of this type are expected to be small and would fall well within the limits of uncertainty involved in the choice of potential shape in Eq. (2) anyway.

By substituting the last two terms in Eq. (1) into Eq. (21), Section 5.1, we obtain the perturbation interaction

$$U = U_1 + U_2 \qquad (3)$$

with

$$U_1 = -\varepsilon(r\,V')P_2 + \tfrac{1}{2}\varepsilon^2(r\,V') \qquad (4)$$

and

$$U_2 = -\tfrac{1}{16}\varepsilon b^2[(r\,V')P_2\,\nabla^2 + 2\,\nabla\cdot(r\,V')P_2\,\nabla + \nabla^2(r\,V')P_2] \qquad (5)$$

where the primes denote differentiation with respect to r. Our perturbed eigenvalue problem then reads

$$(H_0 + U)u = Eu \qquad (6)$$

for the energies E and intrinsic wave functions u in the deformed field, where H_0 denotes the spherical Hamiltonian in Eq. (2). Expanding u in terms of the complete set of eigenfunctions $\Psi(nlj\Omega)$ of H_0 (which belong to the same projection Ω of the particle's angular momentum along the nuclear symmetry axis, and have the same parity w since only these quantum numbers are conserved when all perturbations are included), Eq. (6) reduces to the matrix eigenvalue problem

$$\sum_{nlj} C(q, \Omega w; nlj)[E_0(nlj) - E(q, \Omega w) + (n'l'j'\Omega|U|nlj)] = 0 \qquad (7)$$

for the energies $E(q, \Omega w)$, and the eigenvectors $C(q, \Omega, w; nlj)$ which are (at the same time) the expansion coefficients for the wave functions u in terms of the $\Psi(nlj\Omega)$. The additional quantum number q in the above expressions serves to label the different roots of the matrix Eq. (7) belonging to the same Ω

and w. A deformed state is then specified by the set (q, Ω, w); and, due to the assumed axial symmetry in our potential, a degeneracy with respect to the sign of Ω in each state still remains.

Now, in principle, the summations in Eq. (7) should also include integrations over the continuous positive energy spectrum of H_0, so that the matrix is formally of infinite order. The complete diagonalization of this system of matrices is not possible in practice, and a considerable number of simplifications must be introduced to make the procedure a practical one. Therefore, with Gottfried (1956), we first delete the entire continuous spectrum of H_0 so that the matrix elements of U in Eq. (7) refer to bound state wave functions only. We expect the errors introduced by this approximation to be confined mostly to the particle states lying near the top of the potential well. Further simplifications result from the selection rules for the matrix elements of U appearing in Eq. (7). As U is an even operator in space, no parity change is introduced by it, and only even or odd values of l can appear in the summations in Eq. (7). Since the eigenvalues of Eq. (7) fall into definite shells of even or odd parity, well separated from each other in energy, the operation of the parity selection rule makes it sufficient to diagonalize the matrices in the subspace spanned by only those wave functions of H_0 which have the same parity and which belong to the same major shell. The next shell of states having the correct parity to contribute is then energetically too distant to have a large effect, and the contributions of all such distant states can be neglected in the first order (Nilsson, 1955).

In setting up the appropriate matrices for the deformed field it is convenient to break the basic wave functions $\Psi(nlj\Omega)$ down into radial and angular parts by writing

$$\Psi(nlj\Omega) = (1/r)G(nlj)Y_{lj\Omega} \tag{8}$$

where the Y's are the well-known eigenfunctions of j^2 and j_z, and the G's can be numerically determined once the shape of the spherical potential $V(r)$ in Eq. (2) is defined. The matrices of U can then be reduced to simple expressions involving the product of terms depending only on the radial wave functions G and the known matrix elements of $P_2(\cos\theta)$. After some reduction one finds

$$(n'l'j'\Omega|\, U_2\, |nlj\Omega) = -\varepsilon\{I_1 - \tfrac{1}{4}b^2[I_2 + I_3 + f(l',l)I_4]\}$$

$$\times (l'j'\Omega|P_2|\, lj\Omega) + \varepsilon^2 I_1 \delta_{n'n}\delta_{l'l}\delta_{j'j} \tag{9}$$

where

$$f(l',l) = (l+1)(l+2), \qquad l' = l+2$$

$$= l(l+1) - 1, \qquad l' = l$$

$$= l(l-1), \qquad l' = l-2 \tag{10}$$

and the I's denote the radial matrix elements

$$I_1 = (G(\alpha'),\, r\, V'G(\alpha)), \qquad \alpha = (nlj)$$
$$I_2 = (dG(\alpha')/dr,\, r\, V'\, dG(\alpha)/dr),$$
$$I_3 = -(G(\alpha'),\, r\, V'''G(\alpha)),$$
$$I_4 = (G(\alpha'),\, (1/r)\, V'G(\alpha)).$$

(11)

It is clear that the values of these matrix elements are very sensitive to the behavior of the radial functions G and the behavior of the potential at the nuclear surface, and hence, the importance of using realistic nuclear potentials would appear obvious. Since the integrations involved in Eq. (11) are confined to the surface, the task of carrying out the indicated integrations numerically for a realistic well shape is considerably reduced.

Further evaluation of Eq. (11) now depends on the values of the various nuclear parameters (well depth, nuclear radius constant, etc.) defining the well shape chosen for $V(r)$, which in turn determines the functions G. These parameters have been found approximately, in the work of Wyatt *et al.* (1960),

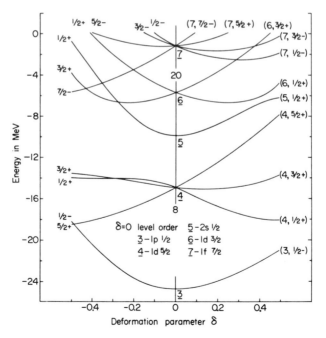

Fig. 1. Energy levels for protons and neutrons from $N = 8$ to $N = 20$ as a function of the nuclear deformation. Each state is labeled by the quantum numbers (q, Ω, w) defined in the text (Lemmer and Green, 1960).

for a well shape very similar to a Woods–Saxon potential by looking at both bound and scattering states for spherical nuclei. We will assume that their values are appropriate for this problem too, although this need not necessarily be so. This is no serious restriction, however, since it turns out that most of the results of the deformed calculation are primarily dependent only on the overall shape of the radial wave functions, which in turn is rather insensitive to the exact well parameters used in their calculation, as long as the general features of the well are retained.

Knowing the radial integrals and spherical energy levels $E_0(nlj)$, it is a simple matter to solve for the eigenvalue numerically for various values of the deformation parameter. The results of such diagonalizations are illustrated in Figs. 1 and 2 where we give the resulting energy level schemes for light and heavy nuclei plotted as a function of the more usual deformation parameter

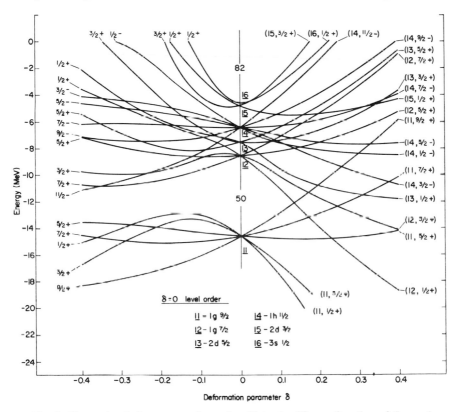

Fig. 2. Energy levels for protons from $A = 50$ to $A = 82$ as a function of the nuclear deformation. The quantum numbers (q, Ω, w) are given on the right for each state and the connection between q and the relevant spherical levels is shown in the inset (Lemmer and Green, 1960).

$\delta = 0.67\varepsilon$. This is used, rather than ε, to allow a direct comparison with other existing calculations, especially those of Nilsson. The quantum number q defined previously in connection with the designation of the deformed levels is given along the vertical axis at $\delta = 0$ in each figure and serves to indicate directly the spherical state from which each deformed level originates. The bracketed numbers labeling each state give the set of quantum numbers (q, Ω, w) appropriate to that state. A table of the coefficients C is also available (Lemmer, 1960). Figure 2 refers to a nucleus with radius corresponding to $A = 177$. However, by repeating the calculation for another value of A (i.e., changing the radius parameter R) we can readily see that the main features of the level scheme are preserved, there being only a slight shift in the overall position of each level. This statement is even more true for the expansion coefficients $C(q, \Omega, w)$ which hardly change at all when the positions of the spherical levels are altered in this way. Thus, we can suppose that the level scheme will be valid for the range of nuclei in this region.

A comparison of the level schemes generated by Lemmer and Green (1960) with the diagrams computed by Nilsson (1955), using an oscillator potential for the nuclear field, shows a very similar behavior in the energy levels as a function of deformation. This might have been expected since the main features of any deformed level scheme will depend primarily on the spherical level ordering. In Nilsson's case this level order is adjusted to reproduce the empirical single particle levels as well as possible. In the present calculation it is determined directly as a result of choosing well parameters which reproduce scattering and bound state data as well as possible (Wyatt et al., 1960).

Mottelson and Nilsson (1959) have made an intensive analysis of the ground state properties of deformed odd A nuclei in terms of the Nilsson level scheme. Lemmer and Green have made a parallel analysis of ground state spins and magnetic moments based on the present calculations.

A comparison of the orbit assignments for the odd particle state in both odd proton and odd neutron nuclei shows no significant difference from, or alternatives for, the Mottelson–Nilsson assignments. This is an expected result. On the other hand, the calculation of magnetic moments in terms of the wave functions does have an independent significance. The determining factors here are the expansion coefficients themselves, which are insensitive to the exact location of the energy states, but directly involve the structure of the radial wave functions G in Eq. (8). These *do* differ considerably from the corresponding oscillator wave functions. It is possible that the main improvement obtained by using a realistic potential is that the wave functions give a much better picture of the situation for a real nucleus than that given by the oscillator functions. In this connection, the calculated coefficients usually show considerably less "mixing" of different angular momentum states than the oscillator potential would lead us to expect. The reasons for this are twofold. The energy levels are, on the average, farther apart in energy in the nonlocal potential than they are in a local well; and, the surface region for the realistic potential is smaller than it is for an oscillator potential (which is all surface), so that the coupling of the nucleons to the nuclear surface is reduced accordingly. In contrast, the direct effect of the nonlocal interaction through the terms proportional to b^2 in Eq. (5) turns out to be very small.

In summary, it appears that the main features of the Nilsson level scheme (and the qualitative conclusions based on it) are retained in a more realistic treatment of the average force field governing the independent motion of the nucleons. We observe, however, that the present level schemes have been generated in a rather systematic way, and are understandable at least in physical terms since the radius, diffuseness, nonlocality, etc., all fall within ranges of values which are reasonable from other independent experimental and theoretical investigations. In this sense there has been no "fitting" of empirical data in any way in the present investigation. Lemmer and Green have simply accepted the results, based on an attempted unification of bound and scattering states in terms of a realistic potential well, and have pursued the effects of deforming this potential spheroidally. The good overall agreement with empirical data certainly indicates that the realistic potential used as the basis of these calculations is capable of producing reasonable results within the independent particle picture of the nucleus.

5.4 Scattering by Velocity Dependent or Nonlocal Potentials

5.4a Early Work

We begin this section with a description of the attempt (Green, 1959; Wyatt *et al.*, 1960) to achieve a unified description of the positive and negative energy states of nuclei in the region of concern in classical nuclear physics. Since we have already discussed the bound state portion of the calculation, we shall concentrate on the scattering aspects of the problem. A kernel $\tilde{V}(\mathbf{r}, \mathbf{r}')$ is chosen which is characterized in a relatively simple way, and, for convenience of computation, the "effective mass approximation" is used.

The transition from bound states to scattering via the nonlocal formalism might at first suggest the simple replacement of $V(r)$ by $V(r) + iW(r)$. This would result in "complex" effective mass terms of the type

$$M(r) = \frac{\mu}{1 - [b^2 \mu / 2\hbar^2][V(r) + iW(r)]}. \tag{1}$$

For an attractive potential [$V(r) < 0$, $W(r) < 0$ *for all* r], the resulting $iW(r)G(r)$ term would be a source of the usual "local" absorption in the customary optical model description where $b = 0$. The additional terms, however, would be due entirely to the nonlocality. It is not difficult to show that the additional imaginary terms arising from nonlocality correspond essentially to *emission*. Indeed, the nonlocal imaginary terms would at best *diminish* the absorption with increasing energy, which could contradict the observation that the absorption increases up to about 100 MeV.

In an effort to simulate the known variation of absorption with energy, a reduced mass of the form

$$M(r) = \mu/\{1 + [\xi(r) + i\zeta_1\eta(r)]\} \tag{2}$$

has been chosen, but the local refractive and absorptive term has been taken as $-V^*[\xi(r) + i\zeta_0\eta(r)]$, where ζ_0 and ζ_1 are two free parameters introduced in scattering, and $\eta(r)$ is a form function associated with the absorption term. It was chosen as

$$\eta(r) = -d\xi/dr. \tag{3}$$

In view of the continuity of $\xi(r)$ and its derivatives, $\eta(r)$ and $\eta'(r)$ are also continuous for the polynomial form. The functional simplicity and continuity of the polynomial form were helpful in dealing with the formidable differential equations which involve many derivatives of form factors.

The WWG scattering code picks up the analytic solution at $r = a$, integrates numerically through the complex potential terms present in the transition region, and evaluates the wave function and its derivative at $r = b$. The scattering amplitude and the various cross sections are then calculated, following the usual optical model analysis.

Because of the two additional parameters (ζ_0 and ζ) occurring in the scattering formulation, the task of finding a complete set of suitable parameters was approached from the bound state problem. A nonlocality distance was fixed at $b = 0.81$ F in the light of estimates from nuclear matter calculations (Gomes *et al.*, 1958). The five potential parameters V_0, V_1, r_0, a_{so}, and T were fixed by the bound state data, then ζ_0 and ζ_1, in the light of the scattering data. Figure 2, Section 3.4, shows representative neutron differential scattering cross sections (solid curves) based upon the final set obtained (Table III, Section 5.2). The dashed curves represent the local predictions of Bjorklund and Fernbach (1958).

Although some of the elastic differential scattering cross section curves in this nonlocal model differ somewhat from experiment (e.g., Bi at 4.1 MeV), others show structural details observed in experiment, but not predicted on the basis of local models (see, e.g., Cu and Fe at 14.6 MeV). This structure is generally high, but nevertheless in good shape agreement with experiment.

Before going into the details of more recent scattering calculations let us consider the physical implications of the nonlocal or velocity dependent potentials in scattering problems. First we comment on the conservation of probability when $\tilde{V}$ is hermetian, i.e., $\tilde{V}(\mathbf{r}, \mathbf{r}') = \tilde{V}^*(\mathbf{r}', \mathbf{r})$. In conjunction with the requirement that V be symmetrical, this means that $\tilde{V}$ must be real and total flux is conserved. The actual problem is more complicated, however, since we want a nonhermetian $\tilde{V}$; one which gives rise to a net absorption. This means that

$$\int \operatorname{div} \mathbf{j} \, d\mathbf{r} = i^{-1} \int d\mathbf{r} \, d\mathbf{r}' [V(\mathbf{r}, \mathbf{r}') - V^*(\mathbf{r}', \mathbf{r})] \Psi^*(\mathbf{r}) \Psi(\mathbf{r}') \le 0. \tag{4}$$

For symmetrical $\tilde{V}$ of the form $U + iW$, this can be written as

$$\int d\mathbf{r} \, d\mathbf{r}' \, W(\mathbf{r}, \mathbf{r}') \Psi^*(\mathbf{r}) \Psi(\mathbf{r}') \le 0 \tag{5}$$

where $W(\mathbf{r}, \mathbf{r}') = \operatorname{Im} V(\mathbf{r}, \mathbf{r}')$. Now the principle contribution to the integral comes from the region of the main diagonal, first because of the phase relations between Ψ^* and Ψ, and second because any physical V is more or less sharply peaked about the diagonal. Consequently, net absorption is presumably guaranteed if $W(\mathbf{r}, \mathbf{r}')$ is negative in the neighborhood of the main diagonal, at least for sufficiently short range potentials.

Tang *et al.* (1959) have considered the implications of the WWG model and have given plausibility arguments as to the meaningfulness of the WWG absorption terms. For a kernel of the Frahn–Lemmer type, the number of particles removed from the incident beam per second is easily found to be given by

$$\int \operatorname{div} \mathbf{j} \, d\mathbf{r} = (2/\hbar) \int W_b [\tfrac{1}{2}(\mathbf{r} + \mathbf{r}')] \delta_b(\mathbf{r} - \mathbf{r}') \rho(\mathbf{r}, \mathbf{r}') \, d\mathbf{r} \, d\mathbf{r}' \tag{6}$$

where $\rho(\mathbf{r}, \mathbf{r}') = \Psi^*(\mathbf{r}) \Psi(\mathbf{r}')$ is the mixed nucleon density and $\mathbf{j}$ is the usual probability current density vector. If we confine the discussion to nucleons interacting in nuclear matter, W is a constant, and we can describe the nucleons by plane waves. The mixed density then becomes

$$\rho(\mathbf{r}, \mathbf{r}') = \exp[-i\mathbf{k} \cdot (\mathbf{r} - \mathbf{r}')] \tag{7}$$

for a nucleon with momentum $\hbar \mathbf{k}$. The expression essentially introduces the Fourier transform of $\delta_b(\mathbf{r} - \mathbf{r}')$ into Eq. (6). Taking a Gaussian representation for the function $\delta_b(\mathbf{r} - \mathbf{r}')$, the right-hand side of Eq. (6) becomes proportional to

$$W_b \exp(-k^2 b^2 / 4) \equiv W_{\text{eff}}(k). \tag{8}$$

Clearly $W_{\text{eff}}(k)$, the effective absorptive potential, is a monotonically decreasing function of the nucleon momentum. This result is contrary to the findings based upon phenomenological fittings which indicate that the coefficient of the absorptive term is an increasing function of energy. To overcome this difficulty Tang *et al.* (1959) proposed a modification to the theory employing two N–$\mathcal{N}$ complex kernels. Thus, the net kernel contains an attractive part which presumably arises from the attractive component of the two-body force, and a repulsive part associated with the influence of the repulsive core when taken in conjunction with the exclusion principle. Then the Fourier transform of Schroedinger's equation leads directly to an expression for the complex potential. Using three parameters, V_b, W_b, and b, for the attractive component and three parameters, V_c, W_c, and c, for the repulsive component, it is easy to fit the declining $V_{\mathrm{eff}}(k)$ and the rising $W_{\mathrm{eff}}(k)$ established by experiment.

5.4b   The Study of Perey and Buck

Next we discuss the interesting work of Perey and Buck (1962), involving nonlocal potentials, which achieves a very satisfactory account for the neutron scattering data up to at least 24 MeV. Furthermore, their work provides a semiempirical recipe for obtaining equivalent local potentials (ELP). Perey and Buck start from a nonlocal potential of essentially the same form as that used by Wyatt *et al.* However for simplicity in the analyses, the kernel was taken to be more special than in our earlier discussion. Thus, it was chosen to depend on the average of the magnitudes rather than on the magnitude of the average of the vectors. In particular they used

$$\tilde{V}(\mathbf{r}, \mathbf{r}') = U(\imath)H(s) \tag{9}$$

where, here, $H(s)$ corresponds to $\delta_b(bs)$ used earlier,

$$U(\imath) = -(V + iW)\xi(\imath; R, a) - i4a_1 W' \, d\xi(\imath; R, a_1)/d\imath \tag{10}$$

and

$$\imath = \tfrac{1}{2}(r + r') = \tfrac{1}{2}(|\mathbf{r}| + |\mathbf{r}'|). \tag{11}$$

The form factor ξ was chosen of the Saxon–Woods type and as usual $R = r_0 A^{1/3}$. The second term is a surface absorption term, of the derivative rather than of the Gaussian type, and contains its own falloff parameter a_1. A local spin orbit term of the usual Thomas form was added to the nonlocal potential. Their potential thus contained nine parameters: b, a, a_s, r_0, V, W, W', V_s, and W_s. In the actual applications discussed by Perey and Buck, which are confined to low and medium energy neutron scattering, W and W_s were taken to be zero so that seven parameters remain, one more than in the Bjorklund–Fernbach analysis of the same energy region.

With the approximation of replacing $\xi(\bar{r})$ by $\xi(\imath)$, the integro-differential equation, itself, became a tractable one. As the first step in the analysis, the cross section $\sigma(\theta)$ was computed exactly (numerically) for the above potential until, by trial and error, a set of parameters was found which gave cross sections similar to empirical ones. Next, using this set of parameters, *without change*, $\sigma(\theta)$ was computed at a number of energies and was observed to exhibit approximately the correct empirical energy dependence. An equivalent local potential was then found at each energy by fitting the nonlocal cross sections, regarded as empirical input data, and using an automatic search routine which minimized the sum of squared deviations. It was found possible to fit the nonlocal cross sections unambiguously and with considerable precision. The energy variation of the local parameters thus found is strikingly similar to that of the empirical optical model parameters.

A study of their numerical results, combined with some qualitative theoretical arguments, then led Perey and Buck to the relation between the nonlocal potential U and the equivalent local potential $\hat{V}$

$$\hat{V}(r, E) \exp\left\{\frac{mb^2}{2\hbar^2} [E - \hat{V}(r, E)]\right\} \approx U(r). \qquad (12)$$

This is easily verified to be the same as the effective mass result up to, and including, terms of order b^2, except for the surface terms.

Using Eq. (12), Perey and Buck then sought to find a single, energy independent set of nonlocal parameters which would fit all the neutron data up to 24 MeV. Their real potential parameters are given in Table I, Section 5.2. Their imaginary potential parameters are $W' = 15$ MeV and $a_1 = 0.47$ F. Note that the range of the nonlocality and the depth of the central potential are generally consistent with the results obtained by Wyatt *et al.* (1960), using the effective mass approximation. Also, note that the radius and surface diffuseness parameters are quite similar to those of Bjorklund and Fernbach (1958). These latter authors used the imaginary potential of the Gaussian form of the width $b = 0.98$ F. The derivative form with $a_1 = 0.47$ F gives very nearly the same shape.

The fits to the data using this energy independent set of parameters are remarkably good, as illustrated in Figs. 1 and 2, which show neutron scattering from several elements at 4.1, 7, 14.5, and 24 MeV. The 4.1 MeV results have been corrected empirically for compound elastic scattering. Also shown in Fig. 3 are the total cross sections as a function of $A^{1/3}$ at these energies. The S wave scattering length was also found to agree very well with experiment, while the S wave strength function gives a good overall fit, but suffers from the usual difficulty of being too large between resonances. Fits to scattering and polarization data below 2 MeV are also good, after empirical corrections for compound elastic scattering are introduced.

The reason for the better fits achieved by Perey and Buck to the experimental cross sections (as compared with those achieved by Wyatt *et al.*)

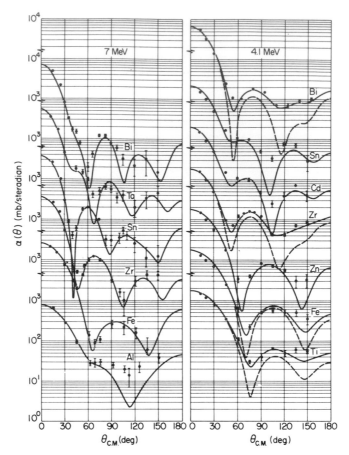

Fig. 1. Comparison of predictions of the energy independent nonlocal optical model with experimental elastic differential cross sections of neutrons at 4.1 and 7 MeV.

(The parameters are given in Table I of Section 5.2. Some of the shape elastic differential cross sections (dashed curves) have been corrected for compound elastic contributions (full curve) [Perey and Buck, 1962].)

is somewhat obscure. The approximation of replacing $\xi(\bar{r})$ by $\xi(\imath)$ is good only in the limit of rather small nonlocality. This is illustrated in Fig. 4 which shows $\bar{r}$ and $\imath$, (a) when $r = 3$, $r' = 3$, and $b = 1$ and (b) when $r = 3$, $r' = 2$, and $b = 1$. The circles about the arrowhead of $\mathbf{r}$ give the e^{-1} and e^{-4} contours of $H(s)$. The figure shows that $s \gg b$ when $\imath \neq \bar{r}$, so that the error due to the disparity of $\imath$ and $\bar{r}$ is limited. Nevertheless the error of the Perey–Buck approximation is probably comparable to that due to the neglect of b^4 terms in the effective mass approximation.

The most plausible explanation for the better fits obtained by Perey and

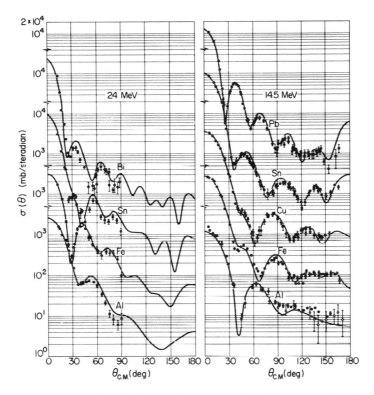

Fig. 2. Comparison of predictions of the energy independent nonlocal optical model with experimental elastic differential cross sections of neutrons at 14.5 and 24 MeV. The potential parameters are given in Table I of Section 5.2 (Perey and Buck, 1962).

Buck is the fact that they varied seven parameters to fit the neutron scattering data and used automatic search techniques. On the other hand Wyatt *et al.* finally varied only two parameters (visually) to fit the scattering data (having fixed the remaining five with bound state data). The explanation is suggested by the significant (albeit small) differences in their final sets, e.g., $[V_0 - V_1(N - Z)/A]_{WWG} \approx 65$ vs. $V_{PB} \approx 71$ for Pb, and $a_{so}^2 \approx 0.66$ vs. $a_{so}^2 \approx 0.41$.

5.4c Recent Studies of ELP

A number of recent attempts have been made to find equivalent local potentials more rigorously from kernels of the form $V(\bar{r})H(s)$. Perey and Saxon (1964) resort to a Fourier transform description similar to that of Wheeler (1936). Accepting the usual kernel, they define

$$V\Psi = \int V(\mathbf{r}, \mathbf{r} + \mathbf{s})H(s)\Psi(\mathbf{r} + \mathbf{s}) \, d^3s \tag{13}$$

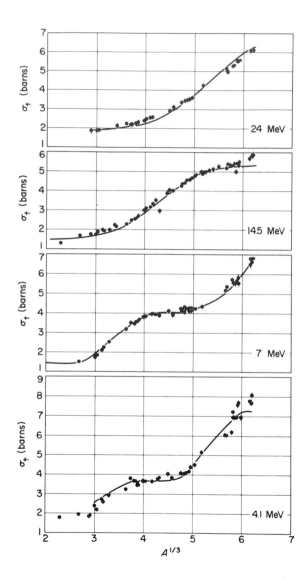

Fig. 3. Comparison of predictions of the energy independent nonlocal optical model with experimental total cross sections at 4.1, 7, 14.5, and 24 MeV. The potential parameters are given in Table I of Section 5.2 (Perey and Buck, 1962).

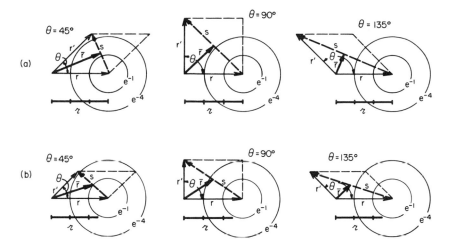

Fig. 4. Illustration of the approximation of Perey and Buck, i.e., the replacement of $\bar{r}$ by z.

where the integration extends over an effective domain of radius b. Over this domain V changes little and hence Ψ oscillates with some reasonably well-defined local wave number κ, to be specified later. As a result, the integration singles out the κth Fourier component of $H(\mathbf{s})$. To make this explicit, we write

$$H(\mathbf{s}) = \left(\frac{1}{2\pi}\right)^3 \int \tilde{H}(k^2)e^{i\mathbf{k}\cdot\mathbf{s}}\, d^3k. \tag{14}$$

Thus

$$V\Psi = \left(\frac{1}{2\pi}\right)^3 \int d^3s \int d^3k\, V(\mathbf{r}, \mathbf{r}+\mathbf{s})\tilde{H}(k^2)e^{i\mathbf{k}\cdot\mathbf{s}}\Psi(\mathbf{r}+\mathbf{s}). \tag{15}$$

Now we make our basic (and only) approximation by expanding $\tilde{H}(k^2)$ about $k^2 = \kappa^2$

$$\tilde{H}(k^2) = \tilde{H}(\kappa^2) + (k^2 - \kappa^2)\tilde{H}'(\kappa^2) + \cdots \tag{16}$$

and eventually adjust $\kappa^2 = \kappa^2(r)$ to make this expansion converge as rapidly as we conveniently can. The double integrations are now trivial. If κ^2 were (arbitrarily) chosen to be zero, this would be the familiar effective mass approximation. No matter how slowly V varies, it is clearly a low energy approximation. Instead we choose κ^2 such that $(\nabla^2 + \kappa^2)$ annihilates Ψ to first order. We obtain, directly, a result very similar in form to the effective mass approximation. We might expect, however, that by choosing κ^2 appropriately the new result could be employed at higher energies where the effective mass approximation should break down.

Just as in our studies of purely velocity dependent potentials, the $\mathbf{\nabla} \Psi \cdot \mathbf{\nabla} V$ term can be transformed away. Thus letting $\Psi = FX$ where

$$F = [\tilde{H}(\kappa^2)/\tilde{H}(k^2)]^{1/2} < 1 \qquad \text{for} \quad \kappa^2 > k^2$$

$$\geq 1 \qquad \text{for} \quad \kappa^2 < k^2 \qquad (17)$$

it follows that X satisfies

$$-\frac{\hbar^2}{2m} \nabla^2 X + V_E(r)X = EX \qquad (18)$$

where

$$V_E(r) = \tilde{H}V(r) - \frac{1}{4}\frac{\tilde{H}'\langle \nabla^2 V \rangle}{\left[1 + \frac{2m}{\hbar^2}\tilde{H}'V\right]} - \frac{\hbar^2}{2m}\left[\frac{\nabla^2 F}{F} - 2\left(\frac{\nabla F}{F}\right)^2\right]. \qquad (19)$$

The evaluation of $V_E(r)$ for simple forms of H (such as a Gaussian) is straightforward but tedious.

Fiedeldey (1967) also starts from Eq. (14), Section 5.1, or nonlocal potentials of the form $U(\bar{r})H(s)$ where U is a WS type form factor and H is a Gaussian form factor, and gives two methods for finding equivalent local potentials which are in a sense complementary. Proceeding by an iterative method he finds ELP's which are rather independent of l. The results agree very well with the Perey–Buck ELP after only one iteration. Fiedeldey suggested that the fact that their equivalent local potential is l independent was the reason for the success obtained with local l independent optical models.

Gersten (1967) goes beyond Fiedeldey's work in deriving explicit rules for the parameters of the equivalent local potential by an expansion technique. Without going into the details, we might indicate that he obtains a local equivalent potential which may be written in the form

$$V_L(r) = \frac{e^{-\alpha E}U(r)}{1 + \alpha e^{-\alpha E}U(r)} + \frac{1}{\alpha}\left[\frac{\alpha e^{-\alpha E}U(r)}{1 + \alpha e^{-\alpha E}U(r)}\right]^3. \qquad (20)$$

Gersten gives numerous graphs and tables providing the parameters of the local potentials which are equivalent to his initial NLP.

In concluding this section we must emphasize that the results to date are strongly indicative of the need for a nonlocal or velocity dependent potential. However, pending a successful fundamental derivation we must be open-minded as to the detailed nature of the nonlocal or velocity dependence. There are indications (Brown et al., 1963) which suggest that the velocity dependence may be more complicated than that assumed in most of the studies which we have discussed. These complications can probably be encompassed by letting $\xi_0(r) \neq \xi(r)$; However, this has yet to be established in detail.

VI

Recent Phenomenological Studies

6.1   Scattering of Nucleons

6.1a   Methods of Analysis

In Section 3.4, the early quantitative results of the optical model analyses for nucleons have been discussed, together with the parametrization of the potential. Numerous analyses of more recent data usually employ the criterion of least χ^2, where χ^2 is the sum of the squares of the differences between the theoretical angular distributions and the experimental values divided by the corresponding experimental uncertainties; and they utilize various automatic search methods to locate the minimum χ^2 points in the multidimensional parameter space. Compilations of these recent analyses [e.g., Hodgson (1963b) or Winner and Drisko (1965)] show that the values of the parameters fluctuate considerably from element to element and energy to energy, although the general trend is similar to that observed by Bjorklund and Fernbach (1958). This is due mostly to the various ambiguities in the optical model parameters, although we expect some fluctuation due to the individual structure of the participating nucleus and the reactions mechanism involved [for the methods of automatic search commonly used, see, for example, Melkanoff et al. (1966)].

In part, this difficulty arises because the experimental data are usually incomplete. If such incomplete data can be fit at all, as they usually can, then it is embarrassingly easy to do so. By this we mean that there exists a range of correlated parameter values over which we can fit the data. As the data become more complete, we can hope that these ambiguities will be resolved.

It may well turn out, however, that the experimental data alone will not fix the parameters of the optical model with any great precision. If so, this can be regarded as indicating, at least in some sense, an inappropriate parametrization.

The question of how to construct an appropriate parametrization remains open. One obvious way out of this dilemma lies in an appeal to the theory of the underlying process. Should this theory become quantitatively reliable, we can use it to fix enough of the parameters of the model to remove the ambiguities. Unfortunately, this task is complicated by the fact that the theoretically calculated quantities are not simply related to the empirically determined ones (as we shall discuss in more detail later).

It became certain that, even at best, analyses of the scattering by a single element at a single energy did not serve to select the parameters of the optical model with any precision, and that, above and beyond dispersion effects, simultaneous analyses of a number of elements at many different energies were required. The more recent optical model analysis has been so directed, with emphasis on finding an average potential which can describe the data over a relatively wide range of mass number and energy simultaneously. We first present the current status of the average nucleon optical potential, its ambiguities within an energy region, and the fluctuation from one energy region to another.

The major features revealed by these analyses can perhaps be summarized briefly as follows:

i. The presence of a symmetry term in the real well depth U_0 has been well established. There are indications that the symmetry effect is concentrated near the surface. Its presence in the surface imaginary part is also proved.

ii. The coefficient of energy in the real well depth U_0 appears to decrease as E increases, being ~ 0.55 (Perey, 1963) or ~ 0.30 (Rosen *et al.*, 1965; Buck, 1963) at $E \leq 22$ MeV, and ~ 0.22 (Fricke *et al.*, 1967; Fulmer *et al.*, 1967) at $30 \leq E \leq 6.14$ MeV, although direct comparison is difficult due to the different geometrical parameters used.

iii. The analyses at lower energies assumed the imaginary potential to be of a pure surface shape type. For this choice of shape factor the strength W' did not show any sign of increase with energy. Subsequently, the analyses at higher energies have revealed that the addition of a volume absorption is definitely needed.

iv. The analyses at higher energies have proved that the geometry used in the lower energy analyses cannot be used at higher energies. It was found that the real well radius must be chosen smaller than the imaginary well radius, and the diffuseness parameter a_1' must be larger than the lower energy value. It is quite possible that the lower energy data could be fitted well by these higher energy geometries, although the converse is unlikely to be true.

v. There are indications that the spin orbit strength is concentrated somewhat inside the surface of the central potential.

vi. Even the overall proton potential in a particular energy region is not free from ambiguity, a fact which may be related to the methods and the scope of the analyses (i.e., the choice of free parameters, the kind of data, its accuracy and angular coverage, the nuclear species considered, etc.), as well as to the influence of nonoptical effects.

vii. It is possible that even the same method and scope of analysis can yield different symmetry dependence depending on where it is particularly looked for (Satchler, 1967b).

A great deal of effort has gone into the determination of overall nucleon optical model potentials. The results of some of these studies are summarized in Tables I and II for neutrons and protons, respectively. Needless to say, these average parameters are meant to provide for overall fits to a vast bulk of data and are not meant for individual precise fits; but, slight deviations from the average parameters are sufficient in most cases to produce precise fits to the data. However, in general, there remain some difficulties at backangles. These difficulties, as well as the deviation of the best fit parameters from the average behavior, warrant detailed studies of individual nuclei, particularly nonoptical effects arising from strong coupling to collective excited states.

Explanations and relevant discussions of the average potentials given in Tables I and II, as well as fits to the data obtained by using these potentials for typical cases, are presented in the following subsections.

6.1b   The Average Potentials for Neutrons

The remarkable success of the energy independent nonlocal potential obtained by Perey and Buck, as discussed in Section 5.4, has made a compilation of the local neutron parameters in this energy range almost unnecessary. However, for the purpose of comparison with the proton potential for which only the local potential has been used so far, we list here the local parameters equivalent to the Perey–Buck potential obtained by solving the equivalence relation, Eq. (12), Section 5.4.

Set $(I.1)$[1] of Table I contains a linear energy dependence in the strength of the real central potential but is otherwise energy *independent*. This is quoted by Rosen *et al.* (1965) as valid for 1 to 25 MeV. Set $(I.2)$ is due to Wilmore and Hodgson (1964). The predicted angular distributions with this potential are reported to be in good agreement with the neutron data over 1–15 MeV for medium and heavy nuclei. We notice that the dependence on E of the real well depth agrees quite well with Set $(I.1)$. However, the strength of the surface absorption W' is seen to decrease somewhat with energy, which is a

---

[1] Hereafter, where sets are referred to by number, without other identification, the numeral before the decimal point will designate the table in which the data are to be found (in Section 6.1).

TABLE I

AVERAGE NEUTRON OPTICAL POTENTIALS[a]

E	U_0	W'	U_{so}	r_0	r'	a	a_i'	b	Set number
1–25	$48 - 0.29E$	9.6	7.2	1.27	—	0.66	0.47	—	(I.1)[b]
1–15	$47.01 - 0.267E$ $- 0.00118E^2$	$9.52 - 0.053E$	—	$1.322 - 0.00037A$ $+ 4 \cdot 10^{-6}A^2$ $- 8 \cdot 10^{-9}A^3$	$1.266 - 0.00037A$ $+ 2 \cdot 10^{-6}A^2$ $- 4 \cdot 10^{-9}A^3$	0.66	0.48	—	(I.2)[c]
4–24	$49.3 - 0.33E$	5.75	5.5	1.25	—	0.65	0.70	—	(I.3)[d]
14.2	$45.5 - (17 \pm 2)\mathscr{S}^f$	$14.5 - (26 \pm 9)\mathscr{S}^f$	8.3	1.26	—	0.70	—	1.0	(I.4)[e]

[a] See footnote on p. 117.

[b] Equivalent local parameters to the Perey–Buck potential quoted by Rosen et al. (1965).

[c] Wilmore and Hodgson (1964).

[d] Rosen et al. (1965).

[e] Dukarevich et al. (1967).

[f] The symbol $\mathscr{S}$ denotes $(N - Z)/A$.

TABLE II
AVERAGE PROTON OPTICAL POTENTIALS[a]

E	U_0	W	W'	U_{so}	r_0	r_I	r_{so}	a	a_I	a_I'	a_{so}	Data	Set number
9–17} 17–22}	$53.3 - 0.55E$ $+ 0.4\mathscr{C} + 27\mathscr{S}$	—	13.5 ± 2.0} $3A^{1/3} \pm 1.5$}	7.5} 8.5}	1.25*[l]	—	—	0.65*[l]	—	0.47*[l]	—	σ	(II.1)[e]
7–22	$53.8 - 0.33E$} $47.7 - 0.33E$ $+ 0.4\mathscr{C} + 26.2\mathscr{S}$}[b]	—	7.5	5.5	1.25	—	—	0.65	—	0.70	—	p	(II.2a)[f] (II.2b)[f]
11–18	$52.6 - 0.2\varepsilon E\,1.0$	—	10.6 ± 1.6	8.0	1.25	—	—	0.65*[l]	—	0.47	—	CCC	(II.3)[g]
30	$39.6 + 0.4\mathscr{C}$ $+ (17 \pm 10)\mathscr{S}$	—	$3.4^{1/3}$	6.0	1.25*[l]	—	—	0.65*[l]	—	0.47*[l]	—	σ	(II.4)[h]
30	$43.0 + 0.4\mathscr{C}$ $+ (20 \pm 5)\mathscr{S}$	c	c	c	1.20	1.25	1.10	0.70	0.70	0.70	0.70	σ, p	(II.5)[i]
30	$47.5 + 0.4\mathscr{C}$} $+ (30 \pm 5)\mathscr{S}$}	3	$4.5 - 16\mathscr{S}$}	6.4}	1.12}	—	—	—	0.58 (Fe, Co, and Cu) 0.65 (Sn) 0.75 (Pb)		—		(II.6a)[i]
30	$51 + 0.4\mathscr{C}$}	3	$4.5 + 16\mathscr{S}$}	6.1}	1.09 $+ 0.25\mathscr{S}$}	1.33}	—	0.75		$= a_I$	—	σ, p	(II.6q)[j]
40 (30)	$49.9 - 0.22E$ $+ 0.4\mathscr{C} + 26.4\mathscr{S}$	[d]	[d]	6.04	1.16	1.37	1.064	0.75	0.63	$= a_I$	0.738	σ, p	(II.7)[k]

[a] See the footnote on p. 117 (the symbols $\mathscr{C}$ and $\mathscr{S}$ denote $Z/A^{1/3}$ and $(N - Z)/A$, respectively).
[b] This expression is obtained by using the proton results only. If combined with neutron results, we would have $51.3 - 0.33E + 0.4\mathscr{C} + 9\mathscr{S}$.
[c] See Table V of Greenlees and Pyle (1966).
[d] See Table III of Fricke et al. (1967).
[e] Perey (1963).
[f] Rosen et al. (1965).
[g] Buck (1963).
[h] Barrett et al. (1965).
[i] Greenlees and Pyle (1966).
[j] Satchler (1967b).
[k] Fricke et al. (1967).
[l] Fixed parameter.

consequence of nonlocality, well known from the effective mass approximation for an energy independent nonlocal potential, as we have seen in Section 5.4. However, this behavior of W' is quite contrary to theoretical expectations, particularly since there is no appreciable change in the shape of the equivalent potential with energy which can possibly compensate for the decrease in W'. This question seems to us to be an open one and in any case will clearly limit the domain of applicability of the model.

We should emphasize that the Perey–Buck nonlocal potential, or its equivalent local potential, is by no means unique. Recent analysis by Rosen et al. (1965) of their own proton polarization data, as well as a wide range of other data on protons and neutrons, which we discuss further in the next subsection, has proved that Set (I.3) can describe quite well the differential, total, and reaction cross sections over the range of energy 4–24 MeV and of mass number $A \geq 27$. The main difference between this set and Set (I.1), for example, is seen to be in the imaginary potential. Potential (I.3) has a much greater width a_1 compared to that of Potential (I.1). It seems as if there exists a $(W' - a_1')$ ambiguity, in the sense that the product $W'a_1'^n$ ($n \simeq 1$) is approximately constant for the neutron average potential with a pure surface absorption, if everything else is kept equal.

The handicap caused by the large experimental uncertainties in the neutron angular distributions compared to the protons could be compensated for by accurate measurements of neutron total cross sections. In the most recent work by Dukarevich et al. (1967), the total neutron cross sections σ_t for a number of isotopes of Ni, Zn, Cd, Sn, and Te were measured at 14.2 MeV. The experimental results are shown in Fig. 1. The following characteristic features were observed:

i. For a given element, σ_t increases approximately linearly with increasing mass number A, as shown in Fig. 1 by the straight lines (drawn by the method of least square deviations).

ii. Comparison of σ_t among isobaric nuclei shows that σ_t for neutron deficient nuclei is larger than for neutron rich nuclei in the Ni–Zn region and smaller in the Cd–Te region.

iii. The increase of σ_t as a function of A for isotopes of a given element is larger in the Cd–Te region than in the Ni–Cd region.

iv. The data show no peculiarities for even-odd or odd-even nuclei as compared with even-even nuclei.

These fairly precise systematic trends seem to warrant a detailed optical model analysis, including symmetry dependence. Dukarevich et al. have done this, looking for a set of parameters which would fit, not only their data on total cross sections for isotopes, but also all other available data on total, reaction, and differential cross sections for elements with natural isotopic composition. The optical model potential with a Gaussian surface absorption was used with the parameters b and U_{so} fixed to the values of Bjorklund and Fernbach, and the parameters U_0, W', r_0, and a were then varied within a narrow region around the values of Bjorklund and Fernbach. The dependence of σ_t on U_0 and W' at the regions $A = 64$ and $A = 118.7$ is shown in Fig. 2, from which it can be seen that the dependence of U_0 and W' on $(N-Z)/A$ (with a negative coefficient) is going to give the observed behavior of σ_t for isobaric nuclei near $A = 64$ and $A = 118.7$, respectively. Their final set of parameters is given by Set (I.4). The predicted total cross sections for isotopes

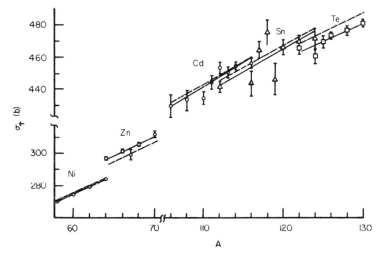

Fig. 1. Comparison of experimental and calculated neutron total cross sections for isotopes. Dashed lines are lines calculated with Set (I.4) of Table I. Full lines are experimental lines (Dukarevich *et al.*, 1967).

with this set are also shown in Fig. 1 (the dashed lines). The fits to the differential, total, and reaction cross sections, for 14.5 MeV neutrons elastically scattered from elements around $A = 64$, 118.7, and 207 with natural isotopic composition, are about as good as those obtained by Perey and Buck.

The importance of their work is that they established the presence of the symmetry term directly from the analysis of the neutron data alone. Especially, they have eliminated the doubt that the symmetry dependence in W' found in the proton analyses (as explained in the next subsection) might be a coincidence and due to different sources, such as a strong coupling to excited states. The magnitudes of their symmetry dependence also appear to be in accord with the proton values as we shall see in Section 6.2.

Finally, we mention the recent experiment on the differential cross sections for neutrons elastically scattered from Pb and Bi^{209} at 7 MeV, performed by Zafiratos *et al.* (1965) with high precision over the entire angular region.

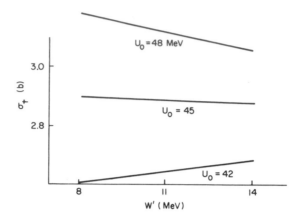

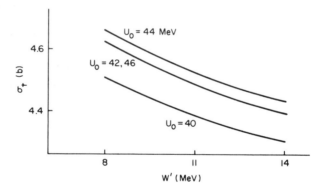

Fig. 2. Neutron total cross section as a function of U_0 and W' for $A = 64$ and 118.7. Parameters not specified at the curves are $r_0 = 1.26$ F, $a = 0.66$ F, $b = 1.0$ F, $U_{so} = 8.3$ MeV (Dukarevich *et al.*, 1967).

Since the neutron data on Pb at 7 MeV played an important role in determining the nonlocal potential of Perey and Buck, the optical model analysis of these new data presented a rather interesting test of the model. The parameters given by Perey and Buck (1962) for Pb are listed as "Potential 1" in Table III. The new data for Bi^{209} are shown in Fig. 3a, together with the data previously used by Perey and Buck. The fit to the data by "Potential 1" is shown by the solid curve. The best fit parameters obtained by Zafiratos *et al.* with a 7 parameter search are given in Table III as "Potential 3," and the fit is shown in Fig. 3b. The chief difference between "Potential 1" and "Potential

TABLE III
NEUTRON OPTICAL MODEL PARAMETERS AT 7 MeV

Potential	U_0	W'	r_0	r_1'	a	a_1'	U_{so}
1[a]	45.31	6.57	1.25	1.25	0.65	0.47	6.7
2[b]	45.08	9.15	1.265	1.240	0.66	0.48	—
3[c]	45.93	5.16	1.23	1.34	0.69	0.48	5.6

[a] Potential 1 is given for Pb (Perey and Buck, 1962).
[b] Potential 2 is calculated from Set (I.2) of Table I for Bi^{209}.
[c] Potential 3 represents the best fit parameters (Zafiratos *et al.*, 1965) for Bi^{209}.

3," to which the improved fit at backangles must be attributed, lies in the fact that in " Potential 3 " the imaginary radius r_1' is extended farther than the real radius r_0.

The necessity for larger r_1' than r_0 has also been evidenced, for example, in nuclear matter calculations and in calculations of s wave strength functions (as discussed in Section 4.2), as well as in proton elastic scattering analyses, as we shall see shortly.

For the sake of comparison, the parameters obtained from Set (I.2) for Bi^{209} at 7 MeV are also given in Table III as " Potential 2." It is seen that the equivalent local potential has the opposite tendency of pulling the imaginary radius slightly inside the real radius.

In any event, the precise determination of neutron average potentials from neutron elastic scattering data alone must wait until more complete data become available.

Neutron potentials can also be inferred from the proton average potentials if we assume the charge independence of the nuclear interactions. This will be discussed next.

6.1c   The Average Potential for Protons

The question of the Coulomb correction for a velocity dependent potential has been discussed in Section 5.2 (see Eq. (17), Section 5.2, and discussion related to it), and we have noted the apparent conflicts in studies in the 1955–1959 period. On the one hand, Lane (1957) suggested that a Coulomb correction, given by γV_c where $\gamma = \beta/(1 + \beta)$, develops for the velocity dependent potential. On the other hand, the proton potential anomaly has been explained as arising in a non-Coulomb symmetry dependent term in an IPM potential, as has been discussed in Sections 2.3, 5.2, and 5.4 in connection with the studies by Green and his collaborators, whose works indicated relatively little change in the symmetry coefficient V_1 in going from static to velocity

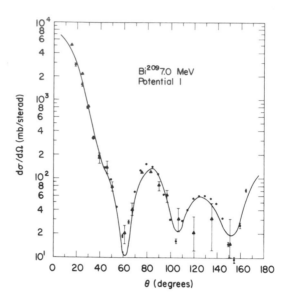

Fig. 3a. The neutron elastic scattering from Bi^{209} at 7.0 MeV. Solid circles represent the data by Zafiratos *et al.* (1965). Triangles represent the data by Beyster *et al.* (1956). Solid curves represent theoretical values with Potential 1 of Table III (Zafiratos *et al.*, 1965).

dependent potentials. Almost all current studies embody a symmetry term. However, many studies also embody a Coulomb correction of the form γV_c. Before describing these studies in detail, we might note that the apparent conflict may reside in the detailed method of solution of the intrinsically non-local or velocity dependent potential used by different investigators. The bound state studies for neutrons and protons in velocity dependent potentials by Green (1957) and Wyatt *et al.* (1960) involved direct solutions of the non-local equation. By incorporating the Coulomb potential in the proton case, we automatically obtain a corrective reduction of its effect. On the other hand, most of the current proton scattering studies are carried out using the energy dependent equivalent local potential. In such cases we might expect to find it necessary to embody explicitly a correction which reduces somewhat the influence of the Coulomb potential.

For convenience of further discussions of the Coulomb and symmetry effects we shall introduce the symbols $\mathscr{S} = (N - Z)/A$ and $\mathscr{C} = Z/A^{1/3}$. For stable nuclei $\mathscr{S}(A)$ and $\mathscr{C}(A)$ vary in a rather similar fashion. Indeed, $\mathscr{C}/\mathscr{S} \approx (0.75A + 250)/A^{1/3}$ for the empirical line of beta stability (Eq. (10), Section 2.1), which might be given the nominal constant value 67. This near constancy of $\mathscr{C}/\mathscr{S}$ makes it difficult to discriminate phenomenologically between the two effects.

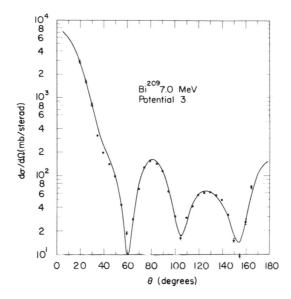

Fig. 3b. The best fit to the neutron data with all parameters free to vary (Potential 3 of Table III) (Zafiratos *et al.*, 1965).

Lane (1962) has noted that the dependence on $\mathscr{S}$ can be introduced by using a real optical model potential of the form

$$U(r) = -U_0\,\xi(r) - \frac{4}{A}\,V_1(\mathbf{t}\cdot\mathbf{T})\xi_1(r) \tag{1}$$

where $\mathbf{t}$ and $\mathbf{T}$ are the isobaric spins of the incident nucleon and target, respectively, and $\xi_1(r)$ is the shape factor. The diagonal element of this operator for the target state, with $T = T_z = (N - Z)/2$, is $V_1\mathscr{S}\xi_1(r)$ for a proton and $-V_1\mathscr{S}\xi_1(r)$ for a neutron. It has been customary to assume that $\xi_1 = \xi$ so that the symmetry effect is contained in the real well depths $U_{0,p}$ and $U_{0,n}$ for the proton and the neutron. This, combined with the consideration of the Coulomb correction just discussed, gives

$$U_{0,p} = V_{00} - \gamma E + \gamma \bar{V}_c + V_1\mathscr{S} \tag{2}$$

$$U_{0,n} = V_{00} - \gamma E - V_1\mathscr{S} \tag{3}$$

where $\bar{V}_c$ is an average Coulomb correction.

We summarize in Table II the work at 9 to 22 MeV by Perey (1963) on average proton potentials, the subsequent analyses at 7 to 22 MeV (Rosen *et al.*, 1965), at 30 MeV (Barrett *et al.*, 1965; Greenlees and Pyle, 1966; Satchler, 1967b), and at 40 MeV (Blumberg *et al.*, 1966; Fricke *et al.*, 1967).

The parameter which was kept fixed during the analyses is shown with an asterisk. The last column of Table II shows the data which played the key role in determining the parameters, i.e., the data which were fitted by means of a least χ^2 criterion using an automatic search code. The rest of the data were usually checked against the predictions of this now determined average potential and, in general, fits were found to be quite satisfactory. Since the proton data are, in general, more accurate and more complete than the neutron data, we can hope to learn more about the potential parameters.

Perey (1963) analyzed the differential cross sections of protons elastically scattered from nuclei heavier than Al at the energies 9.4, 12.0, 14.3, 17.0, and 22.2 MeV. First, automatic searches were carried out for the optimum set of parameters U_0 and W' keeping the rest of the parameters as shown in Table II. To find the dependence of U_0 on $\mathscr{S}$, Perey first subtracted γV_c. At the time of Perey's analysis, it was known from the neutron analysis and also from the coupled channel analysis of Buck (1963) that the coefficient of E is about -0.3. Thus, using $\gamma = 0.3$, replacing V_c by its average value $\overline{V}_c$ inside the nucleus, and assuming a uniform charge distribution of radius $1.25A^{1/3}$ F, i.e., $\overline{V}_c = 1.38\mathscr{C}$ MeV, the Coulomb correction term was determined to be

$$\gamma V_c = 0.4Z/A^{1/3} = 0.4\mathscr{C} \quad \text{MeV.} \tag{4}$$

The plot of $U_{0,p} - 0.4\mathscr{C}$ against $\mathscr{S}$ is shown in Fig. 4, from which the coefficient of the symmetry number was set at 27 MeV for all energies. From the

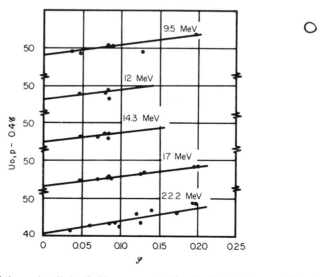

Fig. 4. Plot of the real well depth $U_{0,p}$, corrected for the Coulomb potential variation $-0.4\mathscr{C}$, as a function of the symmetry parameter $\mathscr{S}$. The slope of the lines (27 MeV), gives the coefficient of the symmetry term in the optical potential (Perey, 1963).

intercepts of these lines with the axis, $\mathscr{S} = 0$, as a function of E, the coefficient of E is determined to be -0.55, as given by Set (II.1). Using the expression of U_0 thus determined, a search for the best fit values of W' was made. Typical fits to the differential cross sections at 17 MeV with these parameters are shown in Fig. 5. The best fit parameter W' thus obtained does not show any

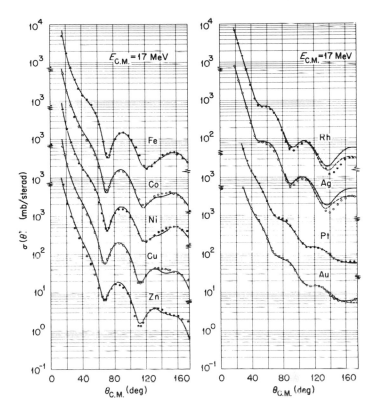

Fig. 5. Comparison of the proton optical model calculations with the 17 MeV data. (The geometrical parameters are fixed to the values given by Set (II.1). $U_{0,p}$ was read off the appropriate curve in Fig. 4. W' was the only parameter adjusted to yield an optimum χ^2 in each case. The dashed curves for Rh, Ag, and Au are the results when the diffuseness parameter a_{I}' is set to 0.65 F instead of to 0.47 F as for the full curves [Perey, 1963].)

marked systematic trends, except that it increases as we go from lighter to heavier nuclei. Perey summarizes the situation for the medium weight elements as given by Set (II.1).

Although the reaction cross sections and polarizations were not considered in the search, the results are in reasonably good agreement with the experimental values. However, the predicted polarization for two lower energies show considerable disagreement beyond $\sim 140°$.

The energy dependence of U_0 found in Set (II.1) is rather strong compared to the results of other studies. Besides, it is apparently in contradiction with Eq. (2). Perey attributed this difference to the neglect of the strong coupling to the collective excited states, and showed that the energy dependence is very sensitive to the deformation parameter β_D. However, the effect of nuclear deformation on the optical potential when averaged over a variety of nuclei could be weaker, as indicated by the analysis of Rosen et al. (1965) which we discuss next.

Rosen et al. (1965) have measured, over a wide range of angles, the azimuthal asymmetry resulting from the scattering of incident polarized protons by various nuclei from H to Sn at 10.5 and 14.5 MeV. The optical model analysis of their data was carried out with the expectation that the polarization would be more sensitive to the scattering potential than the differential cross section, especially more sensitive to the spin orbit interaction and the nuclear surface, although this expectation is usually hindered by the large experimental uncertainty. The experimental error of their polarization was quoted as 5%, in general, and somewhat larger in some cases. On the basis of the analysis of their data, they have succeeded in arriving at an average potential for both protons and neutrons which quite accurately describes a wide range of available data. The procedure was to determine first the 6 parameter proton optical potential by averaging the "best fit" parameters for their polarization data at 10.5 and 14.5 MeV. The average parameters are given as Set (II.2a). The fits to their polarization data, with this average potential, are shown in Fig. 6 for 14.5 MeV. To obtain an average set of parameters for neutrons, the geometrical parameters and the spin orbit potential were chosen to be the same as above, and the real and imaginary well depths V and W' were determined by fitting the neutron differential elastic cross section data at 14.5 MeV. Assuming the same energy dependence as for protons, the neutron potential was determined as given by Set (I.3).

These average parameters, thus obtained, were found to predict quite satisfactorily the data available at that time on the differential cross sections, polarizations, and reaction cross sections for protons from 7 to 38 MeV, and for neutrons from 4 to 24 MeV on various nuclei, with a slight correction for compound elastic scattering for the low energy neutrons. However, for nuclei $A \lesssim 60$ the proton reaction cross sections predicted at 10.5 and 29 MeV lay rather far above the upper limits placed by the experimental errors.

In order to find the dependence of the real well depth U_0 on the symmetry number, searches were made on U_0 for the best fits to each of the polarization data at 14.5 MeV, fixing the rest of the parameter to the average Set (II.2). With the energy dependence $-0.33E$ obtained by them, the result can be expressed as given by Set (II.2b). We should emphasize that this expression for U_0 is valid for protons only. We shall come back to this point later.

The energy dependence of the real well depth $-0.33E$ obtained here is in good agreement with the results of neutron analyses and Buck's coupled channel calculation. It may indicate that the effect of nuclear deformation on the average potential parameters is smaller than Perey previously assumed (Perey, 1963).

The analyses by Perey and by Rosen *et al.* have produced rather different sets of average parameters. In view of the drastic difference in the width of the surface absorption a_1' in Sets (II.1) and (II.2) it may be possible to differentiate them by comparing the predicted reaction cross sections with the recent data at 14.5 MeV (Dicello *et al.*, 1967). It has been pointed out that, for a pure surface absorption, there is some interplay between W' and a_1' (Olkowsky and Raynal, 1961; Baugh *et al.*, 1966). If the product $W'a_1'$ is kept constant (roughly), equally good fits to the angular distributions can be obtained. In fact, this $W'a_1'$ ambiguity seems to be the only major difference between the average potential of Buck [Set (II.3)] and that of Rosen *et al.* [Set (II.2a)]. Similar ambiguity was also noted for neutrons. This is precisely the place where accurate measurements of proton reaction cross sections are expected to play a crucial role.

We have seen no evidence for systematic increase of W' which is expected theoretically as we move to higher energy. However, the shape factor used is an extreme one, that is, a pure surface form. Unless we investigate the possibility of mixing in volume absorption, we cannot draw any definite conclusion about the magnitude of W'. In actual fact, there is an indication that the addition of a small volume absorption improves the fits to the data at 22.2 MeV (Perey, 1963).

More accurate measurements of polarization have been made recently by Baugh *et al.* (1966) at 17.8 MeV for a number of elements. The optical model analyses of these data, made by them, indicated that the fits to the polarization data could be considerably improved by using a smaller radius for the spin orbit potential than for the central potential [also see Griffith and Roman (1965), Goldfarb *et al.* (1966)].

Recent data on proton elastic scattering measured at 30 MeV from Ca to Pb with good accuracy over a wide range of angles (Ridley and Turner, 1964; Turner *et al.*, 1964; Craig *et al.*, 1964; Makino *et al.*, 1964) have stimulated a number of extensive optical model analyses by several groups. The result obtained by Barrett *et al.* (1965) is given by Set (II.4) where the geometrics are the same as those of Perey. It was found that, except for Pb^{208}, pure surface absorption is satisfactory but not pure volume absorption; and, that with pure surface absorption the predicted polarizations and reaction cross sections are also in substantial accord with the experimental data, although the predicted

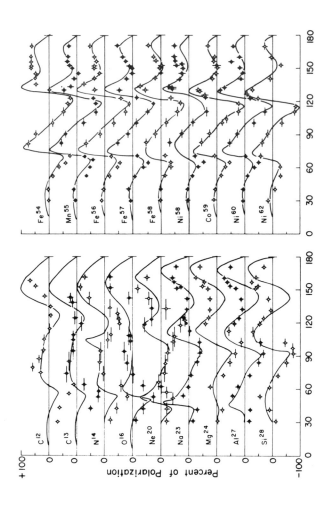

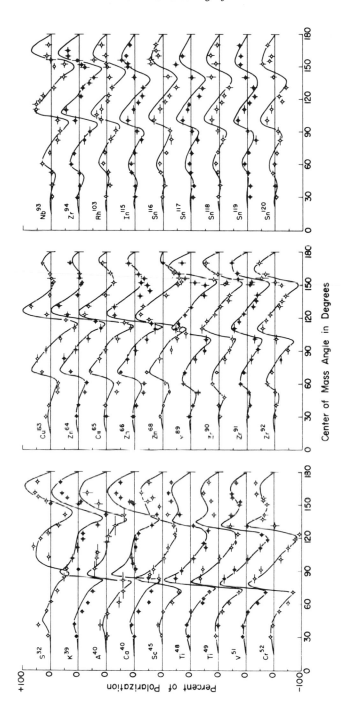

Fig. 6. Angular dependence of the polarization in the elastic scattering of 14.5 MeV protons. Solid curves are optical model predictions with Set (II.2a) (Rosen *et al.*, 1965).

reaction cross section is $\sim 10\%$ lower than the data. The differential cross section is given well in the forward hemisphere but shows too much structure in the backward angles, a feature which is typical of all elements using these geometries. They found that extrapolation of the Perey potential is not permissible, but that the real well depth V is in reasonable agreement with the formula as given by Set (II.4), although Perey's estimate of $W' \simeq 3A^{1/3}$ is still approximately valid in this energy region. A typical fit to the differential cross section and polarization data for Ni^{60}, obtained by using the fixed geometry of Perey, is shown by the dashed curves in Figs. 7 and 8. The calculation was

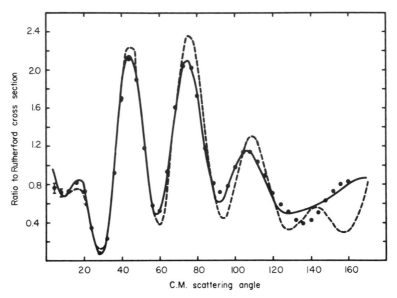

Fig. 7. Fits to the Ni^{60} differential cross section data of 30 MeV protons. The dashed line shows the fit obtained with the Perey geometry parameters, and the solid line is obtained with Set (II.5) (Greenlees and Pyle, 1966).

done by Greenlees and Pyle (1966) with the well depths $U_0 = 45.6$, $W' = 11.3$, and $U_{so} = 5.8$.

Greenlees and Pyle found that the agreement with the differential cross section could, in general, be improved considerably by lifting the restriction imposed by Barrett *et al.* and taking $r_0 < r_1$. They also found that the geometry for the central potential as given by Set (II.5) was satisfactory for all the elements considered. The marked improvement in the differential cross section for Ni^{60} using the geometry is shown in Fig. 7 by a solid curve. There had been a number of indications, mostly from lower energy experiments, that the polarization data could be improved by allowing the spin orbit geometry to differ from the real central geometry. Greenlees and Pyle also found that the spin orbit geometry of Set (II.5) with $r_{so} < r_0$ was quite satisfactory for all the elements. The improved fit for the polarization with this geometry is shown in Fig. 8 by a solid curve.

With central and spin orbit geometries fixed to these values, a search was made for the best fit values of the well depth parameters. The results are given in Table V of Greenlees and Pyle (1966). The real well depth U_0 was seen to be given accurately by Set (II.5). The predicted reaction cross sections agree quite well with the experimental values, except for Ni isotopes and Cu, for which the predictions are too large.

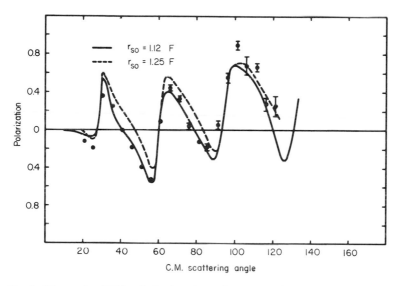

Fig. 8. Fits to the Ni^{60} polarization data. See the caption to Fig. 7 (Greenlees and Pyle, 1966).

An analysis, which is in many ways similar to the one made by Greenlees and Pyle, has also been reported by Satchler (1967b). He gave two alternative expressions for the average potential, Set (II.6a) or (II.6b), depending upon how the symmetry term was incorporated in the real potential. These alternative expressions of the symmetry effect in the real central potential are related to the well known $U_0 r_0^n$ ambiguity. However, the physics implied by them is rather different since the symmetry term of Set (II.6a) is included in the potential depth U_0 in a conventional manner and hence it is a volume term, whereas that of Set (II.6b) is exhibited near the nuclear surface. The evidence of the symmetry effect being concentrated near the nuclear surface has been investigated in the study of the (p, n) transition between analog states (Satchler *et al.*, 1964).

The differential cross sections and the polarizations predicted by Sets (II.6a) and (II.6b) are in excellent agreement with the experimental data over the entire angular range, except for Ca^{40} which presents difficulty in the back-angle. The predicted reaction cross sections are also in substantial accord with the data, but suffer some disagreement for Ni^{58}, Ni^{60}, Cu, and, especially, for Pb^{208}, the predicted reaction cross sections being too high for these nuclei.

The real potential radius found in this analysis ($r_0 = 1.1$–1.2) was con-siderably smaller, and the diffuseness parameter $a \sim 0.75$ was considerably larger than found previously. An analysis with no restriction on the spin orbit geometry has also been performed and yielded a value of $r_{so} \simeq r_0$. This result seems to be in conflict with more recent findings, but probably it is due to the smallness of r_0 required here.

We must point out that Satchler (1967b) took into account the difference of the mean energy of the polarization measurements ~ 29 MeV, and that for the cross section measurements ~ 30.3 MeV, whereas Greenlees and Pyle used an average energy ~ 29.6 MeV. In a more careful future analysis, we may also have to take into account the experimental angular resolutions, especially in the polarization data.

The addition of a volume absorption of the order $2 < W < 4$ MeV is found to be definitely required in this energy region, both by Greenlees and Pyle, and by Satchler. The fact that the volume absorption in Satchler's Sets (II.6a) and (II.6b) is independent of mass number indicates that this may be characteristic of nuclear matter. Specifically, finite size effects are expected to appear in the surface region. In fact, the strength W' and the width a_1' of the surface absorption are both found to increase with increasing mass number. The real and imaginary parts of the average Set (II.6b) are plotted in Fig. 9 for Ni^{58} and Pb^{208}. The increase of the strength W' of the surface absorption with increasing mass number is expressed very well here in a form such that it is correlated to the symmetry number $\mathscr{S}$.

The analysis by Fricke et al. (1967) of their own recent proton data at 40 MeV for the range of nuclei from C^{12} to Pb^{208} has proved to bear out most of the aspects found in the analysis at 30 MeV. Excluding those for C^{12}, the average values of the geometrical parameters and the spin orbit strength were obtained as given by Set (II.7). The dynamical parameters U_0, W, and W' are given in Table III of Fricke et al. (1967), which shows the need for volume as well as surface absorption.

The average geometrical parameters of Set (II.7) are quite similar to those found by Satchler (1967b) at 30 MeV, who also suggested the possibility of $r_{so} < r_0$ and $a_{so} < a$.

With the Coulomb correction $0.4\mathscr{C}$, the dependence on the symmetry number was identified as $26.4\mathscr{S}$, which is also in reasonable agreement with the lower energy results.

Fricke *et al.* have also used the same average geometrical parameters and the spin orbit strength as given here, and have readjusted the well depths U_0, W, and W' to get the best fits to the 30 MeV data. They found fits equally as good as those obtained previously at 30 MeV. The resulting parameters are shown in Table IV of Fricke *et al.* (1967). From these results at 30 and 40 MeV, they inferred an energy dependence of the real well depth to be $dU_0/dE = -0.22 \pm 0.03$. Together with the symmetry dependence obtained above, they found the expression for U_0 given as Set (II.7).

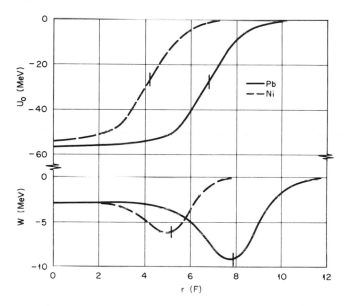

Fig. 9. Plots of the real and imaginary parts of the average potential, Set (II.6b), for Ni^{58} and Pb^{208} (Satchler, 1967b).

The energy dependence found here is markedly weaker than the value obtained in the lower energy region. Similar energy dependence was reported by Fulmer *et al.* (1967) who measured the differential cross sections at 61.4 MeV on Al^{27}, Ni^{58}, Zr^{90}, Sn^{116}, and Pb^{208}, and performed an analysis using the same geometry as Set (II.7). They found that the real well depth is well described by

$$U_0 = 36.7 + 0.4Z/A^{1/3} + 27.2(N - Z)/A. \tag{5}$$

A comparison with the previous results at 40 MeV shows that $dU_0/dE = -0.21$. It may be necessary, however, to reevaluate the symmetry dependence in Set (II.7) and Eq. (5) using the correct Coulomb term corresponding to this energy dependence.

6.1d   The Symmetry Parameter V_1

The determination of V_1 from various reactions has been reviewed by Hodgson (1963a, 1964) and by Soper (1966). There are various methods and not all of them yield consistent values of V_1. In Table IV, some of the recent work is summarized.

It is seen that the presence of a symmetry term appears to have been well established, although the value of V_1 shows considerable fluctuation. The consensus on the value of V_1 resulting from scattering and from reactions involving protons seems to remain at the value quoted by Hodgson (1964), namely

$$V_1 = 24 \pm 4 \quad \text{MeV}. \tag{6}$$

Some exceptions are found in the work of Kossanyi-Demay *et al.* (1967) for isotopes of Ti, Cr, Fe, Ni, and Cu at ~ 18 MeV, and in the work of Durisch and Gould (1965) on Sn^{112}, Sn^{116}, Sn^{120}, and Sn^{124} at 9.8 MeV. They see little evidence for any symmetry dependence of the real well depth. This latter result, however, was explained by Sood (1965) as arising from the effect on U_{0p} of the crossing of a subshell gap at about Sn^{114}. The selection of isotope sequence should be within a subshell to avoid any shell discontinuity, and with even neutron numbers only to avoid any pairing energy effects. Thus, Sood obtains $V_1 = 18$ MeV from the results of Durisch and Gould, excluding Sn^{112}.

The values of V_1 obtained from the neutron scattering data alone are scarce and differ widely, yet they are not inconsistent with the proton value. For some unexplained reason, the value of V_1 obtained by Rosen *et al.* (1965) using their results, for neutrons and protons [Sets (I.1) and (II.2a)] together, differs markedly from the value obtained by the proton analysis alone [Set (II.2b)]. Using the value of $\bar{V}_c$ given by $1.38\mathscr{C}$ as before, and the relation for stable nuclei

$$\mathscr{C} \simeq 65\mathscr{S} \tag{7}$$

obtained from the empirical mass formula, the difference $U_{0p} - U_{0n}$ becomes from Eqs. (2) and (3)

$$U_{0p} - U_{0n} = (90\gamma + 2V_1)\mathscr{S}. \tag{8}$$

Rosen *et al.* found $\gamma = 0.33$. Thus their Sets (I.3) and (II.2a) yield approximately $V_1 = 9$ MeV if we use the rough average of $\mathscr{S} \simeq 0.1$ appropriate for intermediate to heavy elements. On the other hand, if the Coulomb correction is neglected, Eq. (8) gives $V_1 \simeq 23$ MeV. Quite similar results are obtained by using Perey and Buck's Set (I.1) for neutrons and Buck's Set (II.3) ($V_p = 52.6 - 0.28E$) for protons. Sood (1966) has emphasized this discrepancy and has suggested that the neglect of the Coulomb correction leads to more consistent values of V_1, pointing out that the Coulomb correction is not required in the

TABLE IV

SYMMETRY DEPENDENCE

Author	E (MeV)	V_1 (MeV)	W' (MeV)	$V_0 - \gamma E$ (MeV)	γ	Description
Green (1956c)		26.5				A shift method static well
Green and Sood (1958)		28.5				Individual nuclei, static well
		25.0				VDP[b] Oracle solutions
Green (1958b)		28.0				VDP[b] mass formula derivation
WWG (1960)[a]		22 ± 6				NLP[c] Bound Scattering
Bochin et al. (1964)		37				Shift of single particle neutron levels after addition of two neutrons to the nucleus
						(d, p) reaction at $E_d = 6.6$ MeV
Sood (1966)		5.6(30)[d]				Last proton binding energy
		32				Last neutron binding energy
Marinov et al. (1966)		33.4				Separation energy in Sc isotopes
Sliv and Kharitonov (1965)		30–35				Single particle spectra of doubly closed shell ± one nucleon
Brueckner and Dabrowski (1964)		31.5				Nuclear symmetry energy
						Nuclear matter (K matrix) with rearrangement contribution

TABLE IV—(continued)

Author	E (MeV)	V_1 (MeV)	W' (MeV)	$V_0 - \gamma E$ (MeV)	γ	Description
Perey (1963)	9–22	27			0.55	
Picard (1965)	14–24	25			0.52	(p, p)
Rosen et al. (1965)	14.5	26.2		42.9	0.33	Range of nuclei
Kossanyi-Demay et al. (1967)	18.6	9.3 ± 7.8	9.9 ± 0.6 $+(16.2 \pm 7)\mathscr{S}$	46.5 ± 0.70		
Barrett et al. (1965)	30	17 ± 10		39.6		
Greenlees and Pyle (1966)	30	20 ± 5		43.0		
Satchler (1967a)	30	30 ± 5	$4.5 + 16\mathscr{S}$	47.5		
Fricke et al. (1967)	40	26.4		41.1	0.22	
Fulmer et al. (1967)	61.4	27.2		36.7	0.21	
Ball et al. (1964)	22.5	27.8 ± 6.0		43.4		$Zr^{90}, Zr^{91}, Zr^{92}, Zr^{94}, Zr^{96}$
Durisch and Gould (1965)	9.8	3 ± 5		48 ± 1		$Sn^{112}, Sn^{116}, Sn^{120}, Sn^{124}$ (p, p) iso-
Sood (1965)	9.8	18 ± 0.5		45.4		$Sn^{116}, Sn^{120}, Sn^{124}$ topes
Thomas et al. (1964)	12.29	23				Cu^{63}, Cu^{64}
Baugh et al. (1965)	17.8	23 ± 6		43.9		Ni^{58}, Ni^{60}

Benveniste et al. (1964).	~10	23.1	$6.47 + 39.9\,\mathscr{S}$	45.1		(p, p) (p, p') coupled channel calculation, isotopes and isobars
Satchler (1967b)	24	30	$4.5 - 16\,\mathscr{S}$	47.5		(n, n) Range of nuclei
Hodgson (1960a)	96	38		24		
Dukarevich et al. (1967)	14.2	17 ± 2	$14.5 - (26 \pm 9)\,\mathscr{S}$	45.5		(n, n) Isotopes and isobars near $A = 64$ and 118
Rosen et al. (1965)	14.5	$9(23)^d$		$46.5(48)^d$	0.33	(n, n) and (p, p)
Perey and Buck (1962)	11–18	$\sim 10\,(\sim 23)^d$			0.29	Range of nuclei
Buck (1963)					0.28	
Satchler et al. (1964)	~8	25 ± 5				DWBA Impulse approximation (p, n)
Valentin (1965)	155	$(\sim 30)^d$		18		

[a] WWG: Wyatt et al. (1960).
[b] VDP: Velocity dependent potential.
[c] NLP: Nonlocal potential.
[d] The values in parentheses were obtained without a Coulomb correction for protons.

bound state problem. However, the appearance of the Coulomb correction in a velocity dependent or nonlocal potential seems unavoidable for the scattering problem, even though the self-consistent field for the bound state problem may not need any such correction related to V_c. Thus, this inconsistency due to the Coulomb correction remains as a serious unsolved question until more accurate neutron data become available.

For the study of proton elastic scattering from a sequence of isotopes, the Coulomb correction is expected to become a secondary effect since $\mathscr{C}$ is almost a constant (of course, care has to be exercised as to the choice of the isotopes as has been mentioned above). On the other hand, spurious dependence on $\mathscr{S}$ caused by different degrees of deformation among neighboring nuclei can be avoided by explicitly taking into account the strong coupling to collective excited states, thus providing a more reliable determination of V_1. These expectations seem to have been borne out by the optical model analyses of Ball et al. (1964), Thomas et al. (1964), and Baugh et al. (1965) on sequences of isotopes, and by the coupled channel calculation of Benveniste et al. (1964) on Fe^{56}, Fe^{58}, Ni^{58}, Ni^{64}, and Zn^{64} around 10 MeV, all of which yield values consistent with Eq. (6).

The more direct determination of V_1 comes from the (p, n) quasi-elastic scattering. The isospin dependent interaction of Eq. (1) is not merely another way of writing the symmetry term in the optical model potential, but also can induce the (p, n) transition to the isobaric analog state of the ground state through its nondiagonal element $(t_- T_+)$. In either coupled channel calculations or DWBA calculations of this problem, coupling matrix elements are directly proportional to V_1 whereas the Coulomb correction enters only indirectly. Furthermore, the DWBA calculation of Satchler et al. (1964) proved that the (p, n) angular distribution is sensitive to the shape factor $\xi(r)$, and that the surface peaking of the isospin dependent interaction is definitely preferred. The value listed in Table IV is the strength of the surface coupling converted to its equivalent volume coupling (Satchler et al., 1964). We see that it is also well in accord with Eq. (6). Also, at least some indication has been seen from elastic scattering that the symmetry dependence of the real central part might be peaked near the surface (Satchler, 1967a; Fulmer et al., 1967).

The question of the symmetry dependence of the strength W' of the surface absorption is a little more complicated. The strength of the absorptive potential is expected to increase as we move to heavier nuclei since it depends on the strength of the couplings to collective oscillations or rotations of the target nucleus, which increase in general with mass number. Thus, the analysis of proton elastic scattering alone cannot settle this question, although there have been a number of occasions when W' was found to be well expressed as a linear function of $\mathscr{S}$. Satchler (1967a) has shown, however, that Set (II.6a), found from the analysis of proton elastic scattering at 30 MeV, can be used to reproduce the total and nonelastic cross sections of neutrons of about 24 MeV for a wide range of mass numbers, if the sign in front of the symmetry term in W' is reversed (after being appropriately adjusted for the energy dependence of the real well depth). More conclusive evidence was presented by Dukarevich *et al.* (1967) as we have seen in Section 6.1b. Other evidence of the necessity for a complex coupling term may be seen, for example, in the coupled channel calculation of the analog state resonance (Auerbach *et al.*, 1966).

6.1e Spin-Spin Interaction

The inclusion of a term dependent on the spin of the target nucleus in the optical potential was first suggested by Feshbach (1958a, 1960). The simplest such interaction is the spin-spin interaction of the form

$$- V_{ss} \xi(r) \frac{(\mathbf{I} \cdot \boldsymbol{\sigma})}{I} \tag{9}$$

where $\mathbf{I}$ is the spin of the target nucleus, $\boldsymbol{\sigma}$ is the Pauli spin operator of the incident nucleon, and $\xi(r)$ is some shape factor. Considerable effort has been expended to determine the strength V_{ss}, but to the present the results indicate that the magnitude of V_{ss} is quite small.

Rosen (1960) and Rosen *et al.* (1961, 1962) found that the polarizations of protons elastically scattered from unoriented nuclei were almost identical for $Mg(I = 0)$ and $Al(I = 5/2)$, or for $Co(7/2)$ and $Ni(0)$ around 10 MeV. Similar negative results were obtained (Rosen *et al.*, 1965) with initially polarized protons scattered from $Na^{23}(3/2)$ and $Mg^{24}(0)$, $K^{39}(3/2)$ and $A^{40}(0)$, $Al^{27}(5/2)$ and $Si^{28}(0)$, and, $Ti^{49}(7/2)$ and $Ti^{48}(0)$. They have also performed a triple scattering experiment in which completely polarized protons were scattered from Be^9 and then analyzed for polarization; but no change in the polarized beam was detected to within less than 10%. All these results, incidentally, justify the neglect of target spins in the usual optical model analysis.

More conclusive information is to be expected from the scattering of a polarized nucleon beam from oriented nuclei (Wagner *et al.*, 1965; Fisher *et al.*, 1966, 1967). First the total and differential cross sections, σ_t and $\sigma(\theta)$, of unpolarized neutrons from unoriented Ho^{165} were measured, and a number of sets of optical model parameters which fit these data were found. Since Ho^{165} is a highly deformed nucleus, the satisfactory analysis of all these data required coupled channel calculation with the $(7/2)^-$ and $(9/2)^-$ states

TABLE V
OPTICAL MODEL PARAMETERS

Authors	E_n (MeV)	U_0	W'	r_0	r_1	a	a_1	U_{so}	β_D [a]	V_{ss} (MeV)
Wagner et al. (1965)	0.350	45.18	3	1.25	1.25	0.65	0.47	7.5	0.3	$-0.460 < V_{ss} < 0.980$
Fisher et al. (1966, 1967)	7.85	45.28	6.32	1.25	1.25	0.65	0.47	0	0.3	$-0.340 < V_{ss} < 0.540$

[a] The parameter β_D is the deformation parameter.

coupled (Tamura, 1965). Then, the total cross sections of the polarized neutrons were measured against oriented Ho^{165}, once with parallel spin orientation $\sigma_t^{\uparrow\uparrow}$, and once with antiparallel spin orientation $\sigma_t^{\uparrow\downarrow}$. The difference between σ_t and the mean value of $\sigma_t^{\uparrow\uparrow}$ and $\sigma_t^{\uparrow\downarrow}$, which is called the "deformation effect" $\Delta\sigma_{def}$, is calculated, and a set of parameters among the previously obtained sets is selected which gives good agreement with the experimental value of $\Delta\sigma_{def}$ as well as σ_t and $\sigma(\theta)$. The parameters thus determined are given in Table V. The difference $\Delta\sigma_{pol} = \sigma_t^{\uparrow\uparrow} - \sigma_t^{\uparrow\downarrow}$ is computed next with the spin-spin interaction in the form of Eq. (9) with the same WS shape factor as the real central potential, and the strength V_{ss} determined to yield agreement with the experimental value of $\Delta\sigma_{pol}$. The results are also shown in Table V, and indicate that the strength of the spin-spin interaction [Eq. (9)] is quite small, if present at all, compared to the isobaric spin dependence.

A crude microscopic model of the spin-spin interaction has been presented by Fisher *et al.* (1966, 1967) by assuming Ho^{165} to be a single proton bound in a Nilsson orbit about a spinless core, and by assuming, also, the same spin dependent interaction between the incident neutron and the extra-core proton as for the free nucleon–nucleon force. The crude estimate for V_{ss} thus obtained was $\sim +60$ keV, which agrees with the small value found above.

6.2 Scattering of Nucleons at High Energies

Early phenomenological analyses with the optical model at energies above 100 MeV or so were carried out in most cases with semiclassical approximations, and the data used were restricted to small angles or, for neutrons, total and reaction cross sections only. These analyses have been summarized by Hodgson (1963b). In this energy region, no complete and systematic least square analysis of the data has yet been carried out, and therefore, the optical model parameters are known only roughly. At high energies where relativistic equations are required, if $\lambda\, dV/dr \ll V$, then the Dirac equation reduces to the Klein–Gordon equation. Further, if we assume $V/E_{rel} \ll 1$, where E_{rel} is the relativistic total energy including the rest mass, the Klein–Gordan equation can be brought to the same form as the Schroedinger equation with the wave number k given by $k = [(E_{rel}^2 - m^2 c^4)/\hbar^2 c^2]^{1/2}$ and $\hbar^2 c^2/2E_{rel}$ in place of $\hbar^2/2m$ in the Schroedinger equation. Thus, for the discussion of this section, we assume the Schroedinger type equation with the above understanding. Between a few hundred MeV and a few GeV, perhaps, it would probably be more accurate to use the Klein–Gordan equation for spinless particles and the Dirac equation for spin $\frac{1}{2}$ particles. Using the high energy approximation presented in Section 4.3, the differential, reaction, and total cross sections are given by

$$\sigma(\theta) = |f(\theta)|^2, \qquad f(\theta) = \frac{k}{i} \int_0^\infty b J_0 \left[2kb \sin\left(\frac{\theta}{2}\right) \right] [\eta(b) - 1] \, db \qquad (1)$$

$$\sigma_r = 2\pi \int_0^\infty b[1 - |\eta(b)|^2] \, db = 2\pi \int_0^\infty b\{1 - (\exp[-2\chi_{\mathrm{I}}(b)])^2\} \, db \qquad (2)$$

$$\sigma_t = 4\pi \int_0^\infty b[1 - \mathrm{Re}\,\eta(b)] \, db = 4\pi \int_0^\infty b\{1 - \exp[-2\chi_{\mathrm{I}}(b)] \cos 2\chi_{\mathrm{R}}(b)\} \, db$$
$$(3)$$

where

$$\eta(b) = \exp[-2\chi_{\mathrm{I}}(b)] \exp[2i\chi_{\mathrm{R}}(b)] \qquad (4)$$

is the ratio of the outgoing spherical wave to the ingoing spherical wave with the "classical" impact parameter b, which is related to the orbital angular momentum l by $b = \lambdabar(l + \frac{1}{2})$. From Eq. (17), Section 4.3, the quantities $\chi_{\mathrm{I}}(b)$ and $\chi_{\mathrm{R}}(b)$ are given in terms of the optical model potential $V(r) = U(r) + iW(r)$ by

$$\chi_{\mathrm{I}}(b) = -\frac{1}{2\hbar v} \int_{-\infty}^\infty W[(b^2 + z^2)^{1/2}] \, dz,$$

$$\chi_{\mathrm{R}}(b) = -\frac{1}{2\hbar v} \int_{-\infty}^\infty U[(b^2 + z^2)^{1/2}] \, dz. \qquad (5)$$

For the sake of simplicity, the spin orbit term has been neglected in the above expressions. Equations (1)–(5) tell us that, at high enough energies, σ_r is determined by $W(r)$ alone and is independent of $U(r)$, i.e., $W(r)$ can be well determined from σ_r^{expt} alone, quite independently of $U(r)$, while σ_t depends upon both $W(r)$ and $U(r)$ and its dependence on $U(r)$ is oscillatory. This dependence of σ_r and σ_t on $U(r)$ and $W(r)$ is approximately true even at neutron energies as low as 96 MeV, as has been shown by Hodgson (1960a) in an exact calculation.

As will be explained in Chapter VII, a more fundamental approach yields, in the high energy limit, the relation between the imaginary potential and the effective nucleon–nucleon total cross section $\bar{\sigma}(r)$ inside the nucleus

$$\tfrac{1}{2}\rho(r)A\bar{\sigma}(r) = \frac{W(r)}{\hbar v}, \qquad (6)$$

where $\rho(r)$ is the nuclear density distribution determined by the Stanford high energy electron scattering experiments. In the phenomenological analyses, Eq. (6) is often utilized in order to find $W(r)$ from $\bar{\sigma}$, or vice versa.

The experimental situation is shown in Figs. 1 and 2. As can be seen from Fig. 1, the reaction cross sections σ_r^{expt} are fairly independent of energy. The free nucleon–nucleon total cross section $\bar{\sigma}_{free}$ as plotted in Fig. 2 also shows only a weak dependence on energy. Thus, from either Eq. (2) or (6), we can see that W should increase in approximate proportion to v. Equation (6), for example, can give the radius of the imaginary potential once $\bar{\sigma}(r)$ is assumed to be the same as $\bar{\sigma}_{free}$.

After determining $W(r)$ in this way, the real potential $U(r)$ can be chosen to give the correct total cross section σ_t^{expt}. From Fig. 1 we see that σ_t^{expt} varies considerably with energy, a feature which can be reproduced mainly by adjusting $U(r)$.

Elton (1961) has analyzed the neutron total and reaction cross sections at energies between 0.3 to 5 GeV for C, Al, Cu, and Pb and obtained the fit to σ_r^{expt} and σ_t^{expt} given by the solid curves in Fig. 1. He finds that the radius of the neutron density distribution for light and medium nuclei is almost the same as for heavy nuclei, larger by 0.1 to 0.2 F than the radius of the charge distribution.

A similar analysis has also been carried out by Batty (1961) for protons scattered by carbon at energies from 95 to 1000 MeV, and for neutrons scattered by carbon at 155 MeV. Best fits were sought, not only to the total and reaction cross sections, but also to the differential cross sections and polarizations at small angles whenever they were available. The potential shape used was a modified Gaussian

$$\xi(r) = [1 + f\tfrac{4}{3}(r/R)^2] \exp[-(r/R)^2] \qquad (7)$$

with $f = 1$. The "best fit" parameters and the experimental and predicted total and reaction cross sections are given in Tables 2 and 3 of Batty (1961). The effective nucleon–nucleon total cross section $\bar{\sigma}(0)$ obtained from Eq. (6) is shown in Fig. 2. The quantity $\bar{\sigma}(0)$ thus obtained is almost identical with $\bar{\sigma}_{free}$ for $E \gtrsim 300$ MeV, but it is considerably lower than that for lower energies, due probably to the effects of the Pauli exclusion principle, multiple scattering, and scattering off the energy shell. The ratio of the radius parameter R to the electron scattering radius $R = 1.635$ F is plotted in Fig. 3. We emphasize that these potential parameters are valid for small angles only and are not to be trusted for scattering beyond the first diffraction minimum. Particularly, the values around 180 MeV should be replaced by more recent results which will be discussed shortly.

For protons at 725 MeV, an analysis similar to Batty's has been reported recently by McManigal *et al.* (1965) for seven nuclei from He to Ta.

A more fundamental approach has also been attempted in which the optical model potential is constructed from the nucleon–nucleon scattering amplitude, as will be explained in Chapter VII. However, there is some

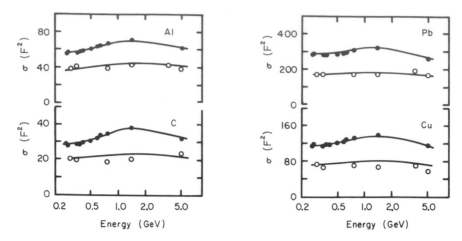

Fig. 1. Total cross sections (solid circles) and reaction cross sections (open circles) for the scattering of neutrons from C, Al, Cu, and Pb. The curves are theoretical fits (Elton, 1961).

uncertainty in the nucleon–nucleon scattering amplitude, particularly in the off the energy shell components, which are scarcely known at all. Besides the high energy treatment is only approximate, after all. In addition, the optical model parameters in this high energy region are not yet well determined, as we have just seen. At the present stage, therefore, it is not possible to say much more than that the phenomenological optical model potentials, obtained from the analysis of small angle scattering at high energies, are consistent with theoretical expectations.

We emphasize that, in any case, the theory is expected to be valid for small angle scattering only, and that there is thus no guarantee that optical model fits over extended angular regions will be simply related to nucleon–nucleon scattering. On the other hand, by the choice of a particular shape factor for the optical model potential, the results of the analyses may be biased against the high energy treatment. These points have remained academic until recently, since no measurements were available at large enough angles to test them. However, the recent Uppsala measurements and analyses of proton scattering at 180 MeV out to angles of the order of 60°–70° (Johansson et al., 1960, 1961) have brought out these points quite clearly. The most striking features of the data at this energy are the lack of oscillatory structure in the differential cross sections, and the strong and rapidly oscillating polarizations. Johansson et al. found that the large angle data cannot be fit very well using optical model potentials calculated from nucleon–nucleon scattering amplitudes, since the predicted cross sections oscillate too strongly at large angles. These authors then carried out a purely phenomenological analysis with a WS potential and

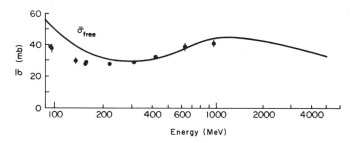

Fig. 2. Mean nucleon–nucleon scattering cross section $\bar{\sigma}$ in the nucleus. The curve was obtained from values for free nucleons (Batty, 1961).

found that the above features can be reproduced only by making r_1 greater than r_0 by a certain amount. The resulting parameters are given in Table I and

TABLE I

OPTICAL MODEL PARAMETERS GIVING THE BEST FIT TO THE EXPERIMENTAL RESULTS[a]

Nucleus	E_{lab}	U_0	r_0	W	r_1	U_{so}	W_{so}	a	σ_r^{theor}	σ_r^{expt}
Lithium	182.7	16	1.00	10	1.55	2.5	−1	0.4	153	149.0 ± 3.0
Beryllium	182.7	16	1.00	10	1.48	2.5	−1	0.5	186	185.5 ± 4.5
Carbon	183.0	16	1.00	10	1.34	2.5	−1	0.5	183	212.3 ± 4.8
Aluminum	183.0	20	1.15	8	1.50	2.5	−1	0.55	393	390 ± 10
Calcium	181.5	16	1.18	8	1.51	2.5	−1	0.55	544	524 ± 14
Iron	182.4	16	1.15	10	1.43	2.5	−1	0.55	711	662 ± 19
Indium	181.8	16	1.20	10	1.39	2.5	−1	0.63	1183	1165 ± 34
Gold	181.5	16	1.15	10	1.38	2.5	−1	0.55	1660	1660 ± 50

[a] Johansson *et al.* (1961).

some typical results are shown in Figs. 4a and 4b for Al. Also shown are the predicted results for optical potentials calculated from the nucleon–nucleon scattering amplitude. These fit the small angle data, as they should, but not

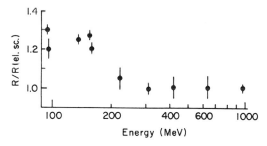

Fig. 3. Ratio of radius to electron scattering value ($R = 1.635$ F) (Batty, 1961).

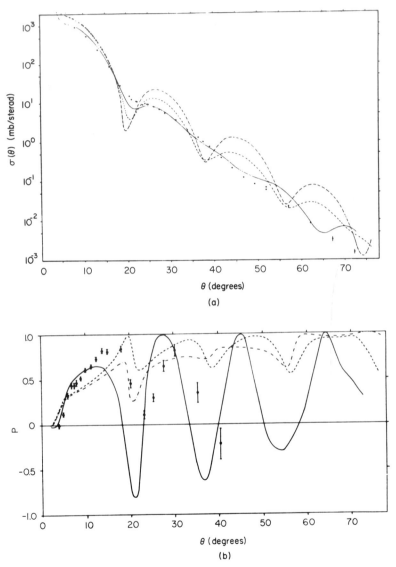

Fig. 4. (a) Differential cross sections for elastic scattering of protons from Al at 180 MeV (Johansson *et al.*, 1961). (b) Polarization of protons elastically scattered from Al at 180 MeV (Johansson *et al.*, 1961).

(Solid curves represent best fit, short dashed curves represent calculated parameters for volume absorption, and long dashed curves represent calculated parameters for surface absorption. The solid dots in (b) are experimental results at 175 MeV (Hillman *et al.*, 1958).)

the large. Satchler and Haybron (1964) reanalyzed the same data and obtained much improved fits to the differential cross sections by using an automatic search program. It was found that for light elements, either a surface or a volume shape absorption can be used to fit the data equally well, but the latter is definitely preferred for heavier elements. For light elements, r_1 is nearly the same as r_0 with a surface absorption, but with a volume absorption r_1 is considerably extended beyond r_0.

With these best fit parameters, however, the reaction cross sections are found to be too large, except for the heaviest elements. Similar difficulty has been encountered in the analyses of Rolland *et al.* (1966) and of Roos and Wall (1965) at nearby high energies.

The fundamental approach certainly needs a lot of improvement as evidenced from the misfits shown by the dotted curves of Figs. 4a and 4b. However, it is expected to be correct at least at small angles, and in particular, Eq. (6) should be approximately correct at high enough energies. Now it seems quite hopeless to reconcile the prediction of this semiclassical relation with the much extended radius of the volume absorptive potential observed in the phenomenological analyses. Elton (1966) has repeated his calculation at 180 MeV and found that the reaction cross sections for all the nuclei investigated above could be reproduced using Eq. (6) with a volume absorption whose radius extends beyond that of the corresponding matter distribution by 0.30 ± 0.05 F, but certainly not by as much as $\simeq 1$ F, as is required by the optical model analyses.

Using semiclassical arguments, Elton then offers a very clear-cut explanation of this dilemma and a remedy for the difficulty of the reaction cross section mentioned above, as subsequently verified by actual numerical calculations.

Particularizing to the scattering of protons by Fe at 180 MeV, Elton (1966) studied the behavior of the real and imaginary parts of η_l given by Eqs. (4) and (5). Previously, Venter and Frahn (1964) had done a direct phase analysis fitting all the data including the reaction cross section beautifully. Their results for Re $\bar{\eta}_l$ and Im $\bar{\eta}_l$, without Coulomb effects, are plotted in Fig. 5 (dashed curves). The bar over a quantity indicates an average over spin directions. Explicitly,

$$\mathrm{Re}\ \bar{\eta}_l = \exp(-2\chi_\mathrm{I}) \cos 2\chi_\mathrm{R}, \qquad \mathrm{Im}\ \bar{\eta}_l = \exp(-2\chi_\mathrm{I}) \sin 2\chi_\mathrm{R} \qquad (8)$$

where χ_I and χ_R are given by Eq. (4). The most notable features are the "hump" in Im $\bar{\eta}_l$ which occurs in the nuclear surface, and the appreciable amount of Re $\bar{\eta}_l$ for small l. Also, notice that the position of the hump in Im $\bar{\eta}_l$ and the half-way "radius" of Re $\bar{\eta}_l$ occur at nearly the same l value.

It is obvious from Eq. (4) that if both $U(r)$ and $W(r)$ are of a volume form as has been the case in the optical model analyses, then both χ_I and χ_R are approximately constant for small l and decrease to zero in the surface. Then it is seen from Eq. (8) that the radial extent of Re $\bar{\eta}_l$ and Im $\bar{\eta}_l$ is governed mainly by that of χ_I and χ_R, respectively. Thus, with the extended imaginary radius, Re $\bar{\eta}_l$ is expected to extend much beyond Im $\bar{\eta}_l$. This has been confirmed by Elton who calculated these quantities as shown in Fig. 5 (solid

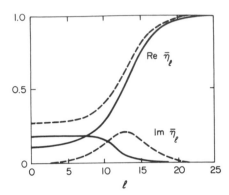

Fig. 5. Comparison of the phases obtained by the optical model potentials of WS shape factors (full curves) with those obtained by the direct phase analysis (dashed curves) for protons scattered by Fe[56] at 180 MeV (Elton, 1966).

curves) using the best fit parameters of Satchler and Haybron. We see that they are quite different from the result of direct phase analysis. To make Im $\bar{\eta}_l$ small for small l as required by the direct phase analysis, we can make either the nuclear media strongly absorptive, or χ_R small, for small l. However, if $W(r)$ is of a volume shape and is large, then χ_I becomes large and hence Re $\bar{\eta}_l$ is small for small l. Since this latter quantity is required to be quite large near $l = 0$, the only alternative is to make χ_I small there. In order to produce the hump in Im $\bar{\eta}_l$ however, χ_I must also be large for large l. Thus, the only possible way to satisfy these two requirements is to choose $U(r)$ repulsive or near zero for small r and strongly attractive near the surface. Without going into details, we give the optical model potential found by Elton in Fig. 6, and the fits to the differential cross section and polarization in Figs. 7 and 8. The predicted reaction cross section is 651 mb as against the experimental value of 662 ± 19 mb. Needless to say this potential is not likely to be unique, and there must be many other similar ones which can fit all the data equally well. However, the qualitative feature presented here is very likely correct.

As for a possible reason for the rather unusual repulsion near the center of the nucleus, Elton speculates on the possibility of relating this to the contribution from off the energy shell two-body amplitudes. Studies of this problem as well as studies of the possible effects of the unusual shape of $U(r)$ on the distorted wave calculation would seem to be very interesting, although they may have to wait until more detailed optical model analyses, with the same characteristic features described here, become available.

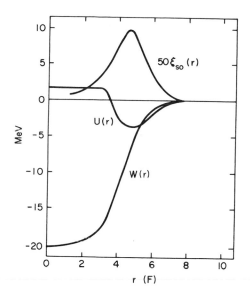

Fig. 6. Optical model potential for 180 MeV protons scattered by Fe[56]. The spin orbit strengths for best fit are $U_{so} = 1.87$ MeV and $W_{so} = 0.98$ MeV (Elton, 1966).

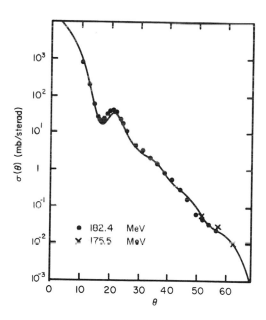

Fig. 7. Differential cross sections for 180 MeV protons scattered by Fe[56] (Elton, 1966).

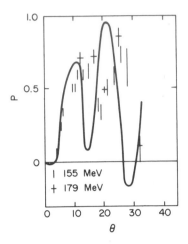

Fig. 8. Polarization for 150–180 MeV protons scattered by Fe^{56} (Elton, 1966).

6.3   The Scattering of Nucleons by Light Elements

In contrast to the situation for intermediate and heavy elements, where the optical model parameters are substantially the same for all elements and where the data can be fit down to quite low energies (provided compound elastic corrections are taken into account), each light element appears to behave differently, and below some minimum energy, the data cannot be fit at all, at least for some of these elements. Both difficulties are easy to understand; they stem from the relative sparsity of low lying states in light nuclei. At low enough energies one or two states dominate, and one can hardly expect the optical model to be applicable. As the energy increases, the number of states participating becomes larger, but the average properties show considerable fluctuation from element to element. At sufficiently high energies, these fluctuations disappear and the light elements should settle down into the normal behavior characteristic of the intermediate and heavy elements. Indeed, such appears to be the case. Not enough work has been done to map out the boundaries of the various domains of energy and mass number with any great precision. It appears that the minimum energy, below which optical model fits cannot be obtained, is of the order of 10–12 MeV, while matters settle down at energies above perhaps 30 MeV. As far as mass number is concerned, it appears that magnesium is in the boundary region. As we shall see, below about 10 MeV it cannot be fit at all; above that energy its optical model parameters are at least roughly similar to those for the heavier elements, although with some striking deviations.

6.3a   The Scattering from Carbon

The first detailed and quantitatively successful analysis of the scattering by light elements at intermediate energies was that carried out by Nodvik *et al.* (1962) for scattering of protons from carbon at energies between 7 and 19.4 MeV (measured at Tokyo and Princeton at about 40 different energies). The data exhibited significant variations over energy intervals as small as 100–200 keV, and thus, it was not expected that the optical model would work at all. For energies below 12 MeV, this expectation was borne out, and it was found that the model could not account satisfactorily for the data. Above that energy, however, they were able to obtain excellent fits to the experimental differential cross sections over the entire angular range.

The most striking feature of the result was the thin absorptive shell and small volume absorption which characterized the potential. Below 17.8 MeV, the optimum fits corresponded to zero volume absorption and $b = 0.25$ F. Above that energy, the optimum fits were characterized by a broadening of the absorptive part of the potential through an increase of W', or an increase in b, or both.[1] The optimum radius parameter was found to be somewhat energy dependent; but, taking into account the reaction cross sections, the value $R_0 = 1.25$ F represents a good overall value. The value of a was also found to be energy dependent, but generally was in the neighborhood of 0.4 F. The predicted reaction cross sections appear too low when compared with the more recent experimental data by Makino *et al.* (1964).

Rosen *et al.* (1962), on the other hand, have analyzed differential cross sections and polarizations in the energy range 5.4–19.7 MeV with emphasis on the fits to the polarization data. These authors found a reasonable agreement between prediction and data over the entire energy range except around 10 MeV and around 20 MeV, where the model failed to work at all.

At higher energies, between 20 to 30 MeV, the situation becomes worse. No complete analysis has yet been published in this energy region, but it has been reported by Dickens *et al.* (1962, 1963) that, although the optical model works quite well at each energy and excellent fits can be obtained, the required variations of parameters from energy to energy are so irregular and violent that, to quote the authors, "it violates the spirit of the model." The parameters obtained by Dickens (1962) are plotted in Fig. 1 (Scott *et al.*, 1967) together with those by Nodvik *et al.* (1962).

Tamura and Terasawa (1964) have proposed a model using the sum of an amplitude derived from an *energy independent* optical potential and resonant amplitudes of Breit–Wigner form. They succeeded in reproducing the rapid

---

[1] To reduce the number of free parameters, the relationship $a_1 = 0.69b$ was introduced by these authors, which makes both volume and Gaussian surface absorptions drop to one-tenth of the maximum value at the same point.

variations of cross sections using three compound nuclear levels of N^{13}. A similar model has been used by Lowe and Watson (1966, 1967) to reanalyze the same data, together with the recent polarizations measured by Craig *et al.* (1966a), using three compound nuclear levels of N^{13} of spin parity assignments partly different from Tamura's. Their energy independent optical model parameters are also shown in Fig. 1, and the level assignments are given in Table I. Neither of these models yield reaction cross sections which

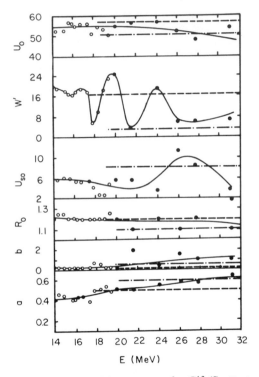

Fig. 1. Collected optical model parameters for C^{12} (Scott *et al.*, 1967).
[Dashed lines are the energy independent parameters of Tamura and Terasawa (1964), and dot dashed lines are the energy independent parameters of Lowe and Watson (1966). Solid curves indicate the trend of the optical parameters obtained by Nodvik *et al.* (1962) (open circles) and by Dickens *et al.* (1963) (solid circles).]

agree very well with experiment. The presence of three simple compound states in N^{13} at such a high level of excitation has also been indicated by Scott *et al.* (1967) in their study of inelastic scattering, $C^{12}(p, p')C^{12*}$ (15.11 MeV, 1^+, $T = 1$) at energies between 20.5 and 30.25 MeV. Their prediction for the "doorway" states is also given in Table I.

At still higher energies, resonance effects are expected to be less important

TABLE I

N^{13} RESONANCE PREDICTIONS

Authors	$E_{\text{C.M.}}$ (MeV)	$\Gamma_{\text{C.M.}}$ (MeV)	(l, j)		Description
Tamura and	19.75	2.49	$d_{3/2}$		$C^{12}(p, p)$
Terasawa			(dominant)		
(1964)	20.05	1.46	$d_{5/2}$		
	24.93	2.17	$p_{3/2}$		
			(a)	(b)	
Lowe and	19.0	1.5	$g_{9/2}$	$d_{5/2}$	$C^{12}(p, p)$
Watson			(dominant)		
(1966, 1967)	20.8	1.0	$h_{9/2}$	$f_{5/2}$	
	$\simeq 22.2$	$\lesssim 0.5$	$f_{7/2}$	$f_{7/2}$	
Scott *et al.*	20.9	—	$d_{5/2}$		$C^{12}(p, p')C^{12*}$
(1967)	22.5	—	$f_{5/2}$		(15.11 MeV)
	25.5	—	$p_{3/2}$		

and we might hope to obtain smoother variations of the optical model parameters. However, even at 50 MeV, the situation does not appear to be particularly simple. A number of analyses have been reported at energies near 30, 40, and 50 MeV (Dickens *et al.*, 1963; Ridley and Turner, 1964; Blumberg *et al.*, 1966; Barrett *et al.*, 1965; Fricke and Satchler, 1965; Craig *et al.*, 1966b; Fannon *et al.*, 1967). Fannon *et al.* analyzed both differential cross section and polarization data over a wide angular range. Pure surface absorption gives the best fit at 30 MeV, but at 40 and 50 MeV pure volume absorption is preferred.

The results of Fannon *et al.* (1967) and Fricke *et al.* (1967) indicate that either a_{so} or a_1 must assume an extremely small value in order to reproduce the observed negative values of polarizations at angles greater than $\sim 140°$. With usual values for both a_{so} and a_1, the large angle polarizations are given very poorly.

6.3b The Scattering from Oxygen

A very extensive optical model analysis of proton elastic scattering from O^{16} was performed by Duke (1963) in the energy range between 8.66 and 19.2 MeV using the same technique of analysis as employed by Nodvik *et al.* (1962) for C^{12}. The experimental differential cross sections (Daehnick, 1964) upon which his analysis was based, exhibited considerable variations over energy intervals of 200–500 keV width, and required a drastic variation of parameters with energy, much worse than for the case of C^{12}. The optimum radius parameter ranged from 1.20 to 1.30 F, but compromise fits, which were only slightly inferior to the excellent optimum fits, were found with $r_0 = 1.25$ F over the entire energy region. With this radius parameter, the imaginary potential of a pure surface form was preferred for all energies except in a narrow interval around 15 MeV where a volume absorption was preferred. On the other hand, by sacrificing fits at large angles, Hardie et al. (1963) have succeeded in obtaining excellent fits at forward angles ($\theta \lesssim 120°$) for all data between 8.5 and 13.6 MeV (except at 8.993 MeV) with little variation of parameters.

At higher energies, between 21 and 53 MeV, a complete set of measurements, including polarizations and reaction cross sections, has been obtained (with good accuracy) at UCLA (Cameron et al., 1967) and LRL (Boschitz, 1966; Boschitz et al., 1966). Both polarizations and differential cross sections above 30 MeV varied monotonically with energy, but below 30 MeV they exhibited nonmonotonic variation. Boschitz (1966) found that for energies greater than 30 MeV good fits were obtained using $r_{so} < r_0$, with most of the geometry parameters held constant, and with the dynamical parameters U_0, W', and U_{so} decreasing monotonically with energy and W increasing monotonically with energy. At $E = 25.0$ and 23.4 MeV, reasonable fits were still possible, but the parameters were no longer consistent with the trends at higher energies. At $E = 21$ MeV, the polarization could not be reproduced at all with reasonable parameters.

Analyses of differential cross sections alone have also been reported by Kim et al. (1964) and Barrett et al. (1965) at around 30 MeV, and by Fannon et al. (1967) at 50 MeV. The fits obtained by these authors suffered some difficulty at backward angles $\theta \gtrsim 110°$.

6.3c   Scattering from Other Light Nuclei

Bauer et al. (1967), Lutz et al. (1963), and Johansson (1965) have analyzed neutrons elastically scattered from N^{14} in the energy region between 4.5 and 14.0 MeV. Johansson (1965) found that the data could not be fit below 4.5 MeV, and below 7 MeV the Hauser–Feshbach formalism was needed to account for the compound elastic contribution. The behavior of parameters as a function of energy was erratic below 8 MeV, which might be associated with the resonances seen in the total cross sections near 7 MeV. Above 8 MeV, however, Bauer et al. (1967) found that differential cross sections could be fit by holding the geometrical parameters to the values $r_0 = 1.2$, $a = 0.65$, and $a_1 = 0.47$ with a relatively small variation of U_0 and W'. Although the fits to the data obtained by these authors need some improvement at backward angles, and the compound elastic correction at lower energies by the Hauser–Feshbach formalism makes it difficult to draw definite conclusions, we may say that the thin absorptive shell required for protons scattered from C^{12} and

O^{16} appears not to be needed for neutrons scattered from N^{14}, and that the parameters are fairly close to the values found for intermediate and heavy elements, at least for $E_n \gtrsim 8$ MeV and higher.

As a second example, we look at the results of Melkanoff and Nodvik (1962) on the scattering of protons from magnesium. Like carbon, magnesium also exhibits rapid energy variation below 18 or 20 MeV, and similarly, cannot be fit below about 10.5 MeV. In Table II, for the fixed grid parameters

TABLE II
SCATTERING OF PROTONS BY Mg AT VARIOUS ENERGIES[a]

E	U_0	W'	a	U_{so}	σ_r (mb)
15.85	46	6	0.54	10	765
15.33	47	5.5	0.41	11	675
14.87	46	5	0.44	10	678
14.45	42	6	0.69	6	827
14.06	46	4	0.50	5	681
13.59	47	4	0.47	4	672
13.15	48	4	0.55	4	712
12.62	47	4	0.48	4	672
12.1	49	5	0.61	6	751
11.62	46	5	0.71	3	883
11.15	46	2.6	0.22	4	493
10.64	46	3	0.53	4	706

[a] The parameters in the table give the optimum fit for the fixed grid parameters $r_0 = 1.25$ F, $b = 1.25$ F, and $W = 2$ MeV. The value of a is in F, the values of E, U_0, W', and U_{so} are in MeV. The relation $a_1 = 0.69b$ is used (Melkanoff and Nodvik, 1962).

$r_0 = 1.25$ F, $b = 1.25$ F, and $W = 2$ MeV, the optimum fit values of the remaining parameters and the reaction cross section are presented as a function of energy. These results are quite striking. Above about 12 MeV, the behavior is quite regular and similar to that for heavier elements, except in the neighborhood of 14.45 MeV where suddenly U_0 decreases and a and σ_R increase. Below about 12.5 MeV, the behavior is rather erratic, particularly the changes in a and σ_R over the interval 11.62–11.15 MeV. The likely influence of good reaction cross section data is apparent, but unfortunately, no data were available at the time of their analysis. It should be mentioned that no polarization data were available either, so that these results were obtained by fitting differential cross sections alone.

Of course, the data can also be fit with other values of the grid parameters; r_0 can vary between 1.2 and 1.3 F with the best value somewhat energy dependent, as for carbon. As far as b is concerned, values as small as those for carbon are ruled out; the range of acceptable values is between perhaps 0.75 or 1.0 F and 1.5 or 1.75 F. The values of W likely lie between zero and perhaps 8 MeV. For example the results for the grid point $r_0 = 1.25$, $b = 1.25$ F, and $W = 6$ MeV also indicate peculiar behavior at 14.45 and 11.15 MeV, so apparently this behavior is not an accidental consequence of the particular grid point being examined.

We next mention the analysis by Rosen *et al.* (1965) of their polarization data for protons scattered from light elements. It is surprising to see that reasonable agreement with the data can be obtained by using Set (II.2a) of Table II, Section 6.1, at 14.5 MeV for elements as light as H^3, He^3, He^4, Li^6, Li^7, and Be^9. The polarization data for Mg at 17.3 MeV are also well reproduced by Set (II.2a) of said Table II. At 8.5 MeV, they also obtain reasonable fits to the polarizations for elements ranging from He^4 to Ag, using slightly different average parameters.

Some work has been reported on neutrons scattered from Li^6 and Li^7 by Batcheler and Towle (1963), who found that the differential cross sections between 1.5 and 7.5 MeV can be reasonably well described by the Perey–Buck nonlocal potentials (Perey and Buck, 1962). On the other hand, the work by Lutz *et al.* (1963) for 14 MeV neutrons on various light elements indicates need for a violent change in parameters from element to element to obtain precise fits to the differential cross sections.

It appears that, for light elements, violent fluctuations of the parameters are inevitable if we require precise fits to the data over the entire angular range.

At sufficiently high energies, these fluctuations disappear and light elements behave quite the same way as heavy elements, as has been shown, for example, by Hodgson for neutrons scattered from Li and Be at 96 MeV (Hodgson, 1960a), and also, as has been discussed in Section 6.2.

Finally, for elements as heavy as Al, optical model parameters begin to behave in a manner typical of heavy elements, as we have already seen in Section 6.1.

6.4   Scattering of Composite Particles

6.4a   General Remarks

Phenomenological optical model analyses of the elastic scattering of deuterons, H^3, He^3, and He^4 from complex nuclei are discussed in this section. The optical model was first applied for deuterons by Cindro *et al.* (1959), Melkanoff (1959), and Slaus and Alford (1959), for helium-3 and tritons by

Hodgson (1960b, 1961), for alphas by Igo and Thaler (1957) and Cheston and Glassgold (1957), and for heavier ions by Porter (1958). Despite the fact that the *a priori* validity of such a simple model is dubious, the optical model not only worked but worked very well for these composite particles. Since then a great deal of work has been done as more experimental data have become available, and the usefulness of the model has been well established. Extensive compilations of early optical model analyses of composite particles can be found, for example, in Hodgson's book (1963b) or in the report by Winner and Drisko (1965). These analyses have been carried out assuming these composite particles to be point particles, neglecting their internal structures, and hence neglecting the effect of polarization or virtual breakup during the collision with the target nucleus.

The effects of real breakup of the composite particles during the collision, and of inelastic scattering and pickup reactions, are included in the imaginary part of the optical model potentials in the usual manner, and thus the projectile appears to be strongly absorbed by the scattering medium, particularly at or near the nuclear surface. This feature greatly enhances ambiguities among the parameters.

Composite particles often excite strong collective oscillations of the target nucleus, and as a consequence elastic and inelastic channels are strongly coupled. Then, it is not really acceptable to describe elastic scattering alone by the simple optical model. This accounts for some of the violent variations of parameters from nucleus to nucleus seen in those compilations mentioned above. Aside from this type of variation, the vast ambiguities found so far can be grouped into two types.

The first type of ambiguity is the same as that encountered in the analysis of elastic scattering of nucleons; that is, the ambiguity which arises when a small change in the value of one parameter is compensated for by a small change in one or more of the other parameters. Also, a choice between the surface and volume shapes of absorption is more difficult to make here. Of course, this first type of ambiguity is much more pronounced in this case than it is for nucleons, and it is most noticeable if the data are restricted to forward angles, or if the angular distribution has little structure.

The second type of ambiguity is characteristic of strongly absorbed particles; it corresponds to the existence of a series of discrete values of the potential well depths which all give nearly the same scattering, provided that the other parameters are readjusted. The value of the real well depth U_0 is known to vary from ~ 30 MeV to even a few hundred MeV with intervals of ~ 30 to ~ 60 MeV. Except for a few exceptional cases, the common features of this sequence of acceptable potentials are first, that all the real potentials become negligible at nearly the same radius, and second, that the tails of the imaginary potentials are practically the same. Furthermore, the reaction cross sections are predicted to have nearly the same values despite the large differences in parameter values.

This discrete ambiguity in the potential strengths is well understood (Drisko *et al.*, 1963). First of all, all the potentials which belong to the series of discrete optimum potentials produce essentially the same reflection coefficients η_l. In other words, what is involved is not a phase shift ambiguity but rather "identical" phase shifts produced by different potentials. As discussed in Section 4.4, Austern (1961) showed that for strongly absorbed partial waves (i.e., for lower partial waves) the WKB approximation is justified, and correspondingly, that the reflection coefficient η_l for the *l*th partial wave can be expressed as the sum of two terms, one arising by reflection from the nuclear surface and the other by reflection from the centrifugal barrier in the nuclear interior. Drisko *et al.* (1963) focus attention on the latter term. If $V(r)$ is changed so that the phase function $p(r_0)$ which appears in Eq. (54), Section 4.4 is increased by π, this contribution to η_l is unchanged. While this can only be done exactly for one value of *l*, the η_l for neighboring partial waves are altered only slightly. It is found that the series of discrete optimum potentials are related in exactly this way, each changing just enough for $p(r_0)$ to increase by π for the lowest values of *l*. For partial waves around the "critical" $l = l_c$, for which $|\eta_l| \simeq 0.5$, this relation begins to break down, and reflection from the surface dominates for values of *l* larger than l_c. Thus there is a restriction on the potential in that the contributions from the surface region must remain approximately the same. If the well is either too shallow or too deep, it appears to be impossible to satisfy the $\Delta p(r_0) = \pi$ rule for all the low *l* partial waves, while at the same time leaving the reflection from the surface unaltered.

This conclusion is, in fact, verified by exact numerical calculations. The potentials in the series are such that each one has just one half-wavelength more of the radial wave function for $l < l_c$ than the preceding potential, as illustrated later in Fig. 2. Thus, we see that the optical model description of the scattering of composite particles depends quite sensitively on details of the interior of the potential, and that this dependence leads to discrete ambiguities in the parameters of the optical potentials. The importance of the $\Delta p(r_0) = \pi$ rule increases with increasing wavelength, because the magnitude of η_l for $l < l_c$ similarly increases with increasing wavelength.

These arguments apply most forcefully to the case of deuteron scattering. For much more strongly absorbed particles, such as α-particles, reflection off the nuclear surface is much more important. Igo (1958, 1959a,b, 1960) had proposed, in fact, that α-particle scattering should be dependent only on the surface of the optical potential, and hence that potentials which yield the same η_l for *l* around l_c should give the same scattering. However, Drisko *et al.* (1963) have pointed out that discrete ambiguities should persist, though to a lesser extent, even for such strongly absorbed particles as He^3, He^4, and still heavier ions. Indeed, this has turned out to be the case as we shall see later.

These discrete ambiguities in the potential strengths are very difficult to resolve by analyses of elastic scattering data alone. Backangle data are, perhaps, most important in discriminating one potential family from another. (For the case of nucleon scattering this type of discrete ambiguity is resolved by the requirement of continuity with the bound state potentials, known to be about 50 MeV.)

For deuterons, there is a strong indication that the inclusion of spin orbit interactions helps to resolve the discrete ambiguities, as is discussed later.

It has been suggested (Watanabe, 1958; Melkanoff, 1959; Rook, 1965) that the optical model potentials for composite particles are given to the first order by the sum of the potentials for each constituent nucleon averaged over the internal motion of the projectile. This model, however, involves approximations which are valid only at sufficiently high energies; and thus, although it can be useful at high energies to resolve the enormous ambiguities expected in the parameters (Sawada, 1965), at lower energies its utility is limited. For the case of deuterons, some idea of the higher order effects neglected in this naive picture has been obtained by Perey and Satchler (1967) by comparing the general behavior of the first order potential with the exact potential (see Fig. 4 and the related discussion). As for the imaginary part of the potential for lower energy deuterons, the naive model predicts much too weak an imaginary part, and it does not give enough absorption at large radii. The higher order corrections must make up this difference. This is rather to be expected since the loose structure of the deuteron permits diffraction breakup which is not included in the first order term. For a tightly bound particle like He^4, the validity of the first order potential is extremely doubtful, especially at lower energies.

Direct reaction calculations are expected to be sensitive to the discrete ambiguities since they depend upon interior wave functions; and thus, comparisons with experimental angular distributions can resolve ambiguities (Lee *et al.*, 1964, 1965; Hiebert *et al.*, 1967). By examining very low energy deuteron stripping where the Coulomb effects start to compete with the nuclear effects, de Shalit (1964) has found that real well depths of ~100 MeV for the deuteron are required in order to reproduce the angular distribution, and that anything else gives gross disagreement with experiment. Deuteron potentials of similar depths have also been reported to give most consistent results for angular distributions and for spectroscopic factors deduced from stripping and pickup reactions at intermediate energies (Lee *et al.*, 1964, 1965).

The more fundamental question which remains to be answered concerns the applicability of the optical model concept, itself. The derivation of a formal optical model is always possible, but it involves coupled integro-differential equations. The resulting potential is certainly nonlocal and *l* dependent. Thus, the success of the simple local optical model, treating the composite particle as a point particle and disregarding the polarization and virtual breakup, is indeed remarkable. Although the study of stripping or pickup reactions probably will lead to a definite preference for one or another potential in the discrete families, the question of the applicability of the simple optical model concept seems to us to be an open one. From the practical viewpoint of applications to direct reaction calculations, however, the determination of optical model parameters for composite particles is extremely useful. For the remainder of this section, we discuss briefly the characteristic features of these phenomenological potentials.

6.4b   The Scattering of Deuterons

There have been many extensive optical model analyses of deuterons elastically scattered from various nuclei in the energy region 3 to 30 MeV. It has been found that very good fits can be obtained at each energy for each target nucleus, but vast ambiguities exist in the values of the parameters. These can be classified into continuous and discrete types as has already been mentioned (Perey and Perey, 1963, 1964, 1966; Halbert, 1964; Bassel *et al.*, 1964). For each discrete family with surface shape absorption, there exists almost always a corresponding family with volume form absorption with nearly the same value of the real well depth. For all discrete families of potentials, nearly the same values of the reaction cross section are predicted. These features are clearly demonstrated in Table I, which is due to C. and F. Perey

TABLE I

OPTICAL MODEL POTENTIALS WHICH FIT THE 11.8 MeV DEUTERON DATA FOR COPPER[a]

Set	U_0	r_0	a	W'	W	r_I	a_I	σ_R	χ^2
1	36.8	1.070	0.987	10.07	—	1.444	0.739	1440	1.4
2	58.5	1.153	0.879	13.32	—	1.434	0.708	1476	0.65
3	90.7	1.172	0.822	18.34	—	1.410	0.661	1468	0.78
4	128.2	1.193	0.775	24.3	—	1.403	0.608	1460	0.84
5	167.8	1.232	0.716	31.9	—	1.394	0.560	1451	0.96
1′	36.8	1.043	1.006	—	4.57	2.048	0.443	1502	0.72
2′	61.6	1.122	0.891	—	6.95	1.891	0.549	1487	0.59
3′	95.5	1.147	0.808	—	9.57	1.789	0.596	1477	0.67
4′	136.9	1.160	0.753	—	12.38	1.719	0.612	1472	0.77

[a] From C. and F. Perey (1963).

(1963) for copper at 11.8 MeV. The reflection coefficient η_l and the moduli of $l = 0$ and $l = 6$ waves are shown in Figs. 1 and 2, respectively. The similarity of η_l and the increase of one half-wavelength for consecutive potentials are apparent. C. and F. Perey (1963) have also analyzed angular distributions for

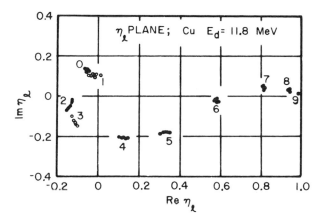

Fig. 1. Distribution of scattering matrix, η_l, from the optical model fits to the 11.8 MeV deuteron data for copper. The parameters are given by Table I. The number associated with each cluster of points indicates the l value (Perey ar. 1 Perey, 1963).

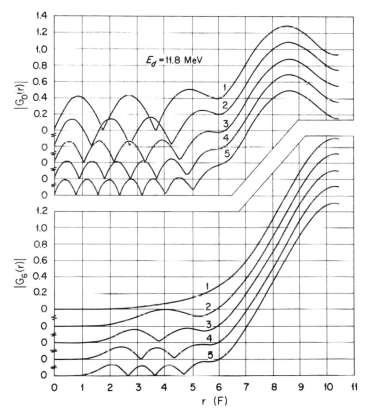

Fig. 2. Moduli of the $l = 0$ and $l = 6$ partial waves as a function of r for the pure surface absorption potential with parameters given by Table I (Perey and Perey, 1963).

target nuclei with $Z \geq 12$ and at energies from 11 to 26 MeV. Typical fits obtained without spin orbit interactions are shown in Fig. 3 for various elements at 11.8 MeV. For medium and heavy nuclei, these authors recommend four sets of average geometries as given in Table II. The dependence on A of the real well depths at 11.8 MeV is plotted in Fig. 4 for fixed geometrical

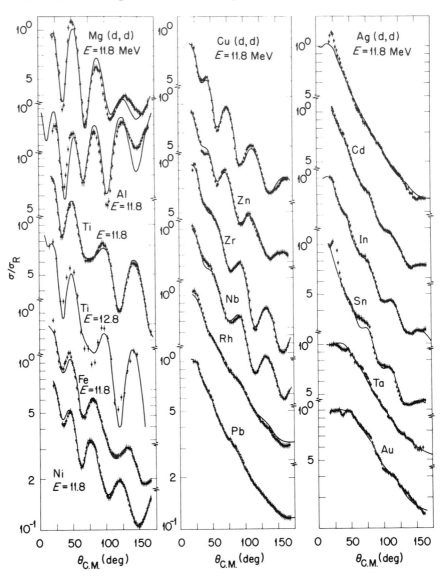

Fig. 3. Optimum fits to the deuteron data at 11.8 MeV (Perey and Perey, 1963).

TABLE II

Set	$r_0 = r_c$	a	r_1	a_1	V_0	K_1	K_2
A	1.15	0.87	1.37	0.70	42	3.3	0.51
B	1.15	0.81	1.34	0.68	81	2.0	0.22
C	1.30	0.79	1.37	0.67	37	2.4	0.51
D	1.30	0.73	1.34	0.65	75	1.14	0.42

[a] The coefficients V_0, K_1, and K_2 are defined by the empirical formula $U_0 - V_0 + K_1 Z/A^{1/3} - K_2 E$.

[b] C. and F. Perey (1963).

sets B and C (Perey and Satchler, 1967). These well depths also include results for targets not included in C. and F. Perey (1963). The solid curve shown for the set B results is simply the curve drawn through the set C results increased uniformly by 46 MeV. It seems that the systematic variation does

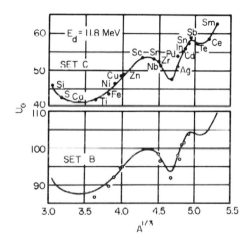

Fig. 4. Depths of real potentials of WS shape factor for 11.8 MeV deuterons with fixed geometrical parameters from sets B and C of Table II (Perey and Satchler, 1967).

not depend upon the choice of geometry. The variation with mass number seen here bears no resemblance to the variation seen for nucleon optical potentials, and may be attributed to the influence of factors such as shell structure upon the higher order corrections to the first order deuteron potential discussed before. Later, Dickens and Perey (1965) found that the deuteron parameters are particularly sensitive to the absolute magnitude of the experimental data, especially when the data do not show any marked oscillations.

The results discussed thus far were all obtained without including spin orbit interactions. These results show, in some cases, difficulties at backangles, i.e., the 11.8 MeV fits for Mg and Al (as can be seen from Fig. 3). Also large discrepancies at large angles occur for Mg and Ca at 21.6 MeV (C. and F. Perey, 1963), and for Ni and Zn at 26 MeV (Tjin A Djie and Brockman, 1965). Raynal (1963) has obtained an excellent fit to the 21.6 MeV Ca^{40} data over the entire angular range by including a vector spin orbit potential of the Thomas type, at the same time reproducing the measured vector and tensor polarizations quite well. He found that a real well depth U_0 of ~ 100 MeV was required. Subsequently, C. and F. Perey (1966) repeated their analysis and found that the inclusion of a spin orbit term greatly improves fits to the data, that otherwise equivalent discrete ambiguities are no longer equivalent, and that the deuteron potential with real well depth close to the sum of that of the neutron and proton optical model potentials gives consistently satisfactory results. This confirms the finding of Raynal (1963).

At $E_d = 34.4$ MeV, Newman *et al.* (1967) have obtained the following average deuteron optical parameters from the analysis of scattering by various elements ranging from C^{12} to Nb^{93},

$$U_0 = 90.2 + 0.89Z/A^{1/3}, \quad r_0 = 0.968 + 0.029A^{1/3}, \quad a = 0.814, \quad U_{so} = 7.0$$

$$W' = 4.33 + 2.20A^{1/3}, \quad r_1 = 1.09 + 0.80A^{-1/3}, \quad a_1 = 0.554 + 0.059A^{1/3}.$$

The deuteron optical model for light elements suffers from difficulties similar to those encountered for the case of nucleons. Good fits can be obtained for each individual angular distribution, but the parameters fluctuate violently (Satchler, 1966).

The influence of the electric polarizability and of Coulomb breakup should be emphasized for deuterons with energy near or below the Coulomb barrier. Dickens and Perey (1965) investigated the effect of electric polarizability on the optical model parameters by adding a dipole term to the best fit optical potential in the Schroedinger equation. They found the effect to be small although not negligible, U_0 being reduced slightly and W' being increased slightly in order to restore the fits. This conclusion is contrary to that of Clement (1963) who found a large effect, but is in agreement with the conclusions of other investigators (French and Goldberger, 1952; Malenka *et al.*, 1953; Sawicki, 1954; Nishida, 1957, 1958). So far there has been no effort to estimate the influence of electric breakup in the low energy deuteron optical model parameters. Probably a long tailed weak imaginary potential would simulate the effects, but its strength and range require theoretical justification in view of the expected ambiguities in the resulting values of the parameters.

At sufficiently high energies, there have been numerous attempts to account for deuteron scattering in terms of the nucleon–nucleon scattering amplitudes or the neutron and proton optical model potentials as calculated in the high energy approximation (Zamick, 1963; Rustgi, 1964, 1967; they include earlier references). It was found that the effect of simultaneous scattering of the neutron and the proton in the deuteron by the target nucleus is very important, and that, with this effect included, the scattering at deuteron energies above approximately 150 MeV can be accounted for well by the impulse approximation for the deuteron (Sawada, 1965).

6.4c   The Scattering of H^3 and He^3

Optical model analyses of the elastic scattering of H^3 and He^3 have been done traditionally with volume absorption only. Early analyses employed equal radii and equal diffuseness parameters for the real and the imaginary parts (Hodgson, 1960b, 1961). With this restriction on the parameters, shallow potentials with $U_0 \sim 25$ MeV seem to be preferred and the inclusion of a spin orbit potential generally improves the fits greatly (Hafele *et al.*, 1967). However, more recent and more complete data have shown that it is necessary to use different geometries for the real and the imaginary potentials in order to obtain good fits over the entire angular range, thus increasing the total number of parameters to six. These are U_0, W, r_0, a, r_1, and a_1. In this case, discrete ambiguities appear, as discussed in Subsection 6.4a.

As a typical example of various potential families, the results for tritons scattered from Ni^{62} at 15 MeV are shown in Table III. These families of

TABLE III

FAMILIES OF PARAMETERS THAT GIVE GOOD FITS TO THE Ni^{62} DATA FOR 15 MeV INCIDENT TRITONS[a]

Family	U_0	W	r_1	a	a_1	σ_R	χ^2
A	37	14.2	1.67	0.952	0.777	1.82	1.80
B	53	14.0	1.66	0.878	0.766	1.81	1.05
C	80	17.7	1.57	0.795	0.797	1.81	0.78
D	113	22.5	1.48	0.736	0.843	1.79	0.80
E	151	29.0	1.36	0.692	0.890	1.81	1.00
F	194	38.0	1.20	0.651	0.995	1.83	1.48

[a] The real well radius r_0 was held fixed at 1.24 F in order to suppress the U_0 r_0^n ambiguity. The families A through F are labeled in Fig. 6 (Hafele *et al.*, 1967)

potentials were obtained by Hafele *et al.* (1967) by fixing the value of r_0 to 1.24 F in order to suppress the $(U_0 - r_0^n)$ ambiguity. Similar ambiguities to those shown here have been known for He^3 for some time. The introduction of spin orbit interactions to the 6 parameter model has only slight effects on the fits to the differential cross sections. Until polarization data become available, the magnitude and shape of the spin orbit potentials remain undetermined.

Systematic studies of the optical model parameters for H^3 and He^3 as a function of mass number and energy have been initiated only recently, and hence, we must await more analyses of elastic scattering, as well as of reactions involving H^3 and He^3, before we can draw any definite conclusions as to the choice among the various families of potentials. The often preferred choice of many authors for the starting values of a search is a potential which has a real well depth close to $3 \times U_0$ (nucleon). Thus, for example, Gibson et al. (1967) obtained the "average" set of parameters given in Table IV for He^3 scattered

TABLE IV

THE STANDARD OPTICAL MODEL PARAMETERS FOR He^3 [a]

Target	E	U_0	r_0	a	W	r_I	a_I
Ca^{40}	37.7	176.9	1.14	0.723	14.5	1.64	0.91
Fe^{56}	37.7	174.2	1.14	0.723	16.8	1.60	0.81
Ni^{58}	37.7	172.6	1.14	0.723	16.2	1.60	0.81
Ni^{58}	43.7	171.75	1.14	0.723	17.2	1.60	0.81
Y^{89}	43.7	175.14	1.14	0.723	14.88	1.60	0.81
Zr^{90}	43.7	170.0	1.14	0.723	17.42	1.60	0.81

[a] Gibson et al. (1967). Values of U_0 and W were obtained with a search procedure, while the geometrical parameters were held fixed to the above "average" values r_0, a, r_I, and a_I.

from Ca^{40}, Fe^{56}, and Ni^{58} at 37.7 MeV, and from Ni^{58}, Y^{89}, and Zr^{90} at 43.7 MeV, with the real well depth around 180 MeV. The values of U_0 and W obtained by Gibson et al. (1967) is plotted in Fig. 5 as a function of mass number. Comparison between theory and experiment is shown in Fig. 6 for Ni^{58} at various energies.

In the case of He^3 scattering from carbon, recent measurements and analysis by Weller and Roberson (1968) indicate that an optical potential which varies smoothly with energy can fit the data from 6 to 18 MeV reasonably well if two resonances are introduced in a manner following that of Tamura and Terasawa (1964).

To date, there seem to exist some conflicting reports as to the sensitivity of direct reaction calculations to the ambiguities of H^3 and He^3 potentials (Hafele et al., 1967; Flynn and Bassel, 1965; Drisko and Rybicki, 1966; Cline et al., 1965).

Comparison of the family E of Table III for H^3 and the parameters in Table IV for He^3 shows that the imaginary potential radius r_I is considerably

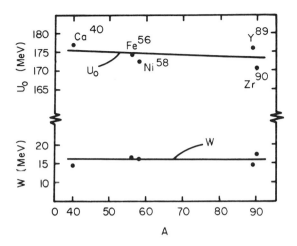

Fig. 5. Values of U_0 and W for 43.7 and 37.7 MeV He^3 elastically scattered from various nuclei (Gibson *et al.*, 1967).

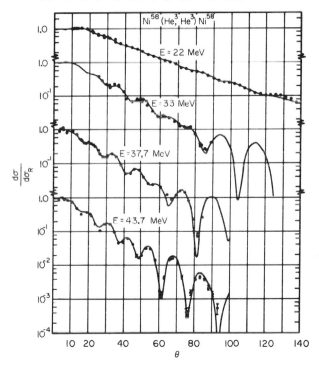

Fig. 6. Elastic angular distributions for He^3 elastically scattered from Ni^{58} at various energies indicated. The solid lines are fits obtained by Gibson *et al.* (1967).

smaller for H^3 than for He^3, a fact which might be associated with the isobaric spin dependence of the interaction. On the other hand, the dependence of U_0 and W on the symmetry parameter $(N - Z)/A$ seems to be very weak as is evidenced from Fig. 5. The introduction of isobaric spin interactions of the form given by Eq. (1), Section 6.1, would be of interest in describing the scattering of H^3 and He^3 and the "isospin flip" reaction (He^3, H^3) in a unified way (Earwaker, 1967).

6.4d   The Scattering of He^4

As we move from the deuteron to heavier ions like He^4, absorption by the nuclear surface becomes stronger at intermediate and high energies, and consequently, the importance of the surface region increases relative to the contribution from the nuclear interior. Thus, even though discrete ambiguities are expected to persist, the continuous ambiguity becomes more prominent.

Four-parameter models with the same geometries for the real and the imaginary parts are, in general, sufficient to reproduce the data. Six-parameter searches often result in insignificant improvements (McFadden and Satchler, 1966). Even if fits are improved, the imaginary potential radius r_1 ends up close to the real potential radius r_0 (Broek et al., 1965). This fact can be interpreted as a manifestation of the tight binding of the alpha particle.

McFadden and Satchler (1966) have analyzed scattering from nuclei ranging from O to U, and found that although it is possible to obtain good fits for intermediate and heavy elements, it is much more difficult to obtain good fits for light elements like O, Mg, Al, Si, and Ca; in fact, no satisfactory fit at all was obtained for O. This is probably due to some compound nucleus contribution, either a statistical fluctuation or individual resonances of higher spin. The fluctuations of parameters from element to element were so great that they were unable to draw any conclusions about an average potential valid for all the nuclei investigated.

At lower energies for intermediate and heavier nuclei, difficulty arises because the strong Coulomb field masks the details of the specifically nuclear interaction. As a consequence, the parameters are determined with much less certainty. The values of parameters for nuclei ranging from Ti to Cr at energies of 16 and 19.5 MeV are given in Table V. These parameters were obtained by Bock et al. (1967). A compilation of earlier results can be found in Winner and Drisko (1965).

At $E_\alpha = 43$ MeV, Broek et al. (1965) carried out an analysis for the scattering from Ni^{58}. At still higher energy, $E_\alpha = 65$ MeV, for the scattering from Zr^{92}, Bingham et al. (1966) found a continuous ambiguity for U_0 which extends from $U_0 = 75$ MeV to as high as 300 MeV in addition to a discrete minimum of χ^2 near $U_0 = 35$ MeV. This is due to the fact that the alpha particles become absorbed more strongly at the nuclear surface at this high energy. The variations of the best fit parameters r_0, U_0, W, and a are shown in Fig. 7, and the fits to the data are shown in Fig. 8. The continuous ambiguity can be understood in terms of the proposals of Igo (1958, 1959a,b, 1960) and

TABLE V

FOUR PARAMETER AVERAGE POTENTIALS FOR
ELASTIC α-SCATTERING FROM THE TITANIUM AND
CHROMIUM ISOTOPES[a]

U_0	W	r_0	r_c	a
183.7	26.6	1.4	1.3	0.564
145.6	23.9	1.395	1.3	0.607
93.6	17.2	1.52	1.3	0.57
61.4	10.8	1.59	1.3	0.59

[a] Bock *et al.* (1967).

of Drisko *et al.* (1963). When particles are strongly absorbed by the nuclear surface and do not penetrate to the interior, the potential inside the nucleus makes little difference to the elastic scattering. Thus discrete ambiguities do not occur and what matters is the asymptotic form of the potential

$$V(r) \to -(U_0 + iW)\,\exp[(r_0\,A^{1/3})/a]\,\exp(-r/a) \qquad (1)$$

which should be the same for all sets of parameters. This requirement is satisfied by the condition

$$a = \text{constant}, \qquad \ln U_0 \propto r_0, \qquad \text{and} \qquad \ln W \propto r_0. \qquad (2)$$

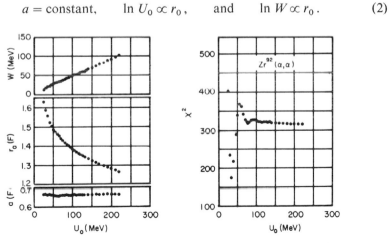

Fig. 7. Interrelationship of ambiguous optical model parameters and χ^2 for each set obtained for α-Zr^{92} at 65 MeV (Bingham *et al.*, 1966).

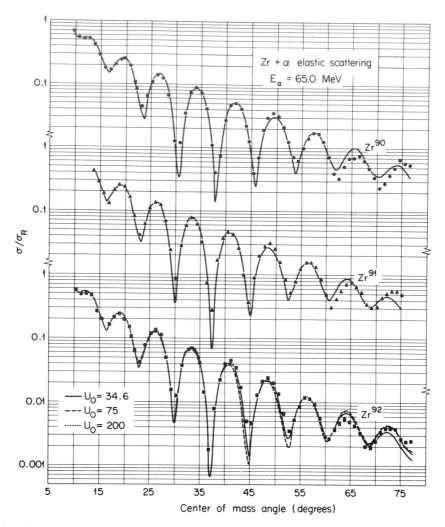

Fig. 8. Ratio of elastic scattering cross sections to the Rutherford cross section for α-Zr^{90}, α-Zr^{91}, and α-Zr^{92} at 65 MeV. Optimum fits with $U_0 = 34.6$, 75, and 200 MeV are shown (Bingham *et al.*, 1966).

In fact, these conditions are well satisfied by the parameters obtained by Bingham *et al.* (1966), as can be seen from Fig. 7.

These authors also found from DWBA calculations of inelastic scattering and of (He^4, He^3) reactions for He^4 against Zr isotopes at 65 MeV that, although inelastic scattering is insensitive to potential ambiguities, the stripping reaction depends very much upon the choice of entrance channel optical parameters. The value $U_0 = 83$ MeV turns out to fit the data best. This result may indicate that the higher order effects neglected in the naive picture mentioned before are quite large and act to reduce the real well depth considerably. As a further evidence for this effect, we mention the work of Wittern (1965) who evaluated U_0 using two-body interactions without a hard core and employing the Fermi gas model for nucleons in nuclei. He concluded that U_0 increases slowly with energy and that $U_0 \simeq 130$ MeV for $E_\alpha \leq 30$ MeV. This is explained as follows. The tight binding of the alpha particle implies a fairly broad distribution in momentum space. Inside the nucleus, the low momentum components are cut out because these states are already occupied by nucleons in the target nucleus. This leads to the reduction in the alpha–nucleus interaction. This reduction, however, should decrease as E_α increases.

Robinson *et al.* (1967) have recently suggested the use of the shell and cluster model to choose the "true" potential. They first find a number of discrete families of potentials for α-particles elastically scattered from Ca^{40} at various energies between 12 and 18 MeV (with a derivative type surface absorption). These potentials are characterized by the number of nodes, N_s, in the internal s wave function. Requiring $U(r)$ to possess a bound s state at -5.23 MeV (which is the separation energy of an α-particle from Ti^{44}), and also assuming that the 2 protons and 2 neutrons in the $(1f)_{7/2}$ shell in Ti^{44} form an alpha cluster, they equate the number of excitation quanta for the $(Ca^{40} + \alpha)$ system and the $(Ca^{40} + 4$ nucleon$)$ system:

$$2(N_s - 1) + L = \sum [2(n_i - 1) + l_i]$$

which is twelve for $n_i = 1$, $l_i = 3$. This yields $N_s = 7$ (with $L = 0$). The real potential depth U_0 which has seven state nodes, i.e., $U_0 = 138$ MeV, is thus chosen with other parameter values $R_0 = 5.20$ F, $R_1 = 5.00$ F, $a = 0.588$ F, and $a_1 = 0.30$ F. The surface imaginary potential depth W' then becomes energy dependent, $W' \simeq 20$ MeV at $E_\alpha \simeq 12$ MeV and $W' \simeq 30$ MeV at $E_\alpha \simeq 18$ MeV.

In any event, for strongly absorbed particles, the problem of choosing the physically most meaningful optical potential among the vast ambiguities is a difficult one and seems to remain open.

VII

Theoretical Basis of the Independent Particle Model

7.1 The Nucleon–Nucleon Interaction—Phenomenological

What holds the nucleus together? This question as to the nature of the fundamental nuclear force has been one of the most challenging in physics since the nucleus was discovered in 1912 by Rutherford. In 1953 Bethe estimated that this question "has consumed more man hours than have been given to any other scientific question in the history of mankind." Seven years later Marshak (1960) restated this view and noted that despite the extra efforts since 1953 "we are not noticeably closer to the goal, a theory that will allow us to deduce nuclear forces from a few basic assumptions and experiments." About the same time a similar appraisal was made by Goldberger (1960), who called attention to the unbelievable confusion and conflict that existed among the various works, and who suggested in a Churchillian phrase that "scarcely ever has the world of physics owed so little to so many."

It would appear that by 1967, some seven years later, our view of the N–N interaction had improved considerably from the bleak picture of 1960. This optimism was engendered by the results reported at the International Conference on the N–N Interaction held at the University of Florida in March of 1967 (Green *et al.*, 1967b), in which representatives of almost all of the active groups assembled to take stock of our knowledge of the N–N interaction. It became clear during the course of the conference that the "One Boson Exchange Model" (OBEM) has emerged as an accurate meson theoretic description of the N–N interaction.

Unfortunately this model has not yet had a major impact upon fundamental studies of the nuclear shell model and optical model. Accordingly, we will postpone our discussion of OBEM until Section 7.4. In this section we shall

confine our discussion to some of the elementary features of the N–N interaction which have played a dominant role in studies of the many body
problem. Detailed treatments of these topics, as well as various pre-OBEM
approaches to the N–N interaction, are well documented in various review
articles and monographs (Hulthén and Sugawara, 1957; Griffith and Power,
1960; Noyes, 1961a,b; Moravcsik, 1963). Let us begin by first developing the
formalism needed in discussions of the N–N interaction.

7.1a   Spin Formalism for Two Spin ½ Particles

In Chapter I we described the Pauli spin formalism for a single particle
having a spin of $\frac{1}{2}$. To treat the N–N problem we must now extend this formalism to deal with two particles having a spin of $\frac{1}{2}$. At the same time we
will introduce the isobaric spin formalism in an essentially identical fashion.

The wave function specifying a system of two identical spin $\frac{1}{2}$ particles will
be a function of the space and spin coordinates of both particles. One generally
tries to find solutions which are either of the product type or a sum of terms of
the product type, i.e.,

$$\Psi(\mathbf{r}_1, \mathbf{r}_2, \sigma_{z1}, \sigma_{z2}) = \psi(\mathbf{r}_1, \mathbf{r}_2)\chi(\sigma_{z1}, \sigma_{z2}). \tag{1}$$

Since σ_{z1} and σ_{z2} both have two possible values corresponding to the α and β
states, there are four basic states of a two particle system. It is possible to
devise a matrix formalism using 4×4 Hermitian matrices to handle the spin
operators associated with a system of two particles. In this matrix formalism
the spin functions will be 1×4 or 4×1 matrices. It is more convenient,
however, to use only 2×2 matrix operators and 1×2 or 2×1 matrix
operands. Such a simple treatment can be sustained if one adopts certain
formal rules for treating the matrix operators and matrix operands associated
with the two particles. Specifically these rules are:

i. In mixed products of the component spin operators connected with
different particles, the order of multiplication is unimportant. For example
$\sigma_{x1}\sigma_{y2} = \sigma_{y2}\sigma_{x1}$. Thus the rules for matrix multiplication do not apply when
the matrices refer to different particles. This rule also applies to spin operands.
Thus $\alpha_1\beta_2 = \beta_2\alpha_1$.

ii. In any sum or difference, each term will be treated as a product of a
matrix operator referring to one particle with a matrix operator referring to
the second. When a matrix referring to a single particle is not explicitly present,
then the unit operator is implied. For example, $\sigma_{z1} + \sigma_{z2} = \sigma_{z1}I_2 + I_1\sigma_{z2}$.

iii. Composite spin operators may be applied to composite spin functions
by allowing the operators associated with one particle to act on its operands
according to the usual matrix laws, and by allowing the operators connected
with the second particle to act on the second particle operands. Operators and

operands associated with different particles may be commuted at will, e.g.,

$$\sigma_{z1}\sigma_{z2}\,\alpha_1\beta_2 = (\sigma_{z1}\alpha_1)(\sigma_{z2}\,\beta_2) = \alpha_1(-\beta_2) = -\alpha_1\beta_2\,.$$

These few rules will suffice for all our applications to combine spin operators and functions. They will also be used in treating isobaric spin and in treating Dirac matrices.

Accepting α_1, β_1, α_2, and β_2 as the basic spin functions for the two particles, we may now form three symmetrical normalized spin functions,

$$^3\chi_1 = \alpha_1\alpha_2$$

$$^3\chi_0 = \frac{1}{\sqrt{2}}\,(\alpha_1\beta_2 + \beta_1\alpha_2) \tag{2}$$

$$^3\chi_{-1} = \beta_1\beta_2\,,$$

and a single normalized antisymmetrical spin function

$$^1\chi_0 = \frac{1}{\sqrt{2}}\,(\alpha_1\beta_2 - \beta_1\alpha_2). \tag{3}$$

Using the orthogonality and normalization properties of the single particle spin functions it is easy to verify that these two particle spin functions represent an orthonormal set. Also, it can readily be shown that these are eigenfunctions of the operator associated with the total component of spin, i.e.,

$$S_z\,^3\chi_1 = \frac{\hbar}{2}\,(\sigma_{z1} + \sigma_{z2})(\alpha_1\alpha_2) = \hbar\alpha_1\alpha_2 = \hbar\,^3\chi_1.$$

Similarly,

$$S_z\,^3\chi_0 = 0\,^3\chi_0\,, \qquad S_z\,^3\chi_{-1} = -\hbar\,^3\chi_{-1}, \qquad \text{and} \qquad S_z\,^1\chi_0 = 0\,^1\chi_0\,.$$

In a similar way we may show that for $M_S = 1$, 0, or -1

$$\mathbf{S}\cdot\mathbf{S}\,^3\chi = 2\hbar^2\,^3\chi \qquad \text{and} \qquad \mathbf{S}\cdot\mathbf{S}\,^1\chi_0 = 0\,^1\chi_0\,.$$

Thus when the system is in the total spin states $^3\chi_1$, $^3\chi_0$, and $^3\chi_{-1}$, the magnitude of the square of the spin angular momentum is certainly $2\hbar^2$, and the magnitude of the z component of spin is certainly $\hbar$, 0, or $-\hbar$, respectively. On the other hand when the system is in the $^1\chi_0$ state, then the square of the magnitude is certainly 0 and the z component of total spin angular momentum is also 0.

We may now indicate a quantum method to evaluate the scalar product $\mathbf{S}_1 \cdot \mathbf{S}_2$ for a system in the state $^3\chi_1$. We let

$$(\mathbf{S}_1 \cdot \mathbf{S}_2)\,^3\chi_1 = \frac{\hbar^2}{4}\,(\sigma_{x1}\sigma_{x2} + \sigma_{y1}\sigma_{y2} + \sigma_{z1}\sigma_{z2})\alpha_1\alpha_2$$

$$= \frac{\hbar^2}{4}\,(\beta_1\beta_2 - \beta_1\beta_2 + \alpha_1\alpha_2) = \frac{\hbar^2}{4}\,\alpha_1\alpha_2 = \frac{\hbar^2}{4}\,^3\chi_1. \tag{4}$$

The identical results follow for $^3\chi_0$ and $^3\chi_{-1}$. However, for the singlet state we have

$$(\mathbf{S}_1 \cdot \mathbf{S}_2)\,^1\chi_0 = \frac{\hbar^2}{4}\,(\sigma_{x1}\sigma_{x2} + \sigma_{y1}\sigma_{y2} + \sigma_{z1}\sigma_{z2})\,\frac{1}{\sqrt{2}}\,(\alpha\beta - \beta\alpha)$$

$$= \frac{\hbar^2}{4\sqrt{2}}\,(\beta\alpha + \beta\alpha - \alpha\beta - \alpha\beta - \alpha\beta + \beta\alpha) = -\frac{3\hbar^2}{4}\,^1\chi_0 \qquad (5)$$

Thus the $^3\chi$ states and the $^1\chi$ state are eigenstates of the operator $(\mathbf{S}_1 \cdot \mathbf{S}_2)$ belonging to the eigenvalues $\hbar^2/4$ and $-3\hbar^2/4$.

7.1b   The Isobaric Spin Formalism

In the historical development of nuclear theory, great weight has been attached to the fact that nucleons may transform into one another. In his first paper on nuclear forces, Heisenberg (1932) assumed that the neutron and proton are two possible isobaric states of a nucleon, analogous to the two spin states of a spin $\frac{1}{2}$ particle. In order to exploit the analogy fully, let us assign to a nucleon the charge character value $\frac{1}{2}$ when it is a proton and the charge character value $-\frac{1}{2}$ when it is a neutron. These two numbers may be viewed as the permissible values, in an abstract space, of the z component of a dimensionless isobaric spin vector $\mathbf{t}$ (sometimes referred to as the isospin or isotopic spin vector). We introduce two quantum numbers t and m_t, which determine the magnitude and the z component of the isobaric spin vector according to the equations

$$|\mathbf{t}| = [t(t+1)]^{1/2} \qquad \text{where} \qquad t \doteq \tfrac{1}{2} \qquad (6)$$

and

$$t_z = m_t \qquad \text{where} \qquad m_t \doteq \tfrac{1}{2}(\text{p}),\ -\tfrac{1}{2}(\text{n}). \qquad (7)$$

We may now assign to a system of two nucleons the derived total isobaric spin vector

$$\mathbf{T} = \mathbf{t}_1 + \mathbf{t}_2. \qquad (8)$$

The same quantization rules which were previously used to determine the allowed values of total spin and z component of total spin here lead to

$$|\mathbf{T}| = [T(T+1)]^{1/2} \qquad \text{where} \qquad T \doteq 0, 1. \qquad (9)$$

We see that, when $T = 0$, $T_z = M_T \doteq 0$, whereas when $T = 1$, $T_z = M_T \doteq 1$, $0, -1$. The $T = 1$ state is sometimes referred to as the isobaric spin triplet state, and the $T = 0$ state is referred to as the isobaric spin singlet state.

Since the z components of isobaric spin are additive, i.e.,

$$M_T = m_{t_1} + m_{t_2} \qquad (10)$$

the $M_T = 1$ state can correspond only to a p–p $(\frac{1}{2}, \frac{1}{2})$ physical system. On the other hand, the $M_T = -1$ state can correspond only to a n–n $(-\frac{1}{2}, -\frac{1}{2})$ physical system. The $T = 1$, $M_T = 0$ and the $T = 0$, $M_T = 0$ states must both correspond to the p–n $(\frac{1}{2}, -\frac{1}{2})$ system. The experimental arrangement selects the $T = 1$, $M_T = 1$ state in studies of p–p systems or the $T = 1$, $M_T = -1$ state in studies of n–n systems. However, to determine which of the two possibilities represent the n–p system will become apparent if we write out the isobaric spin functions which characterize the four possible states of the N–N system.

We restrict ourselves to isobaric spin wave functions which are either unchanged by interchange or else changed in sign, i.e., symmetric or anti-symmetric. The isobaric spin functions which have these properties are

$$^{3}\tau_1 = p_1 p_2 \qquad ^{3}\tau_0 = \frac{1}{\sqrt{2}}(p_1 n_2 + n_1 p_2) \qquad ^{3}\tau_{-1} = n_1 n_2 \qquad (11)$$

and

$$^{1}\tau_0 = \frac{1}{\sqrt{2}}(p_1 n_2 - n_1 p_2). \qquad (12)$$

In the $p_1 p_2$ states and $n_1 n_2$ states it is obvious that we cannot experimentally label the individual particles. The usual exclusion principle is applicable to these systems. Thus the experimental apparatus selects for us the isotopic spin states in studies of p–p and n–n systems. However in studies of n–p systems we must appeal to a generalized exclusion principle to establish the isotopic spin state. This generalized exclusion principle may be expressed as follows.

The total wave function characterizing a system of nucleons must be anti-symmetrical with respect to the complete interchange of the complete set of nuclear coordinates of any two particles.

In the analysis of the N–N system of nucleons we assume that the composite wave function may be written as a product of a space function, spin function and isobaric spin function, i.e.,

$$\Psi(\mathbf{r}_1, s_{z1}, t_{z1}, \mathbf{r}_2, s_{z2}, t_{z2}) = \psi(\mathbf{r}_1\mathbf{r}_2)\chi(s_{z1}s_{z2})\tau(t_{z1}t_{z2}) \qquad (13)$$

is chosen. If necessary, a sum of wave functions of this form is used to charac-terize a state. If the spatial wave function is an eigenfunction of the operator $\mathbf{L} \cdot \mathbf{L}$ then it will be characterized by a quantum number l. It is well known that when l is even the spatial wave function is symmetrical and that when l is odd the spatial wave function is antisymmetrical. Even if the wave function is not an eigenfunction of the operation $\mathbf{L} \cdot \mathbf{L}$ it may always be represented by a superposition of eigenfunctions of $\mathbf{L} \cdot \mathbf{L}$ belonging either to even l values or odd l values. The evenness or oddness of a wave function determines the parity and the parity determines the spatial symmetry of the N–N wave function.

The generalized exclusion principle thus requires that the spatial, spin and isobaric spin wave functions and quantum numbers for a system of two nucleons conform to that given in Table I. Alternatively, we may say that the generalized exclusion principle requires that

$$L + S + T = \text{odd number}, \quad \text{or} \quad (-1)^{(L+S+T)} = -1. \quad (14)$$

Note that for an n–p system the values of L and S determine whether it is a $T = 0$ or $T = 1$ state. Since $M_T = 1$ is the p–p system, S waves ($L = 0$) can couple only into the ^1S state, P waves into the ^3P state, and D waves into ^1D state, etc.

In early discussions of nuclear forces the following exchange operators were introduced. The spin exchange operator is defined by

$$P_S = \tfrac{1}{2}(1 + \boldsymbol{\sigma}_1 \cdot \boldsymbol{\sigma}_2) \doteq (-1)^{S+1}. \quad (15)$$

The isobaric spin exchange operator is defined by

$$P_T = \tfrac{1}{2}(1 + \boldsymbol{\tau}_1 \cdot \boldsymbol{\tau}_2) \doteq (-1)^{T+1}. \quad (16)$$

The space exchange operator P_L is defined by imposing the requirement that

$$P_L \doteq (-1)^L. \quad (17)$$

The earliest efforts to account for the saturation and incompressibility tendencies of nuclear matter were based upon various types of exchange forces. Bartlett (1936) proposed the potential

$$V_B = -P_S J(r) = (-1)^S J(r). \quad (18)$$

Heisenberg (1932) suggested the isobaric spin exchange potential

$$V_H = P_T J(r) - (-1)^{T+1} J(r) \quad (19)$$

Majorana (1933) suggested the space exchange potential

$$V_M = -P_L J(r) - (-1)^{L+1} J(r) \quad (20)$$

In early studies Wigner (1933) gave consideration to a potential without exchange

$$V_W = -J(r) \quad (21)$$

In each of these expressions we shall assume that $J(r)$ is a positive definite energy function.

While the Bartlett, Heisenberg, and Majorana potentials depend directly upon S, T, and L, respectively, each of these has an indirect dependence upon

TABLE I

ALLOWED VALUES OF EXCHANGE OPERATORS

Physical system	Notation	L	S	T	$\sigma_1 \cdot \sigma_2$	$\tau_1 \cdot \tau_2$	$(\sigma_1 \cdot \sigma_2)(\tau_1 \cdot \tau_2)$	B	H	M	W	S
p–p n–n	^1S	0	0	1	−3	1	−3	1	1	−1	−1	−1
n–p	^3S	0	1	0	1	−3	−3	−1	−1	−1	−1	−1
n–p	^1P	1	0	0	−3	−3	9	1	−1	1	−1	0
p–p n–p n–n	^3P	1	1	1	1	1	1	−1	1	1	−1	0

the other two quantum numbers by virtue of the exclusion principle. This fact is illustrated in the columns of Table I which are labeled B, H, M, and W, in which the coefficients of $J(r)$ are given for the four types of interactions. Also given in the column headed S is the coefficient of $J(r)$ for the Serber exchange interaction which may be defined by

$$V = -\tfrac{1}{2}(1 + P_L)J(r). \tag{22}$$

This force is attractive for even L and vanishes for odd L, and in consequence, should lead to differential cross sections which are symmetric about 90°.

Exchange forces were first given serious consideration in nuclear physics because they afforded the possibility of accounting for the observed saturation tendencies of nuclear forces. With the advent of meson theory, the dependence of nuclear forces upon isobaric spin has been related to the existence of positive, negative, and neutral mesons. In neutral theory, nuclear forces result from the interaction with a neutral meson field, just as electronic forces result from the interactions with a neutral photon field (electromagnetic field). In charged theory, the forces are a consequence of the couplings of nucleons with positive and negative meson fields. In symmetric theory, the forces are connected with a particular mixture of positive, negative, and neutral meson fields. If the interaction based upon neutral meson theory has the form

$$V_n = J(\mathbf{r}, \mathbf{s}_1, \mathbf{s}_2) \tag{23}$$

which we here allow to depend upon the spin of the nucleons, then the corresponding charged theory leads to the interaction

$$V_c = \tfrac{1}{2}(1 + \boldsymbol{\tau}_1 \cdot \boldsymbol{\tau}_2)J(\mathbf{r}, \mathbf{s}_1, \mathbf{s}_2) \tag{24}$$

and the symmetric theory yields

$$V_s = (\boldsymbol{\tau}_1 \cdot \boldsymbol{\tau}_2)J(\mathbf{r}, \mathbf{s}_1, \mathbf{s}_2). \tag{25}$$

The seventh column of Table I contains the values of $\boldsymbol{\tau}_1 \cdot \boldsymbol{\tau}_2$ for various states. The interaction propagated by the isotopic spin 1 mesons, e.g., the π- and ρ-mesons may be described in this way.

7.1c Low Energy Properties, Effective Range Theory

Of the three N–N systems, the n–p, p–p, and n–n systems, only the n–p system exists in a state of binding, i.e., the deuteron. While we tend to view the N–N interaction as a strong interaction we might note that in the natural energy unit $E_0 = \hbar^2/2\mu a^2 = 41.46$ MeV (when $\mu = M/2$ and $a = 1$ F are used), the binding energy of the deuteron $B = 2.2245$ MeV is very weak, i.e., $B \ll E_0$. This contrasts, for example, with atom–atom interactions for which $B \sim 50E_0$ in typical diatomic molecules. Thus, for the distances and masses involved, nuclear forces could be considered to be rather weak forces. Let us consider now some of the other important properties of N–N systems. In giving experimental numbers it will be understood that the last digit listed is uncertain. For precise, recent specifications of experimental errors we refer the reader to the monograph by Wilson (1963), the Proceedings of the International Conference on the N–N Interaction (Florida, 1967), and the recent Supplement of *Progress of Theoretical Physics* (PTP, 1967) which is devoted to the N–N problem.

The total angular momentum of the deuteron in the natural unit $\hbar$ is characterized by the quantum number $J = 1$. The magnetic moment of the deuteron is given by $\mu_d = 0.85741$, in the natural unit $\mu_N = e\hbar/2m_p c$. The deuteron also has a quadrupole moment $Q = 0.282$ F^2.

The deuteron binding energy has been obtained from the $H^1(n, \gamma)H^2$, $H^2(p, n)2p$, and $H^2(\gamma, n)H^1$ reactions. The spin, magnetic, and quadrupole moments have been obtained from molecular beam experiments.

In the early days of N–N cross section measurements, great pains were taken to determine the total and differential cross sections as functions of energy with the hope that this information could be used to determine the shape of the N–N potential. However, Breit *et al.* (1936), and Landau and Smorodinski (1944) called attention to the fact that the theoretical low energy scattering results should be quite insensitive to the shape of the well for any reasonable shape. Schwinger (1950), Bethe (1949), Blatt and Jackson (1949), and others have in fact developed a so-called shape independent method of analysis for the interpretation of low energy scattering, which shows that for a central potential the low energy S wave phase shifts may always be characterized by the equation

$$k \cot \delta = -a^{-1} + \tfrac{1}{2} r_0 k^2 \tag{26}$$

where r_0 and a are the so-called effective range and fermi scattering length. The lengths should be obtainable directly from the experimental data. Thus, a plot of $k \cot \delta$ vs. k^2 should indicate a straight line with slope equal to $r_0/2$ and intercept $-a^{-1}$.

To derive Eq. (26), we start from Schroedinger's equation for $l = 0$ and energies E_1 and E_2 (Hulthén and Sugawara, 1957)

$$u_1'' + [k_1{}^2 + v(r)]u_1(r) = 0 \tag{27}$$

$$u_2'' + [k_2{}^2 + v(r)]u_2(r) = 0. \tag{28}$$

Here $k_i = (ME_i/\hbar^2)^{1/2}$ is the propagation constant in the CM system and $v(r)$ is assumed simply to be a central two body potential. We shall assume that there is a bound level or ground state wave function for which

$$u_g'' + [-\alpha^2 + v(r)]u_g(r) = 0 \tag{29}$$

where $\alpha = (BM/\hbar^2)^{1/2}$. All of these wave functions satisfy the boundary conditions

$$u_1(0) = u_2(0) = u_g(0) = 0. \tag{30}$$

Let us now introduce a set of barred functions which are asymptotically the same as $u(r)$ but which satisfy Eqs. (27)–(29) with $v(r) = 0$. These functions are normalized by requiring

$$\bar{u}_1(0) = \bar{u}_2(0) = \bar{u}_g(0) = 1. \tag{31}$$

This determines them to have the forms

$$\bar{u}_i(r) = \sin(k_i r + \delta_i)/\sin \delta_i \qquad (i = 1, 2) \tag{32}$$

and

$$\bar{u}_g(r) = e^{-\alpha r}. \tag{33}$$

It is important to note that $\bar{u}(r)$, as given by Eqs. (32) and (33), fixes the normalization of $u(r)$ uniquely.

If we multiply Eq. (27) by $u_2(r)$ and Eq. (28) by $u_1(r)$ and subtract one equation from the other and integrate between 0 and R, we get

$$[u_2(r)u_1{}'(r) - u_1(r)u_2{}'(r)] \Big|_0^R = (k_2{}^2 - k_1{}^2) \int_0^R u_1(r)u_2(r)\, dr. \tag{34}$$

The same procedure for the barred functions gives

$$[\bar{u}_2(r)\bar{u}_1{}'(r) - \bar{u}_1(r)\bar{u}_2{}'(r)] \Big|_0^R = (k_2{}^2 - k_1{}^2) \int_0^R \bar{u}_1(r)\bar{u}_2(r)\, dr. \tag{35}$$

Taking next the difference of these two equations, and letting $R \to \infty$, we have

$$k_2 \cot \delta_2 - k_1 \cot \delta_1 = (k_2{}^2 - k_1{}^2) \int_0^\infty [\bar{u}_1(r)\bar{u}_2(r) - u_1(r)u_2(r)]\, dr \tag{36}$$

where we have used Eqs. (31) and (32). If we start from Eqs. (27) and (29), instead of Eqs. (27) and (28), the same procedure gives

$$k_1 \cot \delta_1 + \alpha = (k_1{}^2 + \alpha^2) \int_0^\infty [u_g(r)u_1(r) - u_g(r)u_1(r)]\, dr \tag{37}$$

We now define the scattering length a, according to Eq. (26)

$$\lim_{k^2 \to 0} [k \cot \delta] = -a^{-1}. \tag{38}$$

Dropping the index 1 in Eq. (36) and making $k_2{}^2$ approach zero, we get

$$k \cot \delta = -a^{-1} + \tfrac{1}{2}k^2 \rho(0, E). \tag{39}$$

Similarly, from Eq. (37) we obtain

$$k \cot \delta = -\alpha + \tfrac{1}{2}(k^2 + \alpha^2)\rho(-B, E) \tag{40}$$

where we define

$$\rho(0, E) = 2 \int_0^\infty [\bar{u}_0(r)\bar{u}(r) - u_0(r)u(r)] \, dr \tag{41}$$

and

$$\rho(-B, E) = 2 \int_0^\infty [\bar{u}_g(r)\bar{u}(r) - u_g(r)u(r)] \, dr. \tag{42}$$

The index and argument 0 means the zero energy wave function. When E approaches zero in Eq. (40), we get

$$a^{-1} = \alpha - \tfrac{1}{2}\alpha^2 \rho(-B, 0) \tag{43}$$

where $\rho(-B, 0)$ is the "mixed effective range"

$$\rho(0, -B) = \rho(-B, 0) = 2 \int_0^\infty [\bar{u}_g(r)\bar{u}_0(r) - u_g(r)u_0(r)] \, dr. \tag{44}$$

We can show now that all ρ's defined above can be regarded as constants in a good approximation in the low energy region since $\bar{u}(r)$ and $u(r)$ differ from each other only inside the nuclear force range. The main contribution to the integrals above comes from the inside region, where for the N–N problem the potential energy is numerically much larger than the total energy. Thus, the above three ρ's depend only slightly upon E, and we can approximate them by

$$r_0 = \rho(0, 0) = 2 \int_0^\infty [\bar{u}_0{}^2(r) - u_0{}^2(r)] \, dr. \tag{45}$$

In this approximation, we obtain Eq. (26) or

$$k \cot \delta_0 = -\alpha + \tfrac{1}{2}(k^2 + \alpha^2)r_0 \tag{46}$$

and

$$a^{-1} = \alpha - \tfrac{1}{2}\alpha^2 r_0. \tag{47}$$

This effective range theory implies that we can determine only the two shape independent parameters a and r_0 for each spin state from the low energy scattering data. Furthermore, effective range theory predicts a simple relation between the scattering parameters a and r_0 and the binding parameter α. According to Eq. (39), the shape of the nuclear potential cannot be decided even with the combined knowledge of the deuteron binding energy and the low energy scattering data.

If, now, we accept Eq. (26), then by solving for $\sin^2 \delta$ it follows that the low energy (i.e., S wave) cross section should be given by

$$\sigma^0 = \frac{4\pi}{k^2 + (-a^{-1} + \frac{1}{2}r_0 k^2)^2} \tag{48}$$

In actuality the low energy n–p cross sections do not conform to so simple a formula. Wigner (1936) removed the major difficulty with the suggestion that the interaction for the spin singlet state of the n–p system differs from the interaction in the spin triplet state. In n–p scattering with unpolarized particles, the statistical weight of the singlet system is $\frac{1}{4}$ as compared to the statistical weight $\frac{3}{4}$ for the triplet system. Hence the total S wave n–p cross section is given by

$$\sigma = \tfrac{3}{4}\sigma_t + \tfrac{1}{4}\sigma_s \tag{49}$$

where σ_t denotes the S wave scattering cross section associated with the triplet state and σ_s the S wave scattering cross section associated with the singlet state.

When the singlet and triplet n–p cross sections are related to the effective range and scattering lengths r_s, a_s and r_t, a_t, we can indeed fit the low energy (0–10 MeV) n–p data quite well. The success of the theory in itself, however, must not be taken too seriously, since by using four adjustable parameters we might force a variety of functions to fit the same experimental data. There is, however, the interrelation given by Eq. (47), as well as independent means of determining a_s and a_t. Using $\alpha = 0.232$ F^{-1} and $a_t = 5.38$ F we obtain $r_t = 1.70$ F. The reciprocal of α, i.e., $\alpha^{-1} = 4.31$ F, is a measure of the radius of the deuteron. Indeed for some purposes we may characterize the radial wave function of the deuteron by

$$\psi = \left(\frac{\alpha}{2\pi}\right)^{1/2} \frac{e^{-\alpha r}}{r}. \tag{50}$$

This is called the zero range approximation since it corresponds to a solution of Schroedinger's equation for a delta function potential. The fact that the deuteron is such a loosely bound and extended structure has been used to provide convenient neutron targets for high energy p–n and n–n experiments. Here the view is taken that the proton is a "spectator" whose effects can be allowed for by small corrections.

The independent means of determining a_s and a_t involve using cold neutrons ~ 0.01 eV, scattered coherently by orthohydrogen and parahydrogen, or by various liquid hydrocarbons. Recent values obtained from such experiments are listed in Table II along with recent values of r_s and r_t.

Besides the spin–spin dependence, the existence of a noncentral component

TABLE II
$^1S_0$ AND $^3S_1$ SCATTERING LENGTHS, EFFECTIVE RANGES, AND MORSE PARAMETERS

System	a (F)	r_0 (F)	V_0 (MeV)	a_m (F)	r_m (F)
$^1S_0$ of n–p	-23.678 ± 0.028	2.44 ± 0.11	61.99	0.3957	0.9365
$^3S_1$ of n–p	$+5.397 \pm 0.011$	1.727 ± 0.013	119.49	0.3408	0.8668

of the N–N interaction was noted in the fact that the deuteron has a quadrupole moment and the fact that the magnetic moment of the deuteron departs from that expected for a pure S state. If the deuteron wave function were a pure S state, we would not expect any contribution to the magnetic moment due to the orbital motion of the proton. Since the spins of the proton and neutron are parallel, the deuteron magnetic moment, when expressed in nuclear magnetons, should be

$$\mu_d^{\ 0} = \mu_p + \mu_n = 2.79268 - 1.91304 = 0.87964. \tag{51}$$

The experimental value is 0.85741. Accordingly we must explain the magnetic anomaly

$$\mu_d - \mu_d^{\ 0} = 0.02223. \tag{52}$$

To account simultaneously for the anomalous magnetic moment and the quadrupole moment of the deuteron, Rarita and Schwinger (1941) used the tensor force as a noncentral force in the n–p interaction which couples the even parity $^3S_1$ and $^3D_1$ states together so that the ground state contains a small $^3D_1$ mixture. Let us show how a small $^3D_1$ component may account for the magnetic anomaly.

If the orbital angular momentum of the deuteron is $\mathbf{L}$, then $\mathbf{L}/2$ is the angular momentum of each nucleon about the center of mass. Since the proton has the charge e, the proton orbital angular momentum gives rise to a magnetic moment $\mu_N \mathbf{L}/2\hbar$. Consequently, the magnetic energy of the deuteron in a magnetic field is

$$W_m = (\tfrac{1}{2}\mathbf{L} \cdot \mathbf{H} + 2\mu_p \mathbf{s}_p \cdot \mathbf{H} + 2\mu_n \mathbf{s}_n \cdot \mathbf{H})\mu_N \hbar^{-1}. \tag{53}$$

For the coupling arrangement illustrated in Fig. 1a, a quantum mechanical or vector model calculation of $\langle W_m \rangle = {}^{2S+1}\mu_J{}^L H\mu_N$ with the state $M_J = J$ gives

$$^{2S+1}\mu_J{}^L = \frac{J}{2}\left[\mu_d^{\ 0} + \tfrac{1}{2} - (\mu_d^{\ 0} - \tfrac{1}{2})\frac{L(L+1) - S(S+1)}{J(J+1)}\right]. \tag{54}$$

Inserting the L, S, J quantum numbers 0, 1, 1, we find, as is expected, that the magnetic moment for the $^3S_1$ state is just $\mu_d^{\ 0}$. The set 2, 1, 1, which corresponds to the $^3D_1$ state, leads to

$$^3\mu_1{}^2 = \tfrac{3}{4} - \tfrac{1}{2}\mu_d^{\ 0} = 0.3101. \tag{55}$$

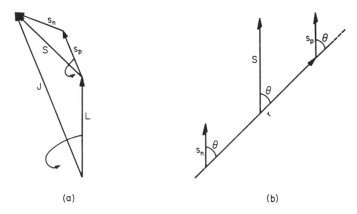

(a)   (b)

Fig. 1. (a) Semiclassical vector diagram for $^3D_1$ state. (b) Diagram showing orientation of parallel spin vectors relative to a radial vector.

A state which is a combination of $^3S_1$ and $^3D_1$ states may be written in the form

$$\Psi = {}^3\Psi_1{}^0 \cos w + {}^3\Psi_1{}^2 \sin w \tag{56}$$

where $^3\Psi_1{}^0$ and $^3\Psi_1{}^2$ are normalized wave functions. Then, since $\sin^2 w$ represents the $^3D_1$ probability, we find that the appropriate weighted combination of the $^3S_1$ and $^3D_1$ moments is

$$\mu_d = \mu_d{}^0(1 - \sin^2 w) + (\sin^2 w)(\tfrac{3}{4} - \tfrac{1}{2}\mu_d{}^0). \tag{57}$$

Accordingly,

$$\mu_d - \mu_d{}^0 = -\tfrac{3}{2}(\mu_d{}^0 - \tfrac{1}{2}) \sin^2 w. \tag{58}$$

Inserting the experimental value for the anomaly, we obtain for the fractional $^3D_1$ admixture in the ground state of the deuteron

$$\sin^2 w = 0.039 \approx 4\%. \tag{59}$$

The small admixture of the $^3D_1$ state needed to account for the magnetic moment of the deuteron may also account for the quadrupole moment of the deuteron. The D state wave functions correspond to a distribution of the proton, which varies with θ, and hence would be expected to give rise to an electric quadrupole moment. To determine this moment, we must calculate the radial parts of the $^3S_1$ and $^3D_1$ wave functions, a calculation which depends upon the detailed nature of the noncentral force which causes the small $^3D_1$ admixture. Rarita and Schwinger (1941) assumed that this noncentral force is a tensor force which has the form

$$V_T = -S_{12} K(r) \tag{60}$$

where

$$S_{12} = 3(\sigma_1 \cdot u)(\sigma_2 \cdot u) - \sigma_1 \cdot \sigma_2 \tag{61}$$

and $u = r/r$ $(r = r_p - r_n)$.

It can be shown by strict quantum mechanical methods that the tensor force operator acting upon a $^3S_1$ wave function will convert it into a $^3D_1$ wave function. The $^3S_1$ and $^3D_1$ states are thereby coupled by the tensor force so that the state of minimum energy is a combination of the two states.

In the deuteron, the net spin vector $\mathbf{S} = \mathbf{s}_n + \mathbf{s}_p$ establishes an intrinsic direction in space, and the tensor force acts to concentrate the spatial distribution relative to this intrinsic direction. To obtain a physical insight into the effect of such a potential, let us consider its classical effect. In the singlet spin state there is no net $\mathbf{S}$. Hence the S_{12} operator may be set to zero, since the tensor force cannot act to alter the central field distribution relative to a nonexistent preferred direction. In discussing the spin triplet state, let us, for convenience, take the $\mathbf{S}$ direction to be the z direction. In Fig. 1b, we show the orientation of the two parallel spin vectors relative to the radial vector joining the two nucleons. Treating the $\boldsymbol{\sigma}$'s as unit vectors, the tensor potential in this classical case may be written as

$$V_T = -S_{12} K(r) = -[3(\cos^2 \theta) - 1]K(r) \tag{62}$$

If $K(r)$ is a positive definite function, then for any r, the potential energy will have the minima $-2K$ at $\theta = 0°$ and $180°$, and the maxima K at $\theta = 90°$ and $270°$. This potential will thus act to force the radial vector to lie along the resultant $\mathbf{S}$ vector. A combination of a large central force, which has no preferred orientation, and a small tensor force will tend to produce a distribution of the radial vector which is elongated along the line of resultant spin $\mathbf{S}$. Such a cigarlike distribution will have associated with it a positive electric quadrupole moment. We will discuss the quantum mechanical derivation of the mixing due to the tensor force in Section 7.4.

Rarita and Schwinger made use of the interaction function

$$V = -I_{12} V_0(1 + c_\sigma \boldsymbol{\sigma}_1 \cdot \boldsymbol{\sigma}_2 + \gamma S_{12})\xi(r) \tag{63}$$

where $\xi(r)$ has the square well form with radius a, and I_{12} is the neutral, charged, or symmetric isobaric spin operator. They found it possible to account for the then available low energy N–N data, including the magnetic and quadrupole moments of the deuteron, by using the four parameters

$$I_{12} V_0 = 13.5 \quad \text{MeV}, \qquad a = 2.8 \times 10^{-13} \quad \text{cm},$$

$$c_\sigma = 0.036, \qquad \text{and} \qquad \gamma = 0.775.$$

The photodisintegration cross section, i.e., the cross section for the reaction $H^2(\gamma, n)H'$ and the neutron capture cross section for the reaction $H'(n, \gamma)H^2$ can also be calculated from an assumed interaction. For the former reaction the experimental differential cross sections in the center of mass system are consistent with the formula

$$\sigma(\theta, \varphi) = a + (b + c \cos \theta) \sin^2 \theta. \tag{64}$$

In general, the low energy photodisintegration agrees with theoretical predictions except that the experimental isotropy coefficient a/b is much larger. The experimental neutron capture cross section $\sigma_{\text{expt}} = 3.29 \text{ F}^2$ is slightly larger than the theoretical value of 3.14 F^2 (Hulthén and Sugawara, 1957).

We might conclude this discussion by saying that at first it appeared that a 4-parameter phenomenological interaction, embodying central, spin–spin, and tensor components could account for all low energy data. Subsequent studies however, indicated that, no matter what well shape is chosen, Eq. (63) is not sufficiently versatile to account for all the low energy N–N data. Somewhat better success was achieved by introducing N N interactions with a fifth adjustable parameter. Thus it appeared possible, using a 5 parameter phenomenological interaction, to give a fair account of the deuteron's binding energy, magnetic moment, quadrupole moment, n–p, and p–p scattering at low energies, the photodisintegration cross sections, and the neutron capture cross section. We must recognize, however, that the wavelengths of matter waves in this energy region are rather large compared to the range of nuclear forces. Hence we cannot really expect to "see" the fine details of the N–N interaction by means of low energy experiments. Accordingly, the fact that it was possible to interpret a large amount of experimental data in the low energy region in terms of 5 parameter N–N models was more a demonstration that quantum mechanics was applicable than an indication of the reliability of the postulated interaction.

7.1d   High Energy Scattering

It was expected that we would learn more about the N–N interaction by investigations in the high energy region where the De Broglie wave lengths are either comparable to or smaller than the range of nuclear interaction. According to the semiclassical model, the impact parameters assigned to individual partial waves are given by

$$b_l \approx (l + \tfrac{1}{2})/k \approx (l + \tfrac{1}{2})(83/E_l)^{1/2} \quad \text{F} \tag{65}$$

where E_l is the laboratory energy in MeV. Thus, at 83 MeV, P, D, and F waves would sense to 1.5, 2.5, and 3.5 F, respectively, in contrast to 3, 5, and 7 F at 21 MeV. On the other hand at 330 MeV they would sense to 0.75, 1.25, and 1.75 F. Thus in the high energy region, it was anticipated that we should learn whether nuclear forces are attractive or repulsive in these states, and thus verify or contradict various assumptions as to the exchange character of the N–N interaction. The scattering was also expected to reveal whether the n–p and p–p nuclear forces in like states are identical, as was expected according to the charge independence hypothesis.

This was the basic motivation underlying one of the most extensive sets of experimental scientific studies in the history of mankind, an effort which still continues.

With the post war development of high energy accelerators, data on n–p and p–p scattering in the high energy range began to accumulate quite rapidly. The pioneer work with the Berkeley 184 inch cyclotron has now been supplemented by work at many other laboratories, so that the overall nature of the differential p–p and n–p cross sections and the total n–p cross sections in the energy range up to about 330 MeV was fairly well established by the early 1950's. This energy is often used as a convenient cutoff for N–N studies, since above this energy π-meson production becomes appreciable. Then the scattering analysis in terms of real potentials is no longer applicable. Figure 2

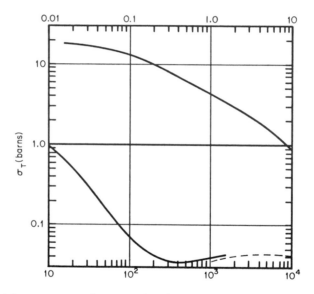

Fig. 2. Total n–p cross sections as a function of neutron kinetic energy (in MeV). Upper scale for upper curve, lower scale for lower curve. Dotted curve represents results of measurements of p–d cross sections, with corrections for the spectator proton.

gives the total n–p cross section. For simplicity, we do not show individual data points or errors, since these are not of major significance to our discussions. Figure 3 gives the differential cross sections for n–p scattering at a selection of energies taken from recent compilations. Figure 4 gives the differential cross sections for p–p scattering at several energies. Note the remarkable constancy of the observed cross section at particular energies for angles between 30° and 90°. This contrasts with the n–p results, which are fairly anisotropic with angle, although they are approximately symmetrical about 90°.

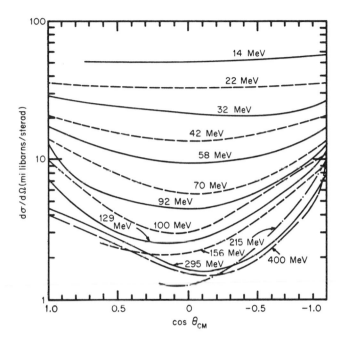

Fig. 3. Differential cross sections for n–p scattering at several energies.

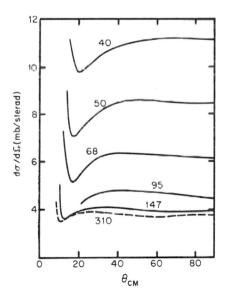

Fig. 4. Differential cross sections for p–p scattering at several energies.

The isotropy of p–p scattering suggested (in 1950) that only S waves were scattered, even at high energies. On the other hand the anisotropy of n–p scattering with approximate symmetry about 90° suggested that D, G, and other even partial waves were scattered, which conforms to the suggestion of the Serber force. As we noted earlier, this force vanishes for odd L, and hence, leads to differential cross sections which are symmetric about 90°. In general, the high energy results were so completely at variance with what was anticipated on the basis of simple phenomenological low energy N–N interaction models that they led to the creation of an entirely new game. As new data became available, those pursuing the phenomenological approach found it increasingly necessary to use more elaborate models with additional parameters. While in 1947, 5 parameters were used, by 1957, 20 parameter models were being used, and by 1967, 40 (give or take 10) parameter models had arrived.

A major influence in the development of phenomenological models was the suggestion by Jastrow (1951) that n–p and p–p scattering could be accounted for qualitatively by using potentials with repulsive cores. This hard core was to have a major impact upon the development of nuclear structure theory (see Section 7.2).

Probably a more permanent milestone was the experimental discovery of the polarization induced in high energy p–p scattering using double scattering techniques (see Chapter III) (Oxley and Schamberger, 1952; Oxley *et al.*, 1953). Figure 5 presents a recent compilation of high energy p–p polarization results. Figure 6 indicates the trends of n–p polarization data.

The N–N interaction, as it unfolded, has appeared so complex that the study has proceeded in separated steps. The first step is to measure the parameters that can be measured. The major parts of these are elastic scattering parameters. There are now almost 2,000 items of data made up of differential cross section, polarization correlation, and triple scattering measurements at various energies and angles. According to the analysis of Wolfenstein and Ashkin (1952), the most general form of scattering matrix in spin space for two spin $\frac{1}{2}$ particles subject to invariance under rotation, space reflection, and time reversal, which can be built out of the spin operators $\boldsymbol{\sigma}_1$ and $\boldsymbol{\sigma}_2$, and the incident momenta $\mathbf{k}$ and outgoing momenta $\mathbf{k}'$ (in the center of mass system), is

$$M(\boldsymbol{\sigma}_1, \boldsymbol{\sigma}_2, \mathbf{k}, \mathbf{k}') = A(q) + B(q)(\boldsymbol{\sigma}_1 \cdot \mathbf{n})(\boldsymbol{\sigma}_2 \cdot \mathbf{n}) + C(q)(\boldsymbol{\sigma}_1 + \boldsymbol{\sigma}_2) \cdot \mathbf{n}$$

$$+ D(q)(\boldsymbol{\sigma}_1 - \boldsymbol{\sigma}_2) \cdot \mathbf{n} + E(q)(\boldsymbol{\sigma}_1 \cdot \mathbf{q})(\boldsymbol{\sigma}_2 \cdot \mathbf{q})$$

$$+ F(q)(\boldsymbol{\sigma}_1 \cdot \mathbf{p})(\boldsymbol{\sigma}_2 \cdot \mathbf{p}) \tag{66}$$

where $\mathbf{q} = \mathbf{k}' - \mathbf{k}$ is the momentum transfer, $\mathbf{p} = \mathbf{k}' + \mathbf{k}$ and $\mathbf{n} = \mathbf{k} \times \mathbf{k}'$. If the forces between nucleons are charge symmetric the quantity D vanishes.

Thus only the real and imaginary parts of A, B, C, E, and F must be determined. The optical theorem (Puzikov *et al.*, 1957) imposes additional constraints, which leave only five experiments to be performed. If, now, we start with an unpolarized beam, a single scattering experiment may give a total cross section σ_t and differential cross section $(d\sigma/d\Omega)$. A double scattering experiment in which the first scattering produces a polarized beam can define five convenient parameters D, R, A, R', and A' which describe how the components of spin of a particle change after the second scattering. In addition, we may determine the parameters C_{nn}, C_{kp} which describe the correlation between the directions of the spin after scattering. Finally we have the parameters A_{xx}, and A_{yy} which describe the scattering of a polarized beam by a polarized target.

Wilson (1963) has given a recent compilation of data, including a large body of data on the N–N interaction at low energy, 68, 95, 140, 210, and 310 MeV. Since that time many more data have accumulated [see Florida (1967) and Nisimura (1967)].

The elastic scattering parameters are best parametrized by a phase shift analysis which separates the various angular momentum states. Recent phase shift efforts throughout the world are summarized in the Proceedings of the International Conference on the N–N Interaction (Florida, 1967), and in a recent Supplement of the *Progress of Theoretical Physics* (PTP, 1967).

The most recent overall sets of phase parameter fits to N–N data in the region up to 350 MeV are those of Breit *et al.* (1968) and MacGregor *et al.* (1968). Figure 7 gives the results of these analyses. We refer the reader to the original articles for the assigned statistical uncertainties. Possibly, a more reliable estimate of current uncertainties is represented by the differences in the final phase shift solutions obtained by these two leading groups. The scale to the left in Fig. 7a is used for the $^1S_0$ and $^3S_1$ phase shifts with respect to the zero degree base line. The upper scale gives the laboratory energy in MeV. The lower scale gives the propagation constant in F^{-1}. The dashed $^1S_0$ and $^3S_1$ curves below 10 MeV and above 330 MeV are extrapolations based upon static Morse functions (Darewych and Green, 1967). The dot dashed curves indicate the effective range expansion. Table II gives the parameters of these Morse functions and the effective range constants used.

The fact that the ^1S phase shift vanishes at low energies is indicative of the fact that there is no bound $^1S_0$ state. The fact that the $^3S_1$ phase shift starts at 180° is indicative of the deuteron ground state. The difference in the ^1S and ^3S potentials is largely represented in the tensor force term. Thus, the ^3S Morse potential must be viewed as containing an effective equivalent of this tensor force, rather than as a realistic representation of the ^3S N–N interaction. It is used here primarily for the purposes of connecting the phenomenological high energy phase shifts to low energies, since there has been a tendency for the past twenty years for the low energy and high energy N–N studies not to join to each other.

Let us now turn our attention to the P and D phase shifts whose scales are given on the right. Note that the ^3P phases range from about 20° to $-30°$. The rather precise agreement between the two sets of phase shifts is due to the fact that these are determined from p–p scattering data which are known rather accurately. The fact that there are appreciable differences in the ^1P state is symptomatic of the fact that these phase shifts are largely drawn from the n–p data for which the experimental errors are much greater. Note that these P wave phase shifts are quite appreciable, which is contrary to the representation of the N–N interaction as a Serber force (which vanishes for odd states). The $^3D_1$, $^3D_2$, $^3D_3$, and ^1D phase shifts are in rather good agreement. Note that D wave phase shifts are quite substantial in the 100–300 MeV energy region, and in fact, are comparable to the S and P wave phase shifts. If ordinary forces were involved, and centrifugal shielding were entirely effective, they would be expected to be much smaller than S and P wave phase shifts. The curves marked ρ_1 are measures of the assigned mixing between the $^3S_1$ and $^3D_1$ states at various energies on the rather enlarged scale (in radians) to the left. From the disagreement between the two analyses, it is clear that the ρ_1 mixing parameter is still a poorly understood quantity. This parameter should

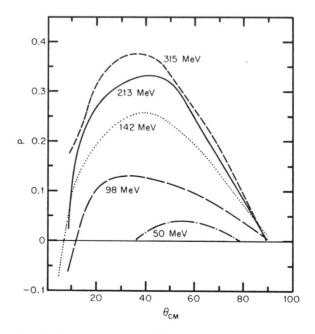

Fig. 5. Schematic diagram of high energy p–p polarization.

go over at -2.2 MeV to a mixing parameter which determines the magnetic and quadrupole moments of the deuteron, but the connection between high energy and low energy work is still not well established. The indicated markings on the three horizontal base lines give the classical impact parameters for the *S*, *P*, and *D* waves according to Eq. (65). These indicate, in a general way, the region of the N–N interaction sensed by the various partial waves at various energies.

Figure 7b gives the *F*, *G*, and *H* wave phase shifts along with the mixing parameters for $J = 2$, 3, 4, and 5 which will be discussed in Section 7.4. Here the vertical scale has been magnified by a factor of five. Note that according to the semiclassical impact parameter description these waves are primarily sensing the very outer regions of the N–N interaction. Note, also, that the phase shifts of the two groups are fairly similar, except at high energies, for several of the waves.

These two sets of N–N phase shifts, in a sense, represent the current signatures of the interaction as extracted from what is probably the most tedious and extended series of experimental and phenomenological scientific studies in the history of mankind. From their complex nature it should be clear the N–N interaction, itself, must have a complex nature. It should be remarked that even within the past two years the phenomenological phase shifts as

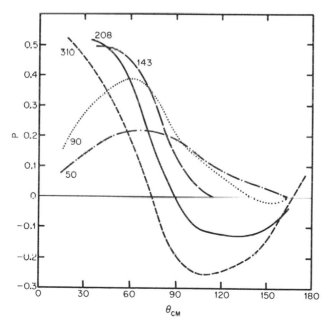

Fig. 6. Schematic diagram of high energy n–p polarization.

284

summarized in recent compilations (Nisimura, 1967; Florida, 1967) have changed quite substantially. It is this complex nature which has been the *bête noir* of nuclear physicists for the past thirty-six years, and which has, in large measure, thwarted the various attacks on the nuclear many body problem.

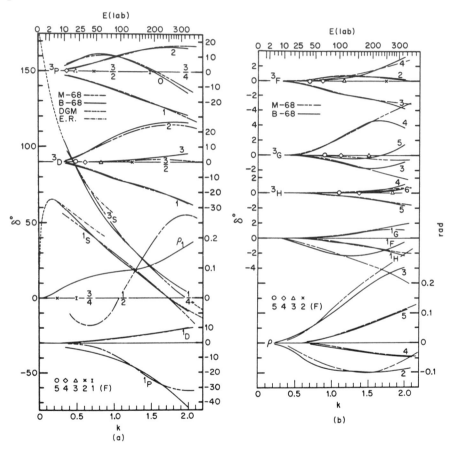

Fig. 7. (a) S, P, and D wave phase shifts and ρ (see Section 7.4), (b) F, G, and H wave phase shifts and ρ_2, ρ_3, ρ_4, and ρ_5.

Before going to the many body problem we should note several of the features of the phase shifts which have been regarded as critical in many body studies. Note that the $^1S_0$, starting out at $0°$, rises to about $60°$, and then goes rapidly down to $0°$ and crosses over to negative values near 250 MeV. A simple attractive Yukawa potential with the same effective range parameters would fall off much more slowly. The phase shifts at high energies would be down only to about $50°$ at $k = 2$ (Dutta *et al.*, 1968). Accordingly, the N–N potential must have a feature at close impact distances or higher energies which drives these S wave phase shifts towards negative values. The hard core was first proposed in this connection by Jastrow (1951). A hard core by itself leads to the S wave phase shift $\delta = -kc$, where c is the core radius, since the wave function must vanish at the core radius. Thus we see that for $c = 0.5$ F and $k \sim 2$ F^{-1}, a hard core effect could easily drive the phase shift downward to $0°$. On the other hand, it should be noted that the $^1S_0$ Morse potential indicated by the dotted line in Fig. 1 of Section 5.1, does a perfect job in fitting the $^1S_0$ phase shifts as does the $^3S_1$ Morse potential in fitting the corresponding phase shift. If these Morse functions with the parameters given in Table II were extrapolated to $r = 0$, they would yield 5.7 GeV for the $^1S_0$ state and 16.3 GeV for the $^3S_1$ state, which, while not infinite, would still be characterized as strongly repulsive. However, as we have noted in Section 5.1, the relatively weak and smooth velocity dependent potential whose $V_c(r)$ and $E_0 w(r)$ are shown in Fig. 1, Section 5.1, give about the same $^1S_0$ phase shifts. Furthermore, since there are two degrees of freedom in velocity dependent potentials, there are a large variety of possible combinations of $V_c(r)$ and $E_0 w(r)$ which will give the $^1S_0$ phase shifts (Darewych and Green, 1967). Tabakin (1964) has used another form of velocity dependent potential to fit the S wave phase shifts. Accordingly, from a purely phenomenological approach it would be difficult to resolve the question as to whether or not the N–N potential has a hard core.

7.2   Foundations of the Nuclear Shell Model

7.2a   *Infinite Nuclear Matter and the Bethe–Goldstone Equation*

The literature on the nuclear many body problem is now so vast that a detailed discussion of this literature would require several books. To this date, the greatest attention has been given to the Fermi gas model of infinite nuclear matter. This is an idealized nuclear system with an infinite number of neutrons and protons in equal numbers with the Coulomb interaction turned off. The great simplification achieved in nuclear matter calculations by this model is the possibility of using plane waves as initial IPM wave functions. We can then examine various N–N interactions to see whether or not they would lead to the saturation of nuclear energies and densities.

In early studies, saturation was attributed to the existence of various exchange forces of the nature discussed in Section 7.1. If nuclear forces were attractive in all states of relative motion, then the attractive interactions which yield a negative potential energy would build up approximately as

$\frac{1}{2}A(A-1) \sim A^2$. On the other hand, the positive kinetic energy as given by the Fermi gas model builds up only as $A^{5/3}$. Accordingly, at sufficiently large A the potential energy would overwhelm the kinetic energy and the system would collapse. Exchange forces which change sign according to the symmetry of various states provide a natural way to reduce the build up of potential energy relative to kinetic energy, and thus, possibly to account for the saturation of nuclear energies and densities.

As knowledge of the N–N interaction at high energies began to emerge in the early fifties, it influenced the approaches to the nuclear many body problem. The proposal of a hard core by Jastrow (1951) was, in part, the motivation for a new approach to the two body correlation problem made by Brueckner and his collaborators (1954). Almost from the beginning (Bethe and Bacher, 1936), this correlation problem was viewed to be a major obstacle to the application of atomic many body techniques to the nucleus. The Brueckner approach, as modified and extended by Bethe (1956a) and Goldstone (1957), is a technique for overcoming the inability of ordinary perturbation theory to deal with infinite hard core N–N interactions and strong short range correlations. In the infinite nuclear matter problem, we assume initially that the A particles are completely free within a volume Ω, and that these particles occupy the single particle levels characterized by plane waves with momentum k_α. The wave function for the state of a total system Φ_0 is written in a form of a Slater determinant of the one particle function

$$\phi_\alpha = \Omega^{-1/2} \exp(i\mathbf{k}_\alpha \cdot \mathbf{r}_i). \tag{1}$$

Φ_0 would be the solution of the problem if there were no interactions at all. Then the energy of the lowest state would be simply

$$T_0 = 4 \sum_{i=1}^{A/4} \frac{\hbar^2}{2m} k_i^2 = \frac{3}{5} A \frac{\hbar^2}{2m} k_f^2. \tag{2}$$

For the case of four different kinds of particles, each numbering $\Lambda = A/4$,

$$k_f = (3\pi^2 \rho/2)^{1/3} = (3\pi^2/2)^{1/3}/d \tag{3}$$

where $\rho = A/\Omega$ and $d = \rho^{-1/3}$. From electron scattering measurements of proton charge densities we may estimate the total particle density at the center of a heavy nucleus at

$$\rho = A/(4\pi R^3/3) = (3/4\pi)r_0^{-3} \simeq 0.166 \approx \tfrac{1}{6} \quad F^{-3}$$

where we have used $R = r_0 A^{1/3}$ with $r_0 = 1.12$ F. Thus we calculate $d \simeq 5/3$ F, $k_f \simeq 1.36$ F^{-1}, and $\lambda = k_f^{-1} = 0.675$ F, and $t_0 = T_0/A = 23.0$ MeV. The problem now is to calculate the total energy per nucleon which from the nuclear mass formula (Section 2.2) is estimated to be $E_0 = -a_1 \approx -16$ MeV.

We now go beyond the independent particle model and allow for the interaction between any pair of particles in the Fermi sea. To do so, in a practical way, we neglect the interactions of all other particles among themselves and with the pair of particles under consideration. This approximation is called by Gomes *et al.* (1958) the independent pair model (IPAM). To implement the IPAM we treat each interaction separately. Hence, we introduce a force which acts between pairs only when the particles are in the levels α and β of the Fermi distribution. If one or both particles are in any other of the occupied levels there is no interaction. Hence all levels $\gamma \neq \alpha, \beta$ are completely undisturbed by the interaction, and their wave functions are treated as plane waves. The particles in the levels α and β, however, are subject to nuclear forces, and the wave functions of such a pair $\Psi_{\alpha\beta}(\mathbf{r}_1, \mathbf{r}_2)$ will not be a product of plane waves any more. The Bethe–Goldstone equation is designed to calculate this wave function and also the energy corrections to the IPM associated with the pairing interaction.

In spite of the fact that the other particles do not interact with the pair, they have an important influence because of the exclusion principle. Thus, if the pair were embedded, it could not perform a scattering process starting with the states having the momenta $\mathbf{k}_\alpha$ and $\mathbf{k}_\beta$, and ending up with the states having different momenta, say $\mathbf{k}_\gamma$ and $\mathbf{k}_\delta$, which are occupied by other particles. On the other hand, interactions at short distances, and with large momenta changes, which require scattering to states above the Fermi surface, are permitted. Thus the Pauli principle does not prevent the wave function from being distorted at short distances.

In the usual mathematical formalism the equation governing the scattering of an isolated pair of particles is

$$(\nabla_1^2 + \nabla_2^2 + k_\alpha^2 + k_\beta^2)\psi(\mathbf{r}_1, \mathbf{r}_2) = J(\mathbf{r}_1, \mathbf{r}_2) \tag{4}$$

where

$$J(\mathbf{r}_1, \mathbf{r}_2) = (2m/\hbar^2)v(\mathbf{r}_1, \mathbf{r}_2)\psi(\mathbf{r}_1\mathbf{r}_2).$$

The solution of this equation expresses the scattering of two particles by the N–N interaction potential $v(\mathbf{r}_1, \mathbf{r}_2)$. The cross section into the end states $\mathbf{k}_\gamma, \mathbf{k}_\delta$ is

$$\sigma(\mathbf{k}_\alpha\mathbf{k}_\beta, \mathbf{k}_\gamma\mathbf{k}_\delta) = \text{const} \left| \int \exp[-i(\mathbf{k}_\gamma \cdot \mathbf{r}_1 + \mathbf{k}_\delta \cdot \mathbf{r}_2)] \, J(\mathbf{r}_1, \mathbf{r}_2) \, d\mathbf{r}_1 \, d\mathbf{r}_2 \right|^2. \tag{5}$$

If the pair is embedded in the Fermi distribution, Eq. (4) is no longer valid. Any scattering into occupied states must be forbidden. Hence the ordinary wave equation for two particles must be replaced by another equation which contains this limitation. The Bethe–Goldstone equation is designed to accommodate this limitation. It may be derived in a variety of ways [see Gomes *et al.* (GWW) (1958)]. Here we simply write it in the form

$$[(\hbar^2/2m)(\nabla_1^2 + \nabla_2^2) + E_{\alpha\beta}]\Psi_{\alpha\beta} = Q_{\alpha\beta}[v(\mathbf{r}_1, \mathbf{r}_2)\Psi_{\alpha\beta}] \tag{6}$$

where $E_{\alpha\beta}$ is the eigenvalue and $Q_{\alpha\beta}$ is a projection operator which rejects all Fourier components that are not outside the Fermi distribution except those corresponding to the level of α and β. Such an operator may be defined as follows. If $F(\mathbf{r}_1, \mathbf{r}_2)$ is an arbitrary function of $\mathbf{r}_1$ and $\mathbf{r}_2$, then the Fourier amplitude associated with the plane waves $\mathbf{k}_\gamma$ and $\mathbf{k}_\delta$ is

$$(\gamma\delta \,|\, F) = \int \phi_\gamma^*(\mathbf{r}_1)\phi_\delta^*(\mathbf{r}_2)F(\mathbf{r}_1, \mathbf{r}_2)\,d\mathbf{r}_1\,d\mathbf{r}_2. \tag{7}$$

Thus we may express $Q_{\alpha\beta} F$ as the expansion

$$Q_{\alpha\beta} F(\mathbf{r}_1, \mathbf{r}_2) = \sum_{k_\gamma > k_f} \sum_{k_\delta > k_f} \phi_\gamma(\mathbf{r}_1)\phi_\delta(\mathbf{r}_2)(\gamma\delta \,|\, F) + \phi_\alpha(\mathbf{r}_1)\phi_\beta(\mathbf{r}_2)(\alpha\beta \,|\, F). \tag{8}$$

Because of $Q_{\alpha\beta}$, the right hand side of Eq. (6) does not have any Fourier components corresponding to any energetically allowed final states differing from the initial states; and therefore, all scattering matrix elements vanish. Thus, all phase shifts are zero asymptotically for $|\mathbf{r}_1 - \mathbf{r}_2| \to \infty$. Hence (for unequal particles)

$$\Psi_{\alpha\beta}(\mathbf{r}_1, \mathbf{r}_2) \to \phi_\alpha(\mathbf{r}_1)\phi_\beta(\mathbf{r}_2). \tag{9}$$

For small distances, however, $\Psi_{\alpha\beta}$ is different from $\phi_\alpha \phi_\beta$. In fact, for very small distances $\Psi_{\alpha\beta}$ goes over to the solution of an isolated pair of nucleons, since for close collisions only the Fourier components above the Fermi distribution are relevant. Thus, we see that the exclusion principle limits the effective interaction and allows only the modulation of the unperturbed wave function at small distances. At large distances the wave function assumes its unperturbed form and, therefore, has no scattered wave. We introduce the difference

$$g(\mathbf{r}_1, \mathbf{r}_2) = \Psi_{\alpha\beta} - \phi_\alpha(\mathbf{r}_1)\phi_\beta(\mathbf{r}_2) \tag{10}$$

which is a measure of the "wound" in the embedded two particle wave function due to $v(\mathbf{r}_1, \mathbf{r}_2)$. The distance beyond which $g(\mathbf{r}_1, \mathbf{r}_2)$ becomes negligible compared to $\phi_\alpha \phi_\beta$ is called the "healing distance." For an isolated pair, the scattered wave represents a permanent effect of the wound at large distances. The healing distance is of great importance for the validity of the independent pair model. The eigenvalue $E_{\alpha\beta}$ of the Bethe–Goldstone equation determines the energy change which the interaction produces. It can be written in the form

$$E_{\alpha\beta} = (\Psi_{\alpha\beta} \,|\, (-\hbar^2/2m)(\nabla_1{}^2 + \nabla_2{}^2) + Q_{\alpha\beta} v(1, 2)|\, \Psi_{\alpha\beta}). \tag{11}$$

The energy correction due to the interaction is, therefore,

$$U_{\alpha\beta} = E_{\alpha\beta} - (\hbar^2/2m)(k_\alpha{}^2 + k_\beta{}^2). \tag{12}$$

The total energy of the system is now written in the form

$$E = T_0 + \tfrac{1}{2} \sum_{\alpha, \beta} U_{\alpha\beta}. \tag{13}$$

We must emphasize that $U_{\alpha\beta}$ is an energy correction coming from the interaction of a pair of particles in the occupied levels α and β. Hence, $U_{\alpha\beta}$ is a correction to E_0 for the hypothetical case that the interaction exists only when the particles are in the levels α and β, and that the interaction is zero for any particle which is not in α and β. These energy corrections can also be used within the framework of the independent pair model for the determination of the average potential V in which the particle moves. If the particle finds itself in the state α, the interaction with all other particles is simply

$$V(p_\alpha) = \sum_\beta U_{\alpha\beta}. \tag{14}$$

The fact that V does not depend upon position but only upon momentum, greatly simplifies studies of nuclear matter.

   To make a better approximation, the independent pair model can be made self-consistent. Here we consider the interaction between particles in a given pair of levels by setting to zero any interaction with a particle in another occupied level. However, we assume all particles move in a momentum dependent one particle potential. We then try to choose $V(p_\alpha)$ in a self-consistent way, i.e., so that the calculated $U_{\alpha\beta}$ reproduce the assumed $U_{\alpha\beta}$ used in deriving $V(p_\alpha)$.

   We come finally to the problem of solving for $E_{\alpha\beta}$ which requires the solution of Eqs. (6) and (11). Investigations as to the nature and effect of the projection operator have been carried out by Bethe and Goldstone (1957) and by GWW, who find that the wound in $\Psi_{\alpha\beta}$ due to the hard core is healed within a healing distance of the order of magnitude of λ_f. Figure 1 illustrates the $l = 0$ wave function for the simple case of a repulsive core interaction between an isolated pair $u_i(r)$ and a pair embedded in a Fermi distribution, $u_e(r)$. Also shown is the case of no interaction $u_0(r)$.

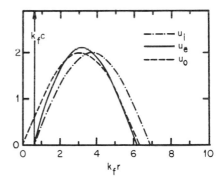

Fig. 1. The wave function of the relative motion in the S state of 2 particles. For no interaction it is given by u_0. For a repulsive core interaction it is given by u_i for an isolated pair, and by u_e for a pair embedded in a fermi distribution. Here $k = 1.48 \ \mathrm{F}^{-1}$ and the relative momentum is $0.3k_f$.

7.2b   The GWW IPAM

In the Gomes–Walecka–Weisskopf study, a Serber type exchange force in conjunction with the central potential is examined in detail. Thus

$$v(r) = v_c + v_a(r)$$

$$v_a(r) = -\tfrac{1}{2}(1 + P_m)v_0\,\eta(r)$$

$$\eta(r) = 0 \quad (r < c,\, r > b), \qquad \eta(r) = 1 \quad (c < r < b) \tag{15}$$

$$v_0 = \hbar^2\pi^2/4m(b - c)^2 = 28.34 \quad \text{MeV}, \qquad c = 0.4 \quad \text{F}, \qquad b = 2.3 \quad \text{F}$$

Figure 2a,b illustrates the wave functions $(R/2)^{1/2}u_e(r)/kr$ (solid lines) and $(R/2)^{1/2}u_0(r)/kr$ (dashed lines) for a pair of embedded particles, with and without interactions. In Fig. 2a, $k = 0.3$ F^{-1} ($k_f = 1.48$ F^{-1}). The average distance d to the next neighbor is indicated. The dotted line labeled s_m represents an estimate of the Moszkowski–Scott separation distance to be described in the next subsection. Figure 2b gives the corresponding graph for $k = 0.6$ F^{-1}.

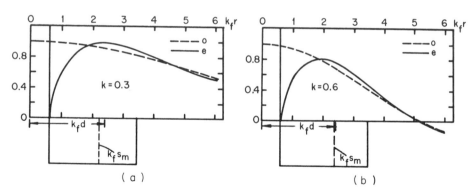

Fig. 2. Value of u_e/kr of the s state wave function for a pair embedded in a Fermi distribution, and value of u_0/kr for a noninteracting pair.

[(a) Here $k_f = 1.48$ F^{-1} and the relative momentum is $k = 0.3k_f$. The Moszkowski–Scott separation distance $s_m = 1.49$ F is indicated by the dotted lines labeled s_m. (b) Same quantities for $k = 0.6k_f$, $s_m = 1.61$ F.]

A number of factors play an essential role in the GWW view and explain what particular features of the nuclear interaction are responsible for the properties of nuclear matter. First, the existence of a repulsive core not only prevents the nucleus from collapsing, but is also small enough to allow the Bethe–Goldstone wave function to heal within a distance less than the average distance between particles ($d = \rho^{-1/3} \approx 1.66$ F). The comparative weakness of the attractive potential also plays an important role. This weakness has two effects. First, it causes the nuclear density to be rather low so that d is much larger than the core radius. The use of a Serber potential which leads to no attraction in the P state is also of importance since this then permits the healing distance to be smaller than d. The D state interaction is assumed to be shielded by the centrifugal barrier. The weakness, together with the relatively long range of v_a has the following effect. The modulation of the isolated pair function caused by the attractive part contains only rather long wavelength Fourier components, i.e., those whose wave lengths are mainly less than k_f^{-1}. Therefore, this modulation is essentially eliminated by the exclusion principle. Thus, at the average separation between particles the effective N N interaction is very weak.

Once the Bethe–Goldstone wave function has been obtained, the $U_{\alpha\beta}$ can be calculated and then $V(p)$ may be found in a self-consistent way. Then Eq. (13) gives the total energy in terms of $U_{\alpha\beta}$. Since all quantities are functions of the Fermi momenta, and therefore of p, we can seek out a density which has a minimum, which then gives the desired a_1 values and ρ for nuclear matter. In their calculations, Gomes *et al.* (1958) found that the embedded $\Psi_{\alpha\beta}$ are not very different from the free particle wave functions at longer ranges. At shorter ranges they approximated $\Psi_{\alpha\beta}$ by a wave function of two isolated interacting particles. Thus, the core contribution to the total energy can be taken as that calculated from a nuclear Fermi gas of particles with mass m^* and with repulsive cores only. From studies by Huang and Yang (1957), Martin and de Dominicis (1957), and Bethe and Goldstone (1957), the repulsive core contributes a pseudopotential given by

$$V_c = 2 \frac{\hbar^2 k_f^2}{2m} (1 + \beta) \left[\frac{2}{\pi} ck_f + \frac{12}{35\pi^2} (11 - 2 \ln 2)c^2 k_f^2 + 0.26c^3 k_f^3 \right] \quad (16)$$

where k_f is the momentum of the particle at the top of the Fermi sea. It is assumed here that this potential is local, i.e., nonvelocity dependent.

To evaluate the contribution to the single particle potential associated with the attractive part of the two body force, we must obtain its expectation with respect to the wave functions which are solutions of the Bethe–Goldstone equation. By virtue of the exclusion principle, which precludes scattering (in N–N collisions) to the occupied states of the Fermi sea, the Bethe–Goldstone wave functions are fairly similar to the free particle wave functions. Accordingly, as a crude approximation we may evaluate the influence of the attractive two body potentials simply by using the Born approximation.

The Serber force has zero expectation for identical particles, i.e., same spin and isotopic spin. For unequal particles with momenta k_α and k_β, the wave function in the Born approximation is

$$\Phi = \Omega^{-1} \exp(i\mathbf{k} \cdot \mathbf{r}) \exp(i\mathbf{K} \cdot \mathbf{R}) \quad (17)$$

where

$$\mathbf{k} = (\mathbf{k}_\alpha - \mathbf{k}_\beta)/2, \qquad \mathbf{K} = \mathbf{k}_\alpha + \mathbf{k}_\beta$$

$$\mathbf{r} = \mathbf{r}_1 - \mathbf{r}_2, \qquad \mathbf{R} = (\mathbf{r}_1 + \mathbf{r}_2)/2 \tag{18}$$

and Ω is the volume of the system. The results of the GWW calculation lead to the self-consistent value $m^* = 0.68m$ at the equilibrium density corresponding to $k_f = 1.35 \text{ F}^{-1}$. The energies at that density are $T_0/A = 22.8$, $V_c/A = 27.7$ MeV, and $V_a/A = -57.4$ MeV. While this $E/A = -6.9$ MeV is considerably less than -16 MeV, nevertheless, the difference is only 14% of the contribution of the attractive potential energy.

Some explicit analytic calculations were carried out based upon GWW by Green (1958b,c), whose purpose was to evaluate the parameters V^*, β and the radial parameter a in a finite nucleus velocity dependent IPM [see Eq. (14), Section 5.2]. The expectation of the attractive two body interaction relative to the two body wave function given by Eq. (17) is

$$U_{\alpha\beta} = \frac{1}{\Omega} \int_0^\infty v_a(r) \Phi^* \Phi \, d\mathbf{r} = -\frac{4\pi v_0}{\Omega} \int_0^\infty \frac{\eta(r)}{2} [1 + j_0(2kr)] r^2 \, dr. \tag{19}$$

For a fixed momentum (k_α) of a single particle, one must now know the distribution of relative momenta k of the other sets of particles. Brueckner (1954), using the results of a study of Hill and Wheeler (1953), has shown that, to an approximation which includes consideration of some surface effects, this distribution function is given by

$$P(k_\alpha, k) = 24\Lambda k^2/k_f{}^3, \qquad k < \tfrac{1}{2}(k_f - k_\alpha)$$

$$= 3\Lambda k(k_f{}^2 - k_\alpha{}^2 - 4k^2 + 4kk_\alpha)/k_\alpha k_f{}^3, \tag{20}$$

$$\tfrac{1}{2}(k_f - k_\alpha) < k < \tfrac{1}{2}(k_f + k_\alpha).$$

Using Eq. (20) in conjunction with Eq. (19), it follows that the potential acting on a single particle of momentum k_α by Λ unequal particles is

$$V(k_\alpha) = \sum_\beta U_{\alpha\beta} = -\frac{\Lambda}{R^3} \frac{V_0}{2} (b^3 - c^3) + \frac{V_0}{\pi} [g(k_\alpha k_f b) - g(k_\alpha, k_f, c)] \tag{21a}$$

where

$$g(k_\alpha, k_f, b) = \tfrac{1}{2}[\text{Si}(bk_f + bk_\alpha) + \text{Si}(bk_f - bk_\alpha)] - \sin(bk_f)(\sin bk_\alpha)/bk_\alpha \tag{21b}$$

where Si is the integral sine function. The momentum dependence of the g function on k_α gives rise to the nonlocality or the effective mass associated with the single particle potential.

To evaluate the effective mass m^* or the corresponding parameter $\beta = (m/m^*) - 1$, we assume that $V(k_\alpha)$ is parabolic in k_α in the neighborhood of the Fermi surface. It then follows simply from the properties of the g function that

$$\beta = \frac{m}{\hbar^2} \frac{1}{k_\alpha} \frac{\partial V}{\partial k_\alpha}\bigg|_{k_\alpha = k_f} = \frac{V_0 m}{\pi \hbar^2 k_f^2} [Z(b) - Z(c)] \tag{22}$$

where

$$Z(b) = \tfrac{1}{4} \sin 2bk_f - \tfrac{1}{2} bk_f - (\sin^2 bk_f)/bk_f \tag{23}$$

We must multiply Eqs. (21) and (22) by three to obtain the total effect of the three sets of unequal particles upon any one particle. Using certain considerations as to surface thickness made by Swiatecki (1951), it is possible to identify approximately the radial parameter a of the exponentially diffuse potential with the radius parameter $R = r_0 A^{1/3}$. Thus using Eqs. (21), (22), and Eq. (14) of Section 5.2, we may calculate E_T, V^*, and β as a function of r_0 in a way which is applicable to a finite nucleus. For the GWW two body parameters we obtain a minimum total energy -4.20 MeV near $r_0 = 1.2$ with $V_a = 93.0$, $V_c = -43.4$ for $V^* = 49.6$, and $\beta = 0.535$. Since surface effects were allowed for at $A^{1/3} = 5$ in this calculation, this number should be compared with a standard value -12.0. An increase of 20% in the two body well depth, i.e., from 28.3 to 34, gave the value $-E_t/A = -10.11$, with $\beta = 0.642$ and $V^* = -65.4$. Here $V_a = 111.6$ and $-V_c = 46.2$. These values are of the same order as those deduced from phenomenological studies of the IPM.

The extension of the work to an actual nucleus for which $N \neq Z$ is straightforward. When different potentials are used for the ^1S and ^3S interactions, which in effect take into account some influence of the tensor force, we find that V^* also depends upon the symmetry parameter in a reasonable way. Thus, the derived potential resembles in a general way the velocity and symmetry dependent potentials inferred from phenomenological investigations. The mass formula so obtained is quite similar to the Bethe–Weizsäcker mass formula, and can be reduced to the BW form with a surface symmetry energy by making some reasonable approximations.

7.2c   The Separation Method and the Reaction Matrix

An important advance in our understanding of the N–N interaction in nuclear matter has been contributed by Moszkowski and Scott (1960) and Scott and Moszkowski (1961) in their development of the so-called separation method. This MS method proceeds by separating the N–N interaction into a short range part v_s and a long range part v_l. The separation distance is chosen at the distance s_m so that

$$(u_i'/u_i)_{s_m} = (u_0'/u_0)_{s_m} \tag{24}$$

where u_i is the radial wave function for isolated two particle scattering in the presence of the N–N interaction, and u_0 is the radial wave function at the corresponding distance when the two particles are noninteracting. For example for the GWW S wave two body potential, this separation point would be in the attractive region at a point which satisfies

$$(k^2 + \kappa^2)^{1/2} \cot(k^2 + \kappa^2)^{1/2}(s_m - c) = k \cot k s_m \qquad (25)$$

where $\kappa^2 = MV_0/\hbar^2 = 0.682$. At $k = 0$, this point would be at $s_m = 1.45$. Other values are illustrated in Fig. 2a, b. Thus, we see that v_s includes a substantial part of the attractive potential. Indeed the separation point has been chosen so that the attractive region of v_s just compensates for the effect of the repulsive core on the logarithmic derivative of the wave function. Recalling that it is u'/u which determines the phase shift, we see that if v_s were acting alone, the N–N phase shift would vanish. In effect the s_m is chosen so that the short range part gives a zero phase shift for free N–N scattering. The long range part is the remaining part of the interaction. Clearly the separation distance depends upon momentum and also upon the angular momentum of the state. Hence, effectively, the long range interaction is velocity dependent, i.e., nonlocal, if expressed in coordinate space. As relative momentum increases, the particle spends less time in the attractive region and thus feels the attraction less. The repulsion does not become any less effective at high energies, but rather, as the momentum increases more of the attraction is needed to cancel away the effect of the repulsion. Thus, the residual long range part becomes weaker and weaker.

Not only is the residual long range part intrinsically weak, but in nuclear matter its influence upon embedded N–N wave functions is greatly suppressed by the effect of the exclusion principle.

The fact that s_m depends on the relative momentum in a fashion such as to "chew" away v_l, is of great importance in accounting for saturation. Thus, if the nucleus were compressed, its average relative momentum would increase. Then the separation distance would become larger which would make the residual interaction weaker.

To calculate now the total energy, we define a reaction operator variously denoted by the symbols K, G, and t using

$$t\phi(k) = v\psi(k) \qquad (26)$$

where ψ denotes the correct two-particle wave function of specified k, in the nuclear medium. The wave function ψ must be normalized such that

$$\int \phi\psi \, dr = \int \phi^2 \, dr \qquad (27)$$

i.e., $\psi - \phi$ is orthogonal to ϕ. Then the diagonal element of the reaction operator or the t matrix is given by,

$$t_{\alpha\alpha} = (4\pi/\Omega) \int v(r)\phi\psi \, dr. \tag{28}$$

According to the theory of Brueckner (1954), Bethe (1956a), and Bethe and Goldstone (1957), the nuclear energy is given by an expression including an exchange term with precisely the usual form from perturbation theory, i.e.,

$$E = \sum_{\alpha} T_{\alpha} + \sum_{\alpha} \sum_{\beta} (t_{\alpha\beta,\,\alpha\beta} - t_{\alpha\beta,\,\beta\alpha}) + \cdots \tag{29}$$

except that the t matrix serves as an effective N–N interaction. We see that a knowledge of the two-particle wave function in nuclear matter is thus needed to calculate the t matrix and then the nuclear energy.

According to Moszkowski and Scott, a simple first approximation to the two-particle wave function ψ for $r < s_m$ is u_i, the wave function of an isolated interacting two nucleon system (in the absence of the Pauli principle), and the purely unperturbed wave function u_0 for $r > s_m$. This enables us to obtain a first approximation to the t matrix, and therefore, to the nuclear energy.

The diagonal element of the expansion for the reaction matrix t in nuclear matter obeys the equation

$$t_{\alpha\alpha} = v_{\alpha\alpha} + \sum_{\gamma} v_{\alpha\gamma} \frac{Q(\gamma)}{e(\gamma) - e(\alpha)} t_{\gamma\alpha}. \tag{30}$$

The quantity $Q(\gamma)$ is unity if, in the intermediate state γ, both nucleons are outside the Fermi sea, and zero if either one or both are inside. We can rewrite the equation in shorthand notation as

$$t = v + v \frac{Q}{e} t. \tag{31}$$

If we now separate the two body interaction into a short range and long range part

$$v - v_{\mathrm{s}} + v_{l} \tag{32}$$

we may calculate the reaction matrix due to the separate parts as a perturbation expansion.

The beauty of the Moszkowski–Scott separation method is that the linear term in t_{s} vanishes and that all terms involving t_{s} in the expansion are small or absent. Furthermore, for a calculation of the energy we may obtain good results by assuming $t_l = v_l$. With this approximation Eqs. (17)–(23) are applicable if one replaces c by s_m and ignores Eq. (16). Thus, v_l can be qualitatively regarded as the effective two body interaction. When we look at the effective interaction (see Fig. 2a,b), we see that it would favor having the two particles about 1 to 1.5 F apart. Furthermore, the fact that the separation distance s_m increases with both k and ρ also plays a role since as the density of ρ increases, the average value of k also increases, and hence the long range potential v_l becomes weaker, which is helpful in achieving saturation.

Moszkowski and Scott (1960) and Scott and Moszkowski (1961), in their detailed calculations with the GWW potential, did not find an equilibrium near $k_f \simeq 1.4$ F^{-1} as obtained by GWW, although their binding energy at this k_f agreed fairly well with GWW. They attributed the discrepancy to the neglect of certain interference terms in the reaction matrix. Using a hard core of radius 0.4 F, followed by an attractive exponential well with parameters chosen to give $a_s = \infty$ and $r_0 = 2.5$ F, they obtained a minimum of -24 MeV at a density corresponding to $1.0A^{1/3}$ F.

In a subsequent effort using the more realistic Gammel–Thaler 17 parameter phenomenological potential (Gammel and Thaler, 1957) they obtained $E/A = -14.2$ MeV at $k_f = 1.5$ F^{-1}. The contributions of the various states were particularly interesting. Their zero order contribution due to the ^1S interaction was -19.5 MeV, and that due to the $^3S_1$ interaction was -8.4 MeV. The second Born correction to the triplet was -5.8. The various short range corrections associated with the singlet converged rapidly. The triplet tended to give a series of large components coming mainly from the tensor force. The largeness was a feature only of terms up to the second order, however, since third and fourth order terms were much smaller (Brown, 1967).

The approximation $t = v_l$ is clearly rather crude, and recent work has been heavily concerned with finding more precise ways of arriving at the reaction matrix. This problem was attacked by Brueckner and Gammel (1958) with computer techniques. However, Bethe et al. (1963) have found a much better method of calculating the t matrix which is called the reference spectrum method (Day, 1967).

In the reference spectrum method, the spectrum of the intermediate states is replaced by a reference spectrum of the form $A + k^2/2m^*$, where the constants A and m^* are chosen so as to approximate as closely as possible the actual particle energies. The region of high virtual excitation is particularly important for the calculation of the short range t matrix. In this region which is far " off the energy shell " the approximations $m^* \sim 1.0$ and $A \sim 0$ are used.

The basic idea of the BBP reference spectrum method is to replace Q/e by a simpler operator which finally yields two advantages: (1) it allows the determination of ψ by a differential equation rather than an integro-differential equation, hence making it much easier to compute than by the Brueckner–Gammel method; (2) it provides a systematic way of improving the approximation which is a major advantage in the quantitative study of higher order diagrams in the Brueckner–Goldstone expansion. The subject cannot be dealt with in full here, but we refer the reader to the recent review articles by Day (1967), Rajaraman and Bethe (1967), and by Brandow (1967) for details on these techniques.

The study by Bethe (1968) of the Thomas–Fermi finite nucleus model represents a recent application of nuclear matter studies to finite nuclei. Realistic forces with a repulsive core are chosen at the outset. Some simplifications are used, e.g., tensor forces are replaced by density dependent effective central forces and the Slater–Dirac approximation to the mixed density is used. The total energy of the nucleus is used to derive an integral equation for the density $\rho(r)$ which is approximated by an analytically solvable differential equation. The density distributions obtained are consistent with electron scattering experiments. The results represent a promising application of the nuclear matter approach to finite nuclei.

7.2d Hartree–Fock Calculations of Finite Nuclei

In the early 1960's, applications of the Brueckner Bethe–Goldstone theory to nuclear matter (Brueckner and Masterson, 1962; Razavy, 1963; Bethe, 1965) appeared to lead to underbinding. Since the calculations were exceedingly complex, a number of investigators began to reexamine the possibility of using smoother N–N interactions in conjunction with ordinary perturbation theory or Hartree Fock techniques. The success of realistic shell and optical models indicated that something like a velocity dependent Hartree–Fock N–$\mathcal{N}$ potential was valid (Peierls, 1959). If the N–N potential were represented by a smooth velocity dependent potential rather than by one with a hard core, perhaps the derivation of the HF energy could be carried out by perturbation theory (Peierls, 1960). This suggestion was the motivation for studies of the N–N interaction by A. M. Green (1962), Razavy et al. (1962), and others referred to in Section 5.1d.

It turns out that there are numerous combinations of nonhard core central potentials and velocity dependent components which can adequately account for the $^1S_0$ and $^3S_1$ phase shifts. For example, without any velocity dependence, we can do very well using a Morse potential or other so-called soft core potentials. Varying quadratic velocity dependent potentials with the smooth $v_0(r)$ and $w(r)$ characterized by Eqs. (7)–(9) of Section 5.1 has also been used successfully. In addition Tabakin and Davies (1966) have successfully utilized a smooth velocity dependent potential of the form

$$V(r, p) = -V_1(r) + p^2 \exp(-s^2 p^2) V_2(r) + V_2(r) p^2 \exp(-s^2 p^2). \qquad (33)$$

A number of meson theoretical potentials which fit the $^1S_0$ and $^3S_1$ phase shifts precisely (Green and Sawada, 1967b,c) have substantially different degrees of velocity dependence (Darewych and Green, 1967). The important point to be made is that the variety of smooth N–N interactions predicated upon phenomenological considerations, and upon field theoretic considerations, possibly affords the opportunity to deal with the many body problem using more conventional Hartree–Fock techniques. Here we write the Hamiltonian

$$H = \sum_{i=1}^{A} T_i + \sum_{i<j}^{A} V_{ij} = H_0 + H_1 \tag{34}$$

where the unperturbed IPM Hamiltonian is

$$H_0 = \sum_{i=1}^{A} (T_i + V_i) \tag{35}$$

and the perturbation

$$H_1 = \sum_{i<j}^{A} V_{ij} - \sum_{i=1}^{A} V_i \tag{36}$$

represents what is left over. The final results should be independent of V. In practice we must choose V in such a way that the perturbation expansion converges as rapidly as possible. A good choice for V would be the self-consistent field obtained from a Hartree–Fock self-consistent field calculation. Presumably the V bears a resemblance to the nonlocal or velocity dependent shell model potentials which have been inferred from the phenomenological studies, and which have been the major concern of this monograph. However, as yet few studies have reached the point of using modern nuclear forces in finite nucleus calculations, so that this remains an article of faith. Thus far, those pursuing HF techniques have adopted the approach of searching for N–N potentials which require only small corrections to the Hartree–Fock approximation. The properties of such potentials, as noted by Davies *et al.* (1967), should be (1) that they be sufficiently simple to permit systematic calculations, (2) that they yield the correct energy, density, and symmetry energy in nuclear matter, (3) that second order corrections be small, and (4) that the N–N data be fitted as well as possible. Proceeding with this pragmatic philosophy, Baranger and his associates first made use of the Tabakin potential as a reasonable one for the purposes of studying the methods of approach to the many body problem (Baranger, 1967; Davies *et al.*, 1967; Krieger *et al.*, 1966, 1967).

It should be noted that the Hartree–Fock approach represents only the first term in a perturbation expansion known as the Goldstone expansion. The Hartree–Fock approximation is valid when the Goldstone expansion series converges rapidly, the second order term (i.e., two body correlation effects) being small with respect to the first, the third order term (i.e., three body correlation effects) even smaller, etc. Thus the primary aim of this approach in selection of N–N potentials was to find one which converged rapidly in this way. The aim, in dealing with such an interaction, was to obtain practical calculations for realistic nuclei. Investigators who have joined in this general effort are Kerman and Pal (1967) and Hughes *et al.* (1967).

Somewhat earlier investigations of this nature were carried out on O^{16} by Talman (1956) who obtained a collapsed nucleus using a simple Yukawa function. Swamy and Green (1957) carried out a similar study using a soft core potential consisting of a long range attractive Yukawa, and a short range repulsive Yukawa, of the form

$$v(\mathbf{r}_1, \mathbf{r}_2) = -a \frac{\exp(-\kappa_a r)}{r} + b \frac{\exp(-\kappa_b r)}{r} \tag{37}$$

where $r = |\mathbf{r}_1 - \mathbf{r}_2|$ and a and b are the attractive and repulsive coupling constants respectively. The calculations were carried out by using analytic functions of the form $r^n e^{-\kappa r}$ for the $1S$ and $1P$ state, which approximated rather well the radial $1S$ and $1P$ wave functions for the Ed potential discussed in Section 2.2. Then scaling factors were used as variational parameters. Using a number of approximations to facilitate hand calculation, reasonable results were obtained when b in the P state was made somewhat larger than in the S state (Swamy, 1961).

In precision Hartree–Fock calculations, two routes are possible, routes which have been used extensively in atomic calculations. The older route uses the coordinate representation in which the wave functions are obtained by the solution of integro-differential equations. The second route expands the radial wave function into a set of orthogonal wave functions which are usually taken as the harmonic oscillator wave functions. Then a variational calculation is used which determines the mixing coefficient in such a way as to minimize the total energy. The advantage of this procedure is obvious. If the IPM functions are close to oscillator functions anyway, only a few terms of the series are needed to get a good representation. In other words, a rather small set of oscillator functions are needed. Instead of solving integro-differential equations, we diagonalize small real symmetric matrices, which is a fairly standard computational procedure. Furthermore, the oscillator representation is easy to use with almost any form of two body interaction. We can write each product of two oscillator IPM wave functions in terms of center of mass and relative coordinates using transformations developed by Talmi (1952) and Moshinsky (1959).

One of the problems of the harmonic oscillator representation is the fact that it is hard to get the tails of the IPM wave functions correctly, since these tails should be exponential while all oscillator functions are Gaussian. A more serious problem is the fact that it is hard to extract the IPM potential in the coordinate representation since this is not needed in any part of the calculation. The IPM potential obtained, however, is nonlocal. Calculations of Kreiger et al. (1967), Davies et al. (1967), and Shakin et al. (1967a,b), indicate that harmonic oscillator wave functions are very good for the occupied states, particularly the strongly bound states. On the other hand, the results are not very accurate for the unoccupied states which are needed also for many calculations, since deviations from harmonic oscillator states are rather large. Baranger (1967) finds that total energies and single particle energies do not change very greatly as the dimensionality of the basis set is changed. Indeed, remarkably consistent results are obtained, and only the levels which are very close to zero energy have difficulty converging as expected.

A substantial group doing Hartree–Fock calculations make use of the t matrix as the effective N–N interaction rather than the N–N potential itself, (Pal and Stamp, 1967). This approach makes use of the studies of infinite nuclear matter which we have discussed, and takes advantage of the quick healing of the correlated wave functions with respect to the uncorrelated wave functions. In effect, the actual short range correlatation, present in the pair wave function, is taken into account by using the effective potential along with the uncorrelated wave functions.

In calculations of the t matrix we must give consideration to three sets of states: (1) the occupied states, (2) the unoccupied states which lie just above the occupied states, and (3) the states which lie well above the occupied states. The importance of the low lying unoccupied states is that they are mixed by the residual interaction, particularly in the nuclei with unfilled major shells. Mixing then may cause pairing phenomena in the ground state or an intrinsic deformation to a nonspherical state. The high lying unoccupied states are important in that these are the states to which a pair of nucleons scatter (virtually) as a result of strong N–N interactions. In the calculation of the correlated pair wave function and hence the t matrix, these high lying, excited, intermediate states play an important role. The effect of these excited, intermediate states must be taken into account in the calculation of the t matrix elements, which then, should be used with the occupied and unoccupied states to calculate the ground state and low energy properties in the nucleus. This double self-consistency requirement is very cumbersome to impose in practice (Kuo and Brown, 1965). To bypass this difficulty, the self-consistency requirement in the calculations of the t matrix is frequently dealt with by using some simplifying assumption. Thus calculations, usually carried out with the t matrix elements of a given phenomenological N–N potential, are determined once and for all by using harmonic oscillator wave functions and energies. Then these t matrices are used as inputs into a standard Hartree–Fock calculation of the type discussed in connection with Baranger's studies. Shakin et al. (1967a,b) report results on closed shell nuclei of O^{16} and Ca^{40} using effective interactions derived from the Yale hard core potentials.

The results show that the binding energies are sensitive to the oscillator parameters $\hbar\omega = 41.6/b^2$ to a degree which depends on many details. They particularly examine the double self-consistency requirement which greatly complicates the Hartree–Fock approach. Their conclusion is that reasonable agreement with the ground state properties of nuclei may be obtained by starting from a realistic potential which fits the N–N scattering data. They call attention to the need for the self-consistent approach to calculating the t matrix.

Pal and Stamp (1967) carry out similar calculations for nonspherical nuclei and obtain rather reasonable results using the hard core Yale potential. They use a rather limited basis set, going only to oscillator states with one additional node beyond the occupied orbitals.

To summarize, the situation seems to be that there are two schools of approach to the finite nucleus problem. The predominant school starts from a N–N force which, to date, has been mostly the Yale, Hamada–Johnston, Reid, or Bressel potentials, which all have hard cores. These groups then use effective t matrix elements in their nuclear structure calculation. The second school uses the smooth potentials of Tabakin, Brink and Boeker, and Baranger, in which case they use the v matrix elements directly (Stamp, 1967).

Moszkowski (1967) recently summarized the work of groups using hard core potentials along with Brueckner–Hartree–Fock techniques. The ground state properties of light nuclei, using a number of hard core N–N potentials, are found to lead to nuclei which are underbound. C. Wong (1967), and Köhler and McCarthy (1967) report similar difficulties. While the methodology of the t matrix and harmonic oscillator functions is complicated and hence somewhat suspect, it would appear likely that it is the N–N interaction that is at fault.

There are many other approaches to the nuclear many body problem which we have not described. These include the statistical mechanics Green's function method invented by Martin and Schwinger (Puff, 1961), the Lee and Yang statistical theory (Mohling, 1962), and the Jastrow–Feenberg method of correlated wave functions (Clark and Westhaus, 1966). In addition there have been extensive recent efforts on the three and four body problems which fall somewhat outside the scope of this work. We refer the reader to the recent articles of Tang and Herndon (1967), Jain and Srivastava (1967), and Meyerhof and Tombrello (1968) for up-to-date guides to these subjects.

7.3 Foundations of the Optical Model

7.3a The Optical Model at High Energies

It should be clear that much remains to be done before we achieve a fundamental understanding of the structure of the nucleus in its ground state.

Such an understanding will be needed before we can hope to explain, from a basic N–N interaction, the additional dynamical aspects of the IPM involved in the optical model. Nevertheless, a vast theoretical literature has developed on the formal derivation of the optical model potential. Since major review articles are available, we shall concentrate our attention on the simplest physical aspects of these studies and simply supply summaries of major results.

Let us derive the N–$\mathcal{N}$ potential in a form suitable for the discussions at high energies. The Schroedinger equation for the N–$\mathcal{N}$ system is

$$\mathcal{H}\Psi = E\Psi \tag{1}$$

where

$$\mathcal{H} = H_0 + V \tag{2}$$

with $H_0 = K_0 + H_A$, and $V = \sum_{i=1}^{A} v(\mathbf{r}_0, \mathbf{r}_i)$. Here K_0 is the kinetic energy operator of the incident nucleon, H_A is the target Hamilton, and $v(\mathbf{r}_0, \mathbf{r}_i)$ is the two nucleon interaction between the incident and the ith target nucleon.

Defining the eigenfunction of H_A with eigenvalue ε_n by Φ_n, the eigenfunction of H_0 can be written as

$$\Phi_{n,\mathbf{k}} = \Phi_n(1, \ldots, A)(2\pi)^{-3/2} \exp(i\mathbf{k}\cdot\mathbf{r}_0). \tag{3}$$

The integral representation of Eq. (1) can be written as (Lippman and Schwinger, 1950)

$$\Psi_{\mathbf{k}}^{(+)} = \Phi_{0,\mathbf{k}} + (E^+ - H_0)^{-1}V\Psi_{\mathbf{k}}^{(+)}. \tag{4}$$

The transition operator T is defined by

$$T(n\mathbf{k}' \leftarrow 0\mathbf{k}) = (\Phi_{n\mathbf{k}'}, T\Phi_{0\mathbf{k}}) = (\Phi_{n\mathbf{k}'}, V\Psi_{\mathbf{k}}^{(+)}). \tag{5}$$

Representing the wave matrix operator Ω by $\Psi_{\mathbf{k}}^{(+)} = \Omega\Phi_{0\mathbf{k}}$, we find from Eq. (5) $T = V\Omega$, and from Eq. (4)

$$\Omega = 1 + (E^+ - H_0)^{-1}V\Omega. \tag{6}$$

Multiplying Eq. (6) by V from the left, we find the integral equation for T

$$T = V[1 + (E^+ - H_0)^{-1}T] = Av[1 + (E^+ - H_0)^{-1}T]. \tag{7}$$

We remark that, since both the initial and final nuclear states are antisymmetric, and V and H_0 are symmetric with respect to the interchange of particles, we can restrict the definitions of the operators appearing in Eq. (7) to the subspace of antisymmetric wave functions of the target nucleus (Kerman et al., 1959).

For isolated two nucleon scattering, we have $A = 1$ and $H_0 = K_0$. Using the symbol t for the two body operator, Eq. (7) becomes

$$t = v[1 + (E^+ - K_0)^{-1}t]. \tag{8}$$

For the collision of two nucleons inside the nucleus this expression is modified by the presence of other nucleons. The corresponding transition operator τ, i.e.,

$$\tau = v[1 + (E^+ - H_0)^{-1}\tau] \qquad (9)$$

is now a many body operator.

Solving Eq. (9) for v, we find $v = [1 + \tau(E^+ - H_0)^{-1}]^{-1}\tau$. From Eq. (7), we find $T = [1 - Av(E^+ - H_0)^{-1}]^{-1}Av$. Substituting the former expression of v into the latter, we find

$$T = A\tau[1 + (E^+ - H_0)^{-1}T] \qquad (10)$$

where terms of order A^{-1} have been neglected.

Equation (10) is of the same form as Eq. (7). As will be explained in the beginning of Section 7.3c by introducing projection operators P and Q, with P on the target ground state and Q off it, we can derive from Eq. (1) the equivalent N–$\mathcal{N}$ potential

$$V_{\text{opt}} = \langle \Phi_0 | V[1 + (E^+ - H_0 - QV)^{-1}QV] | \Phi_0 \rangle \qquad (11)$$

[see Eq. (29)]. Just as Eq. (11) is the equivalent N–$\mathcal{N}$ potential corresponding to Eq. (7), the equivalent N–$\mathcal{N}$ potential corresponding to Eq. (10) is

$$V_{\text{opt}} = \langle \Phi_0 | A\tau[1 + (E^+ - H_0 - QA\tau)^{-1}QA\tau] | \Phi_0 \rangle. \qquad (12)$$

Equations (11) and (12) are the same "generalized" optical potential, but the latter expansion is more convenient for the discussions at high energies.

We now restrict our attention to scattering at high energies. The lowest order treatment is based on the following argument.

Consider the second term in Eq. (12). This corresponds to inelastic scattering of the incident particle accompanied by an excitation of the target nucleus, and subsequent inelastic scattering back to the ground state. Such a process requires the existence of strong correlations among the target nucleons with ranges shorter than the wavelength of the incident particle (Feshbach, 1958b). At sufficiently high energies, these effects are presumably small. The neglect of these effects constitutes the *multiple scattering approximation* (Watson, 1953; Francis and Watson, 1953).

Next consider the first term in Eq. (12). Equation (9) implies that this term corresponds to the scattering of the incoming particle by a target nucleon, with the scattering modified by the presence of the other nucleons. These modifications are also due to correlations among particles and are presumably small at high energies. The neglect of such effects is called the *impulse approximation* (Chew, 1950; Chew and Wick, 1952; Chew and Goldberger, 1952). This implies the replacement of $\langle \phi_0 | \tau | \phi_0 \rangle$ by $\langle \phi_0 | t | \phi_0 \rangle$. The correction for the impulse approximation is of order $1/A$ smaller than the correction for the multiple scattering approximation. Having isolated the dominant terms, we thus write

$$V_{opt} \simeq A\langle\phi_0 |t| \phi_0\rangle. \tag{13}$$

The relation of V_{opt} with the two nucleon scattering amplitude can be found using the momentum space representation $V_{opt}(k', k) = \langle\exp(ik' \cdot r_0) |V_{opt}| \exp(ik \cdot r_0)\rangle$. Neglecting the kinetic energy of the target nucleon before the collision we obtain

$$V_{opt}(\mathbf{k}', \mathbf{k}) = -\frac{4\pi\hbar^2}{m} A\bar{F}(\mathbf{k}', \mathbf{k}) \int d^3\mathbf{r}\, \rho(\mathbf{r}) \exp[i(\mathbf{k} - \mathbf{k}') \cdot \mathbf{r}] \tag{14}$$

where we have introduced the nuclear density $\rho(r)$ which is normalized to unity, and where $\bar{F} = (1/A)[ZF_p + (A - Z)F_n]$ is the amplitude averaged over the Z protons and $(A - Z)$ neutrons in the target nucleus.

In Eq. (14), the amplitude for two particle scattering from $\mathbf{k}$ to $\mathbf{k}'$ in free space is given by

$$F(\mathbf{k}' \leftarrow \mathbf{k}) = -\frac{2\pi^2 m}{\hbar^2} t(\mathbf{k}', \mathbf{k}) \tag{15}$$

where

$$t(\mathbf{k}', \mathbf{k}) = (2\pi)^{-3} \int d^3\mathbf{r}_0 \exp(-i\mathbf{k}' \cdot \mathbf{r}_0)\, t(\mathbf{r}_0) \exp(i\mathbf{k} \cdot \mathbf{r}_0)$$

is the t matrix element when the scatterer is at the origin.

The interpretation of Eq. (14) in the configuration space is

$$V_{opt}\psi = (2\pi)^{-6} \int d^3\mathbf{r}' \iint d^3\mathbf{k}\, d^3\mathbf{k}'\, \exp(i\mathbf{k}' \cdot \mathbf{r})V_{opt}(\mathbf{k}', \mathbf{k}) \exp(-i\mathbf{k} \cdot \mathbf{r}')\psi(\mathbf{r}') \tag{16}$$

which explicitly exhibits the nonlocal character of V_{opt}.

The scattering amplitudes $F(\mathbf{k}, \mathbf{k}')$ are required not only for those obtained from the elastic N–N scattering data, but also for those off the energy shell. However, at sufficiently high energies, off energy shell contributions are expected to become negligible and $V_{opt}(\mathbf{k}', \mathbf{k})$ depends mainly on the momentum transfer, $\mathbf{q} = \mathbf{k}' - \mathbf{k}$ (in the Born approximation, it depends only on $\mathbf{q}$). Hence, to this approximation, replacing $\mathbf{k}'$ by $\mathbf{k} + \mathbf{q}$, the $V_{opt}(\mathbf{r})$ becomes a local operator, and is given by

$$V_{opt}(\mathbf{r}) = -\frac{4\pi\hbar^2}{m} A\bar{F}(0)\rho_{eff}(\mathbf{r}) \tag{17}$$

where

$$\rho_{eff}(\mathbf{r}) = (2\pi)^{-3} \int d^3\mathbf{q} \int d^3\mathbf{r}'\, \rho(\mathbf{r}') \exp[i\mathbf{q} \cdot (\mathbf{r} - \mathbf{r}')] \frac{\bar{F}(\mathbf{q})}{\bar{F}(0)} \tag{18}$$

which is seen to be normalized to unity. In Eq. (18), $\bar{F}(\mathbf{q})$ is the average scattering amplitude for scattering with momentum transfer $\mathbf{q}$. For heavy nuclei, the Fourier transform of $\rho(\mathbf{r})$ is a rapidly oscillating function of $\mathbf{q}$. Thus, we can ignore the dependence of $\bar{F}$ on $\mathbf{q}$. Then we have $\rho_{\text{eff}}(\mathbf{r}) = \rho(r)$, and Eq. (17) becomes

$$V_{\text{opt}}(\mathbf{r}) = -\frac{4\pi\hbar^2}{m} A\bar{F}(0)\rho(\mathbf{r}). \tag{19}$$

This result is very crude, but it is also very simple, and does give the main features of the high energy scattering (Riesenfeld and Watson, 1956). Note that the shape factor is the same for both the real and imaginary parts of the optical model potential. Also note that, utilizing the optical theorem

$$\text{Im } \bar{F}(0) = \frac{k}{4\pi} \bar{\sigma}_t \tag{20}$$

where $\bar{\sigma}_t$ is the total N–N scattering scross section averaged over neutrons and protons, and where k is the wave number of the incident nucleon in the center of mass system of the N–N system, we find

$$\text{Im } V_{\text{opt}}(\mathbf{r}) = -\frac{4\pi\hbar^2}{m} A \frac{k}{4\pi} \bar{\sigma}_t \rho(\mathbf{r}). \tag{21}$$

This relation has already been utilized in Section 6.2.

Equation (19) does not have a spin orbit term. The neglect of the $\mathbf{q}$ dependence of $\bar{F}$ is equivalent to the neglect of the surface effect. Experiments at high energy indicate that the spin orbit potential is small, in qualitative agreement with our result, but of course it is not zero and it does lead to observable effects.

Let us consider the target nucleus with no spin. Then, the N–N scattering amplitude [Eq. (66), Section 7.1] can be taken as

$$M(\mathbf{q}) = A(q) + C(q)\boldsymbol{\sigma}_0 \cdot (\mathbf{k} \times \mathbf{k}'). \tag{22}$$

For a heavy nucleus, the dependence of A and C on $\mathbf{q}$ can be ignored. The term linear in $\boldsymbol{\sigma}_1$ has been dropped from Eq. (22), because the expectation value of $\boldsymbol{\sigma}_1$ with respect to the spin zero target state is zero. Substituting Eq. (22) for $\bar{F}(\mathbf{q})$ in Eq. (15) and taking the Fourier transform of the resulting expression we find for a spherically symmetric density function

$$V_{\text{opt}}(\mathbf{r}) = -\frac{4\pi\hbar^2}{m} A\left[A(0)\rho(r) + \frac{iC(0)}{2} \frac{1}{r} \frac{d\rho}{dr} (\mathbf{L} \cdot \boldsymbol{\sigma}_0) \right]. \tag{23}$$

That is, a spin orbit force of the Thomas form is obtained. If the target spin I is not zero, terms of the order I/A appear (Takeda and Watson, 1955).

In the approximation of Eq. (19), the form of the optical potential is the same as that of the matter density. The neglect of the $\mathbf{q}$ dependence of $\bar{F}$ is equivalent to the neglect of the finite range of nuclear forces. If we use the Born approximation (i.e., $t \simeq v$) to calculate $\bar{F}(\mathbf{q})/\bar{F}(0)$ in Eq. (18), we find

$$\rho_{\text{eff}}(\mathbf{r}) \simeq \int d^3\mathbf{r}' \, \rho(\mathbf{r} - \mathbf{r}')\bar{v}(\mathbf{r}') \bigg/ \int d^3\mathbf{r}' \, \bar{v}(\mathbf{r}'). \qquad (24)$$

This result indicates that, no matter how high the energy, the potential shape factor extends beyond the density distribution by the finite range of nuclear forces.

A detailed study has been carried out recently by McDonald and Hull (1966) in the energy range 98 to 350 MeV for targets ranging from carbon to lead with the N–N phase parameters obtained at Yale (Breit et al., 1960, 1962; Hull et al., 1961, 1962). These results show that the second order multiple scattering terms and the angular dependence of the t matrix are equally important to improve fits to the data. Although some disagreement exists still between the prediction and the data, especially for the polarization near the first maximum, it should be emphasized that generally good agreement is achieved without introduction of any ad hoc parameters. For a recent study in this vein, we refer the reader to Lee and McManus (1968) who treat the elastic and inelastic scattering of 1 GeV protons from O^{16} and C^{12}.

7.3b   Imaginary Potential and the Exclusion Principle

Theoretical derivations of optical potentials at low energies have aspects entirely different from those of the high energy approaches. The elimination of inelastic and reaction states will have serious effects upon the elastic state, and consequently, information about these states, as well as the elastic states, is of essential importance. In addition, the averaging over resonances has to be carried out to smooth out the energy dependence in order that the derived potential be useful at all. In other words, the theory has to be essentially a many body one.

However, the success of the optical model itself indicates that at least a qualitative estimation of the potential parameters should be possible from the primitive IPM point of view, as for that of a Fermi gas model. In fact, it is quite interesting to remark that, with the exclusion principle modification alone, the high energy results actually give quite reasonable results all the way down to the lowest energies. Let us review some of these works for the evaluation of imaginary potentials.

Assuming that whenever an incident nucleon collides with a target nucleon it is removed from the elastic channel and hence contributes to the absorption, we use Eq. (21), which can be rewritten as

$$W(r) = (\hbar/2)vA\rho\bar{\sigma}_t \qquad (25)$$

where v is the velocity of the particle absorbed. The problem here is to take into account the following effects to calculate $\bar{\sigma}_t$.

  i. Certain final states of the collisions are excluded by the Pauli principle.
  ii. The effective masses of the particles are different from their true values.
  iii. The interaction acts differently for a pair within a Fermi gas than for an isolated pair.
  iv. The energy of the interaction is the sum of the incident energy E_i, Fermi energy E_f, and the separation energy S, that is, $E = E_i + E_f + S$.

In the calculation by Gomes (1959), all these effects were taken into account. The success of the Bethe–Goldstone equation in conjunction with the independent pair model (Gomes *et al.*, 1958) as explained in Section 7.2 suggests the use of the same method for point (iii). Gomes solved Eq. (4) of Section 7.2 for the s wave only, using a reduced mass $m/m^* = 1 + [Ak_f{}^3/(1+Bk^2)]$ with $A = 0.48 \ \Gamma^3$ and $B = 1.53 \ \mathrm{F}^2$. He used a central potential with a core radius 0.4 F and an attractive exponential well which reproduces the singlet scattering length and effective range. The effect of the tensor force and of the singlet-triplet difference is neglected. Assuming that the higher partial waves are the same as those for the isolated N–N scattering, the phases of Gammel *et al.* (1957) are used for them. His result in the nuclear matter is shown in Table I. The small value of W reflects the fact that collisions are strongly

TABLE I

IMAGINARY POTENTIAL STRENGTH IN NUCLEAR MATTER WITH $k_f = 1.42 \ \mathrm{F}^{-1}$ [a]

Incident energy (MeV)	IPAM		"Final states" approach[b]	IPAM $(m/m^* = 1)$
	W (MeV)	m/m^*	W (MeV)	W (MeV)
1	1.06	0.77	1.88	2.11
7	2.34	0.78	4.03	4.59
14	4.62	0.80	6.88	7.82

  [a] Gomes (1959).
  [b] Calculated as by Lane and Wandel (1955) and by Clementel and Villi (1955) with the effect of points (i) and (iv) in the text.

repressed by the Pauli principle. Then, using a Thomas–Fermi approximation to estimate the surface effect, he found that the lessening of the effect of the Pauli principle near the surface due to the reduction of the Fermi momentum, together with an increase of the effective mass, gives rise to a strong increase of absorption at the surface, although the reduction in density ρ acts to cancel the effect of the relaxation of the Pauli principle. A typical form of the imaginary potential obtained by him, using a Fermi distribution, has already been shown in Fig. 3 of Section 4.2. The peaking of the absorption near the surface may be due partly to the energy dependence of the two nucleon cross section.

A more realistic shell model approach has been tried by Lemmer *et al.* (1959). They replaced $\rho\bar{\sigma}$ by $\sum_i \rho_i \bar{\sigma}_i$, where the summation runs over all the occupied single particle orbits. They allowed for the effect of the Pauli principle and for doubly closed shell nuclei by setting $\bar{\sigma}_i = 0$ when the energy is less than the binding energy B_i of the ith single particle state. Harmonic oscillator potentials were used to calculate ρ_i and B_i.

These theoretical calculations showed that W is an increasing function of energy below a few MeV, and also that the absorption is strongly concentrated near the surface. The phenomenological analyses of Perey and Buck (1962) and Perey (1963) below 20 MeV, which yielded excellent fits to the data, have actually borne out the latter point; but, their imaginary depth turned out to be a slightly decreasing function of E (Sections 6.1 and 6.2) rather than an increasing function.

In any event, as mentioned at the outset of this subsection, theoretical derivations of low energy optical model potentials are expected to be quite complicated.

7.3c   Formal Derivation of Optical Potential

The older dispersion theories, which define the compound nuclear (CN) states by arbitrary boundary conditions, are extremely general and rigorous, and most suited for the description of compound nuclear reactions (Kapur and Peierls, 1938; Siegert, 1939; Wigner and Eisenbud, 1947; Teichman and Wigner, 1952). A comprehensive review of the subject has been given by Brown (1967). In these theories, the transition amplitudes of direct interaction and optical potential are described as the result of the coherent superposition of the contributions from many different levels (Lane *et al.*, 1955; Bloch, 1957; Lane and Thomas, 1958). In other words, when the optical model and direct interaction theories provide a good description of the reaction amplitude, the older dispersion theories provide a slowly convergent representation. In the work of general unified reaction theories, a more appropriate description of nuclear states is used so that the transition amplitude is described as the sum of a direct reaction amplitude and a series of resonance terms referring to the compound states (Feshbach, 1958a, 1962; Brown, 1959; Newton and Fonda, 1960; Agodi and Eberli, 1960; Humblet and Rosenfeld, 1961).

The following is a sketch of a derivation of the optical model potential. We solve for the scattering states of the Schroedinger equation, Eq. (1). If the N–N interactions contain highly singular parts, then it is assumed that a

Brueckner type self-consistent calculation has already been carried out so that $\mathscr{H}$ is a suitably modified nonsingular version of the many body Hamiltonian. Projection operators P and Q are introduced such that P projects onto a part of Ψ which includes at least the open channel part at energy E, and $Q = 1 - P$ (Feshbach, 1958a, 1962). We find from Eq. (1) that $P\Psi$ and $Q\Psi$ satisfy the following sets of coupled equations

$$[E - \mathscr{H}_{PP}]P\Psi = \mathscr{H}_{PQ}Q\Psi \qquad (26a)$$

$$[E - \mathscr{H}_{QQ}]Q\Psi = \mathscr{H}_{QP}P\Psi \qquad (26b)$$

where $\mathscr{H}_{PP} = P\mathscr{H}P$, $\mathscr{H}_{QP} = Q\mathscr{H}P$, etc. Explicit reference of Eq. (26) to the inelastic or reaction channels can be eliminated by substituting for the $Q\Psi$ in the right-hand side the expression found from Eq. (26)

$$Q\Psi = [E^+ - \mathscr{H}_{QQ}]^{-1}\mathscr{H}_{QP}P\Psi \qquad (27)$$

where the operator $(E^+ - \mathscr{H}_{QQ})^{-1}$ is the full many body Green's function except for the removal of the target ground state. Then we find

$$[E - \mathscr{H}_{PP} - \mathscr{H}_{PQ}(E^+ - \mathscr{H}_{QQ})^{-1}\mathscr{H}_{QP}]P\Psi = 0. \qquad (28)$$

Eigenfunctions of the operator $\mathscr{H}_{QQ}$ which satisfy $(E_s - \mathscr{H}_{QQ})\psi_s = 0$ can be identified as the stationary states of the $(A + 1)$ compound nuclear system with the coupling to the open channel $\mathscr{H}_{QP}$ removed, and the eigenvalues E_s can be regarded as the corresponding resonance energies within the same approximation. Clearly, the resonance term breaks up into two parts, one is the rapidly oscillating term which is due to the levels $E_s \approx E$, and the other is the contribution from the distant levels. The sum, $\mathscr{H}'_{PP}$, of the latter part plus $\mathscr{H}_{PP}$ is a smooth function of energy near E. Thus, the transition amplitude which we obtain from Eq. (28) is simply the sum of a "potential" scattering amplitude due to $\mathscr{H}'_{PP}$ and the rapidly oscillating resonance amplitudes.

The "generalized" optical model potential is thus given by

$$V_{opt} = \langle\Phi_0| V[1 + (E^+ - H_0 - QV)^{-1}QV] |\Phi_0\rangle \qquad (29)$$

where Φ_0 is the ground state wave function of the target nucleus.

V_{opt} is a complex operator. Its imaginary part can be written in the form

$$\text{Im } V_{opt} = -\pi\langle\Phi_0| V \,\delta(E - H_0 - QV)QV |\Phi_0\rangle. \qquad (30)$$

The optical potential thus obtained is exact except for the neglected effects of the exclusion principle. Feshbach (1962) has shown that the effective Hamiltonian method can be generalized to all possible reaction types, as well as to the effects arising from the identity of particles, by suitable choices of projection operators.

In the resonance region, this equivalent two body potential should exhibit all the detailed resonance features. The optical potential, in the proper sense, can be obtained from it only after suitably averaging over many resonances.

The appearance of the integral operator $[E - \mathcal{H}_{QQ} + i\varepsilon]^{-1}$ makes V_{opt} itself an integral operator, that is, nonlocal. Nonlocality is also expected to arise when the exclusion principle is properly taken into account. In addition, V_{opt} is explicity energy dependent. The above expression for V_{opt} is, in any exact sense, entirely formal, since the many body Green's function appears in the result. In other words, V_{opt} is expressed in terms of the solutions to the problem it, itself, purports to solve.

7.3d.   Shell Model States in the Continuum

The main difficulty of the general unified theories is that of providing an explicit representation of the compound nuclear wave function in order to actually compute cross sections. This is remedied in the currently popular theories of elastic, inelastic, and charge exchange scattering, which are based on a more specific model for the origin of the resonances (Newton, 1958; Brenig, 1959; Rodberg, 1961; Fano, 1961; MacDonald, 1964; Danos and Greiner, 1965, 1966; Weidenmüller, 1966; Lipperheide, 1966, 1967). These theories describe the state of the total system as a linear superposition of unbound (i.e., scattering) states and "bound states in the continuum."

The interference phenomena between the compound nuclear and direct reactions have also been investigated with clarity using these theories (Ratcliff and Austern, 1967; Hüfner et al., 1967).

Perhaps the essential features are most clearly presented by considering the simplest case of one open channel coupled to one discrete compound nuclear (CN) state. Our discussion follows closely that of Austern (1967). This will also serve to illustrate the procedure by which bound states in the continuum are excluded, and will provide a simple example of the steps that appear in well known formal derivations of the optical model potentials.

Let us select the following model wave function

$$\Psi^{(+)} = \chi_1(r)\Phi_1(y) + C(E)\Phi(r, y) \tag{31}$$

To simplify the problem, we shall retain only the s wave parts. In Eq. (31), $\Phi_1(y)$ is the eigenstate of the target Hamiltonian $H_A(y)$ with eigenenergy ε_1, and $\chi_1(r)$ describes the scattering state of the projectile. Antisymmetrization is ignored. The CN state $\Phi(r, y)$ is assumed to be an eigenfunction of a Hamiltonian H_0, like that of the independent particle model (IPM), which is closely related to the actual Hamiltonian H. The expectation value of H for such a "bound state," $E' = (\Phi, H\Phi)$, lies well above a threshold for particle emission so that it is embedded into a continuous spectrum, although the structure of Φ distributes E' among many nucleons in such a way that no one nucleon has enough energy to escape. In the language of the shell model, this state Φ is pictured as a number of bound particles and holes in a realistic finite potential, and E' is the sum of the energies of these particles and holes. Let Φ be normalized to unity. It is assumed that Φ_1 and Φ are orthogonal to each other, since in order to construct a bound Φ that lies in the continuum it is probably necessary to use rather high excited states of the target nucleus. The coefficient $C(E)$ determines the amplitude with which Φ is mixed into $\Psi^{(+)}$ at E.

Substituting Eq. (31) into the Schroedinger equation $H\Psi^{(+)} = E\Psi^{(+)}$ with $H = T(\mathbf{r}) + H_A(y) + V(r, y)$, where $T(\mathbf{r})$ is the kinetic energy operator and $V(r, y)$ is the interaction between the projectile and the target nucleus, we find a set of coupled equations for $\chi_1(r)$ and $C(E)$

$$[-d^2/dr^2 + V_{11} - k_1{}^2]\chi_1 = -C(E)W_1(r) \tag{32}$$

and

$$(E - E')C(E) = \int_0^\infty W_1{}^*\chi_1 \, dr \tag{33}$$

where $k_1{}^2 = (\hbar^2/2M)(E - \varepsilon_1)$, and we have defined

$$V_{11}(r) = \int \Phi_1{}^*(y)V(r, y)\Phi_1(y) \, dy \tag{34}$$

and

$$W_1(r) = \int \Phi_1{}^*(y)V(r, y)\Phi(r, y) \, dy. \tag{35}$$

The exact solution of Eq. (32) is given by

$$\chi_1(r) = F_1(r) - \frac{C(E)}{k_1} \int_0^\infty F_1(r_<)H_1(r_>)W_1(r') \, dr' \tag{36}$$

where F_1 and H_1 are the solutions of the homogeneous part of Eq. (32) with the boundary conditions

$$F_1(0) = 0, \quad F_1(r) \underset{r\to\infty}{\longrightarrow} \sin(k_1 r + \delta_1). \quad \text{and} \quad H_1(r) \underset{r\to\infty}{\longrightarrow} \exp[i(k_1 r + \delta_1)].$$

Here δ_1 is the phase shift calculated in the potential $V_{11}(r)$.

Substituting Eq. (36) into Eq. (33) we solve for $C(E)$ and obtain

$$C(E) = J_1{}^*/(E - E' - S_1 + i\Gamma_1/2) \tag{37}$$

where the "level shift" S_1 is defined by

$$S_1 = -(1/k_1) \iint_0^\infty W_1{}^*(r)F_1(r_<)G_1(r_>)W_1(r') \, dr \, dr' \tag{38}$$

with the "level width" Γ_1 defined by

$$\Gamma_1 = (2/k_1)\,|J_1|^{\,2} \tag{39}$$

and

$$J_1{}^* = \int_0^\infty W_1{}^* F_1 \, dr. \tag{40}$$

In Eq. (38), the function $G(r)$ is related to F_1 and H_1 by $H_1 = G_1 + iF_1$. The positive definiteness of the width Γ_1 follows from the outgoing boundary condition in Eq. (36). As $C(E)$ remains finite at $E = E'$ [see Eq. (37)], it follows from Eq. (33) that χ_1 must vanish inside the nucleus at $E = E'$. Thus, near each resonance the single modes of motion characteristic of the open channels disappear from the nuclear interior and the CN wave function $\Phi(r, y)$ dominates.

The scattering amplitude obtained from Eq. (36) is the sum of a potential scattering term due to $V_{11}(r)$ and a resonance term due to $C(E)$.

Now we calculate the quantity $\bar{C}(E)$ averaged over an energy interval I, assuming a narrow resonance.

$$\bar{C}(E) = -i\pi J_1{}^*/I. \tag{41}$$

The energy averaged $\bar{\chi}_1$ is defined by requiring that it satisfy Eq. (32) with $\bar{C}(E)$ in place of $C(E)$, that is,

$$[-d^2/dr^2 + V_{11} - k_1{}^2]\bar{\chi}_1 = i\pi W_1 J_1{}^*/I$$

$$\approx (i\pi/I)W_1(r)\int_0^\infty W_1{}^*(r')\bar{\chi}_1(r')\,dr' \tag{42}$$

where the last step is carried out assuming $F_1 \approx \bar{\chi}_1$ in the definition of $J_1{}^*$ [Eq. (40)]. The error introduced by this approximation is of the order of S_1/I or Γ_1/I, which is presumably small.

The averaging interval I dilutes the influence of the resonance. The energy averaged $\bar{\chi}_1$ no longer conserves the flux even though the elastic scattering alone is possible. This is understood in terms of the time delay of a sharp wave packet, as has been mentioned in Section 4.2. The imaginary part of this "potential" is separable, nonlocal, and a slowly varying function of E.

As mentioned in Subsection 7.3c, the single particle mode of motion of the incident particle occurs since the particle enters into not just one CN state but into many. Then optical model phenomena arise as the result of the coherent superposition of the contributions from many levels (Lane et al., 1955; Brown, 1967).

If a large set of CN states are excluded instead of just one, then the separable imaginary part of Eq. (42) goes over to the generalized form

$$i\pi/I \sum_j W_{1j}(r)W_{1j}^*(r') \qquad (43)$$

where the sum runs over all states j of the excluded space that lie in the interval I. In order that the properties of the optical potential should vary slowly with E, however, it is necessary that the excluded states in the interval I should be typical of the entire spectrum of excluded states in the vicinity of I. In such cases, we can hope to deal with the IPM configurations from which the CN states are built, and use sum rules and closure properties to evaluate Eq. (43), if all states of the nearby IPM configurations are included in I. However, if states with different IPM configurations, such as collective states, are mixed in the interval, simple evaluations of Eq. (43) fail.

It is often necessary to include more than one state in the trial function $\Psi^{(+)}$ of Eq. (31). For example, two collective states "1" and "2" that are projected from the same intrinsic state have a good overlap with each other. Consequently state "2" has to be included explicitly in Eq. (31). After eliminating the CN state ϕ, the resulting coupled channel equation has to be solved with direct coupling between channels "1" and "2". Austern (1967) has shown that in such cases, not only do (separable) imaginary distorting potentials appear in these coupled equations, but (separable) imaginary coupling terms appear also. The necessity for complex coupling terms in DWBA and coupled channel calculations in the phenomenological analyses has already been mentioned in Chapter VI. As seen in the above simple example, the existence of bound states in the continuum then influences the unbound states, since they are coupled by the residual interaction $V = H - H_0$. This coupling is responsible for the decay of the compound nuclear states. If V is assumed to be a sum of one and two particle operators, then the unbound states will couple directly only to those bound states with two particle one hole configurations, which are called the "doorway states" (Block and Feshbach, 1963; Kerman *et al.*, 1963; Lande and Bloch, 1964; Feshbach, 1964; Feshbach *et al.*, 1964, 1967). Through these doorway states the compound nucleus develops into more complicated configurations, (i.e., three particle, two hole states, etc.) or it may decay into the unbound states. Thus, the problem is to select a subset of eigenfunctions of H_0, and diagonalize H in the space spanned by this subset. In practice, these calculations based on the shell model wave functions are limited to light nuclei, where, for excitation energies up to $\lesssim 20$ MeV, probably all states are doorway states and no more complicated states exist.

A comprehensive formalism for nuclear reaction problems which embodies various existing theories as special cases and thereby facilitates comparison of the different theories has been proposed by Lane and Robson (1966) [also see Robson and Lane (1967)].

7.4   Nucleon–Nucleon One Boson Exchange Potentials

7.4a   Development of OBEM

In Section 7.1, we indicated that the "One Boson Exchange Model" (OBEM) has recently emerged as a reasonably simple and accurate description of the nucleon–nucleon interaction. This model is based essentially on meson field theory, although many of the studies have been pursued using the dispersion relations formalism. All OBEM approaches to date involve some phenomenological modifications of theory in the light of experimental information.

The theoretical considerations and viewpoints which led various workers to the OBEM description have been quite varied. Since the work of Taketani et al., (1951) the one pion exchange potential, OPEP, has been known to dominate the outer region of the N–N interactions (i.e., $r > 2$ F). In the 1952–1955 era, calculations of the effects of two pion exchange and multipion exchange were pursued extensively by meson field theorists (Taketani et al., 1952; Brueckner and Watson, 1953; Levy, 1954; Klein, 1955). These 2PEP N–N interactions, however, were unable to account for N–N polarization phenomena as they became known. We shall not go into the various attempts, using phenomenological potentials, to deal with the emerging experimental information on the N–N interaction which are well documented in various review articles and monographs (Hulthén and Sugawara, 1957; Griffith and Power, 1960; Noyes, 1961a,b; Moravcsik, 1963). The experimental work which most immediately stimulated the development of the OBEM was the discovery and classification of strongly interacting mesons or resonances (see Table I), in particular, the ρ-meson (Erwin et al., 1961) and the ω-meson (Maglic et al., 1961). Without doubt these discoveries gave impetus to a number of independent attempts to account for the N–N interaction by including the interactions of these vector (V) mesons, along with the interaction of the pseudoscalar (P) π-meson field. These efforts were unsuccessful until a scalar (S) meson called the s or σ, or an $I = 0$, $J = 0$ 2π-effect, which acts like a scalar meson, was also included. Then the pieces of the intricate jigsaw puzzle began to fit in place. With this PVS approach it was possible for the first time to fit experimental data using models with a modest number of adjustable parameters (1–12), whereas, the only successful models (phenomenological potential models) which had fit the data previously, required some 30–50 adjustable parameters.

TABLE I

STRONGLY INTERACTING MESONS[a]

	Mass (MeV)	Width (MeV)	I^G	$(J^P)C_n$	Tensor	Spect.[b]
π	139.6		1^-	$(0^-)+$	P	$^1S_0$
π^0	135.0	7 ev				
η	548.6	2 kev	0^+	$(0^-)+$	P	$^1S_0$
ρ	765	125	1^+	$(1^-)-$	V	$^3S_1$
ω	783	12	0^-	$(1^-)-$	V	$^3S_1$
σ	$(\eta_v?)$		0^+	$(0^+)+$	S	$^3P_0$
σ_1	$(\pi_v?)$		1^-	$(0^+)+$	S	$^3P_0$
η'	958	4	0^+	$(0^-)+$	P	$^1S_0$
π_v	1016	25	1^-	$(0^+)+$	S	$^3P_0$
ϕ	1019	3	0^-	$(1^-)-$	V	$^3S_1$
η_v	1070	80	0^+	$(0')+$	S	$^3P_0$
A_1	1070	80	1^-	$(1^+)+$	A	$^3P_1$
B	1220	130	1^+	$(A?)-$	A	$^1P_1$
f	1260	140	0^+	$(2^+)+$	T	$^3P_2$
D	1285	30	0^+	$(1^+)+$	A	$^3P_1$
A_2	1305	90	1^-	$(2^+)+$	T	$^3P_2$

[a] Rosenfeld et al. (1968).
[b] Goldhaber (1967).

Publications on OBEM from the scattering amplitude viewpoint, the dispersion relations viewpoint, and the meson potential viewpoint have appeared in rapidly increasing numbers since 1961.

1962: Hoshizaki et al., S. Sawada et al., McKean, and Lichtenberg.
1963: Bryan et al., Scotti and Wong, and Babikov.
1964: Bryan and Scott, Wong, and S. Sawada et al.
1965: Green and Sharma, and Köpp and Kramer.
1966: Green et al., Ball et al., Bryan and Arndt, Arndt et al., and Babikov.

By spring of 1967, the time of the International Conference on the N–N Interaction (Florida, 1967), these efforts began to merge into a fairly homogeneous physical theme with relatively minor variations [see review papers of the 1967 Florida Conference by Green and Sawada (1967b), Lommon and Feshbach (1967), D. Y. Wong (1967), Tamagaki (1967), Signell and Durso (1967), and Köpp (1967)]. Since the proceedings of the conference are available, it will be unnecessary to go into the many technical details. Furthermore, a recent supplement of *Progress of Theoretical Physics* (see PTP, 1967) devotes detailed attention to the entire N–N interaction problem, not only from the field theoretic (Ogawa *et al.*, 1967) and the dispersions relation viewpoints (Furuichi, 1967), but also from the phenomenological potential approach (Tamagaki and Watari, 1967). Here we shall concentrate on the one boson exchange potential (OBEP) approach of Bryan and Scott, and Green and Sawada which utilizes Schroedingers equation in a fashion similar to that used throughout this work on the nuclear IPM. The latter effort, particularly, has been directed towards obtaining meson theoretic potentials which are good in S states, and hence, might serve the needs of nuclear physics.

To place these studies in perspective, it may be helpful to give a brief account of how they fit into the context of earlier work in field theory.

Viewed from the standpoint of the boson field Lagrangian, and quantum electrodynamics, the original form of quantum field theory, as developed in the early 1930's by Heisenberg, Pauli, Dirac, Rosenfeld, Fock, Fermi, Podolsky, Breit, Møller, etc., may be characterized as one in which the photon field Lagrangian depends quadratically upon first derivatives of the field potentials. The extension of field theory to allow for the dependence (quadratic) upon the meson field coordinates themselves was made in 1935 by Yukawa (1935). This explains the short range character of the N–N interaction, i.e., the $\mathscr{C} = r^{-1}$ Green's function of electrodynamics goes over to $Y = r^{-1}e^{-\kappa r}$ of Yukawa's theory where $\kappa = mc/\hbar$ with m the mass of the field bosons. Yukawa's original suggestion, which was made in conjunction with a scalar (S) field coordinate, was extended by Proca (1936) to embrace vector (V) fields. Then Kemmer (1938) extended the theory further by including pseudoscalar (P), axial vector (A), and antisymmetric tensor (T) meson fields, allowing for what would now be referred to as the isospin dependence of these fields and permitting both direct and derivative type couplings.

With the broad realm of possible interactions derivable from such fields, the major problem became that of coping with the highly singular nature of many of the interactions, and that of selecting particular interactions which fit the experimental data. Bethe (1940a), Møller and Rosenfeld (1940), and Schwinger (1942) made the first serious effort in these directions by using phenomenological cutoffs or mixtures of interactions. We refer the reader to the original papers and early text of Rosenfeld (1949) for the details of these developments.

While this work was underway in the early 1940's, the treatment of electrodynamics itself was extended by Podolsky (1942) and by Bopp (1942), who permitted the field Lagrangian to depend quadratically upon second derivatives. Still further extensions of Lagrangian theory to deal with meson fields, by including both the potentials and arbitrarily high derivatives, were made by Green (1948, 1949a), Pais and Uhlenbeck (1950), and by others.

At the same time, Green became involved with the PVS theme in an attempt to deal with the auxiliary condition problem in vector meson theory which, in certain treatments, requires the introduction of a scalar field. While examining various variations of vector–scalar combinations, it became apparent that some lead to cancellation of large static N–N interaction terms. This, then, leads in a simple way to a very complex nuclear force which is largely or entirely relativistic in nature. Then the fact that the pseudoscalar–pseudoscalar interaction is also purely relativistic led to considering this particular interaction.

The singularities associated with relativistic interactions arising in such a PVS theory would normally present great difficulties. However, when used in conjunction with a generalized meson field with higher derivatives in the Lagrangian, these singularity difficulties do not arise.

It would be too great a digression to summarize the trends of the main stream of investigation on the N–N interaction during the intervening years other than to point out that in the early 1960's the only theoretical models which could deal reasonably well with experimental observations required some 30 to 50 adjustable constants.

Then the advances (referred to at the beginning of this section) came in independent works on OBEM. While the formalisms used in these works are somewhat diverse, it seems clear now that the primary reason for their success is their use of common meson ingredients.

The work of Bryan and Scott, who solved Schroedinger's equation with OBE potentials associated with these combinations of pseudoscalar, vector, and scalar fields, prompted Green and Sharma (1965) to reinvestigate the relativistic interaction model. They found, using no adjustable parameters, that both the isoscalar and isovector sets of spin-spin, tensor, and spin orbit interactions implicit in Green's earlier work agreed quite well with those of Bryan and Scott. However, the relativistic model displayed important velocity dependent terms not contained in the Bryan and Scott study.

Green *et al.* (1966), using a modified version of the Bryan–Scott code, then carried out a preliminary study of phase shifts generated by a purely relativistic model consisting of a generalized meson interaction, and isoscalar, scalar, and vector interactions. They obtained encouragingly good results using only three parameters.

At this time the efforts of the two groups, although they use entirely different formalisms in deriving their Schroedinger potentials, have almost merged into one. On the one hand, in recent studies Green and Sawada (1967a,b,c) follow Bryan and Scott by allowing for simultaneous direct and derivative coupling to vector mesons. On the other hand, Bryan and Scott (1967) now include velocity dependent terms in the treatment of the vector and scalar interactions. The one remaining difference relates to the use of regularized fields by Green *et al.*, which may also be interpreted as equivalent to the use of form factors for the nucleons. In practical fitting of data this difference plays an important role, particularly for S waves which are of greatest importance in applications to nuclear physics. Accordingly, let us briefly describe how regularized fields entered this work.

At the outset we might remark that this sojourn in meson field theory (for guidance as to nuclear theory) has many aspects of "the blind leading the blind." For the reader who finds the following two subsections a bit opaque, we suggest going directly to Eqs. (9), (25), (36), and (37), and Table II, which are the principle results; and then, finally to Fig. 1 which shows the final theoretical phase shifts for a regularized OBEP model in relationship to the M-68 phase shifts.

7.4b   Generalized One Boson Exchange Potentials

In studies in which relativistic terms play a major role, singularity difficulties become particularly acute. To deal with them we use a generalized meson field Lagrangian which embodies "regularization" in an essential way. Thus, we assume that all component fields are characterized by a quadratic Lagrangian density (Green 1948, 1949a)

$$L = -(\tfrac{1}{2}a^{-2})[C_0 Q^2 + C_1 a^2(\partial_{\lambda_1} Q)^2 + \cdots + C_N a^{2N}(\partial_{\lambda_1} \partial_{\lambda_2} \cdots \partial_{\lambda_N} Q)^2], \qquad (1)$$

where the nucleon Compton wavelength $a = \hbar/Mc$ is our unit length, the C are dimensionless natural constants, the field coordinate $Q(x_\nu)$ is a real or imaginary function, and

$$x_\nu = (r, ict), \qquad \partial_\lambda = \frac{\partial}{\partial x_\lambda}, \qquad \partial_{\lambda_1}, \ldots, \partial_{\lambda_N} = \frac{\partial^N}{\partial x_{\lambda_1}, \ldots, \partial x_{\lambda_N}}.$$

Here Q represents a scalar field. For other tensorial types we append an appropriate subscript. If we identify $C_0 = (m/M)^2$ (m denoting the meson mass), $C_1 = 1$, and $C_2 = C_3 = \cdots = C_N = 0$, then Eq. (1) becomes the usual meson field Lagrangian implicit in Yukawa's original work.

Using a variational principle, it is possible to obtain the equation of motion of the meson field which is a higher order generalization of the Klein–Gordon equation. Also from our Lagrangian we can derive the energy momentum four vector P_μ and the energy momentum tensor $t_{\mu\nu}$. We may express the energy momentum four vector and hence the field Hamiltonian in terms of Fourier amplitudes. For the field Hamiltonian we obtain

$$H = \sum_\sigma (\gamma_\sigma/c^2) \int \omega_\sigma^2 [Q_\sigma(\mathbf{k})Q_\sigma^*(\mathbf{k}) + Q_\sigma^*(\mathbf{k})Q_\sigma(\mathbf{k})] \, d\mathbf{k}, \qquad (2)$$

where

$$k_{\sigma\nu} = (\mathbf{k}, i\omega_\sigma/c), \qquad \omega_\sigma^2 = c^2(\mathbf{k} \cdot \mathbf{k} + \xi_\sigma^2/a^2). \qquad (3)$$

We may identify $\xi_\sigma = m_\sigma/M$, where the m_σ are "masses" associated with the generalized field, and

$$\gamma_\sigma = \sum_\eta \eta C_\eta (-\xi_\sigma^2)^{\eta-1}. \tag{4}$$

The γ_σ, which arise naturally in a generalized field, are factors whose reciprocals weight the final potentials associated with the different bosons. It can be shown algebraically that

$$B_\sigma = (\gamma_\sigma C_N)^{-1} = \prod_{\tau=1}^{N} (\xi_\tau^2 - \xi_\sigma^2)^{-1}, \tag{5}$$

where we omit $\tau = \sigma$ in forming the product, and that

$$\sum_\sigma B_\sigma = 0, \qquad \sum_\sigma B_\sigma \xi_\sigma^2 = 0, \ldots, \qquad \sum_\sigma B_\sigma \xi_\sigma^{2(N-2)} = 0. \tag{6}$$

These conditions, which follow deductively from the choice of a generalized field Lagrangian, are generalizations of the well-known Pauli–Villars regularization conditions (Pauli and Villars, 1949). They are also closely related to Feynman's (1949) smearing of the electron source function in his quantum electrodynamic calculations, Lee's (1954) peritization method, Heisenberg's ghost state (1957), and Frautschi's (1963) superposition of pole terms.

We may now quantize the meson field by accepting Eq. (2) as a quantal Hamiltonian and requiring that the field obey the Heisenberg equation of motion. Expressing all quantities in terms of their Fourier expansions, it is possible to show that the operators

$$b_\sigma(k) = Q_\sigma(k)(2\omega_\sigma \gamma_\sigma/\hbar c^2)^{1/2}, \qquad b_\sigma^*(k) = Q_\sigma^*(k)(2\omega_\sigma \gamma_\sigma/\hbar c^2)^{1/2} \tag{7}$$

have the commutation properties

$$[b_\sigma^*(k), b_\tau(k')] = (-)^\sigma \delta_{\sigma\tau} \delta(k - k'). \tag{8}$$

For odd values of σ, these are just the familiar commutation rules for a neutral positive definite scalar field. Following Fock (1934), we represent the operator $b_\sigma^*(k)$ for $\sigma = 1, 3$, etc. by functional multiplication of the function $\bar{b}_\sigma(k)$, and the operator $b_\sigma(k)$ by a functional derivative $\delta/\delta\bar{b}_\sigma(k)$. For even values of σ, the operators b_σ^* and b_σ satisfy "wrong-sign" commutation relations (Sudarshan, 1961; Schnitzer and Sudarshan, 1961; Arons *et al.*, 1965).

We shall not discuss the well-known, interpretive problems related to such quantities other than to note that despite many critical discussions (Pais and Uhlenbeck, 1950), they keep reappearing in various forms of field theory. From our present standpoint, we handle them pragmatically by assuming they are related to the experimental fact that nucleons have finite, rather than point, form factors (Hofstadter and Chambers, 1956). Then we simply use the rule (Green 1949a,b) that, if an ordinary meson theory leads to the interaction θJ, a generalized meson theory leads to the interaction $\theta \sum B_\sigma J_\sigma$. Here θ is an operator which may involve isospin, various Dirac matrices, and differential operators; but, may not involve the Compton wavelength of the meson. Specifically, we shall use here, in place of the ordinary Yukawa function, the generalized Yukawa function

$$J(r) = \frac{g^2}{r} \left[e^{-\kappa r} - \frac{U^2 - \kappa^2}{U^2 - \Lambda^2} e^{-\Lambda r} + \frac{\Lambda^2 - \kappa^2}{U^2 - \Lambda^2} e^{-Ur} \right] \tag{9}$$

where g^2 is the intrinsic coupling constant, κ is the inverse Compton wavelength of the meson, and Λ and U are regularization parameters assigned to this meson. This potential originated as the static solution of a sixth order wave equation for a delta function source density. However, the corresponding potential arises as the static solution of the usual Klein–Gordon equation with a source function whose form factor has the characteristic outer length Λ^{-1} and inner cutoff at U^{-1} (Ueda and Green, 1968).

We note that when $U \to \infty$, this goes over to $g^2 r^{-1}[e^{-\kappa r} - e^{-\Lambda r}]$, a weakly regulated combination of Yukawa functions. This then goes over to the ordinary Yukawa function when $\Lambda \to \infty$. In applications of these well-regularized functions at this time we set U to $20M$ and, unless otherwise noted, set Λ at $2M$ which will be referred to as our "standard" regularization. This regularization prescription, which scarcely affects the region from 0.2 F outward, eliminates the singularities of all the relativistic interactions which we will encounter, even those which, in a purely mathematical sense, are manageable singularities. Thus, this prescription is useful in practical numerical calculations, since it minimizes the integration errors caused by taking finite steps near the origin.

The broad picture of N–N interactions arising from direct and derivative type couplings between various tensorial types of meson fields and two nucleons was first considered by Kemmer (1938). Let us examine the same combinations using a procedure based upon the multitime formalism of Dirac et al. (1932). The basic wave equation for each Dirac particle interacting with the field at its location is taken as

$$[c\boldsymbol{\alpha}_i \cdot \mathbf{p}_i + \beta_i M c^2 + I(\mathbf{r}_i, t_i)]\Psi(\mathbf{r}_1, \mathbf{r}_2, t_1, t_2, t, Q) = i\hbar \frac{\partial}{\partial t} \Psi, \tag{10}$$

where I is the interaction between the meson field and the particle, and Ψ is the state functional which depends upon the coordinates and times of both particles as well as the field coordinates and time. A similar equation may be written for the second particle. In the case of direct coupling interactions associated with a meson field, we have

$$I(\mathbf{r}_i, \ t_i) = -g\theta Q(\mathbf{r}_i, t_i) \tag{11}$$

where θ is the appropriate Dirac matrix associated with the component of the meson field. We now add the Dirac equation for the two particles and set the times to be equal. Then we use the transformation of Rosenfeld (1932) to convert the Dirac–Fock–Podolsky multitime wave equation into the Heisenberg–Pauli single time equation

$$(H_p + H_f + H_I - i\hbar\, \partial/\partial t)\Psi(Q, \mathbf{r}_1, \mathbf{r}_2, t) - 0 \tag{12}$$

where

$$H_p = H_1 + H_2, \qquad II_I = H_{I,1} + H_{I,2}. \tag{13}$$

We next use a Fock expansion of our wave functional. Using the properties of annihilation and creation operators, we obtain an infinite series of coupled integro-differential equations the first two members of which are

$$D\Psi_0 - \int dk\, G^*(k_1)\Psi_1(k_1) = 0 \tag{14}$$

and

$$D\Psi_1 + \hbar\omega_1\Psi_1 - \sqrt{2}\int dk\, G^*(k)\Psi_2(k, k_1) - G(k_1)\Psi_0 = 0 \tag{15}$$

where $D = H_p - i\hbar\, \partial/\partial t$, and

$$G(k) = \sum_i g(2\pi)^{-3/2}\theta_i\, c(\hbar/2\omega)^{1/2}\exp(-i\mathbf{k}\cdot\mathbf{x}_i) \tag{16}$$

and where Ψ_0, $\Psi_1(k)$, and $\Psi_2(k_1, k_2)$, the amplitude for the 0, 1, and 2 meson states, are functions of the coordinates of the two nucleons and the common time. To derive the OBEP, we assume in the second equation that we may drop $D\Psi_1$ and the term involving the amplitude Ψ_2. When these steps are taken it follows that

$$\Psi_1(\mathbf{x}_1, \mathbf{x}_2, t, k_1) \approx G(k)\Psi_0(\mathbf{x}_1, \mathbf{x}_2, t)/\hbar\omega. \tag{17}$$

If we insert this into Eq. (14), we find

$$(H_1 + H_2 + V^D - i\hbar\, \partial/\partial t)\Psi_0(\mathbf{x}_1, \mathbf{x}_2, t) = 0 \tag{18}$$

where the Dirac one boson exchange potential V^D is

$$V^D = -\theta_1\theta_2 \int dk\, G^*(k)G(k)/\hbar\omega$$

$$= -\theta_1\theta_2 \frac{g^2}{(2\pi)^3}\sum_{i,j}\int dk\, \frac{\exp[i\mathbf{k}\cdot(\mathbf{x}_j - \mathbf{x}_i)]}{2(k^2 + \kappa^2)} = -\theta_1\theta_2 J \tag{19}$$

with

$$J = g^2 \exp[(-\kappa r)/4\pi r]. \tag{20}$$

The same result follows from the second order term in the usual power series perturbation procedure and indeed from a classical treatment of the field. We now use the rule that for a generalized meson field $J \to \sum B_\sigma J_\sigma$.

Let us consider the case of various isoscalar fields which are directly coupled to nucleons. For a scalar field, simply identify θ with β to obtain the scalar-scalar Dirac potential

$$V_S = -\beta_1 \beta_2 J. \tag{21}$$

For a vector meson field, we represent the field by a four vector $A_\alpha = (\mathbf{A}, iA_0)$. The time-like component of the four vector field leads to a Hamiltonian which is negative definite. The formal consequence of such a negative definite Hamiltonian is that the roles of annihilation and creation become interchanged. We take the interaction for each particle as $I = -g\theta_\alpha A_\alpha(x_\nu)$, where $\theta_\alpha = (\alpha, i)$. The final interaction, when no auxiliary condition is imposed, is simply

$$V_V = (1 - \boldsymbol{\alpha}_1 \cdot \boldsymbol{\alpha}_2)J. \tag{22}$$

A pseudoscalar field is intrinsically a fourth rank, antisymmetric tensor with only one nonvanishing component A_{1234}. For consistency we should, in view of the presence of the fourth index, represent this field by a purely imaginary potential, i.e., $A_{1234} = i\varphi_p$. To insure a Hermitian Hamiltonian, the Dirac matrix associated with the interaction is now $\theta_p = i\beta\gamma_5$. From this it follows that the pseudoscalar direct coupling interaction is

$$V_P = \beta_1 \gamma_{5,1} \beta_2 \gamma_{5,2} J. \tag{23}$$

In a similar way we may treat the axial vector and second rank, antisymmetric tensor fields to derive V_A and V_T.

There are several important aspects of the five OBEP interactions derived in this simple way. In the first place, they are consistent with possible interaction forms between nucleons inferred from invariance considerations prior to the discovery of meson theory and discussed by Pauli (1933) and Bethe and Bacher (1936) in connection with beta decay, and later discussed by Fermi and Yang (1949) in connection with the nucleon–antinucleon interaction. In the second place, they correspond in their static limits to very simple interactions, since $\beta \to 1$, α and $\gamma_5 \to v/c$. Thus in this limit

$$V_P = 0, \qquad V_V = J, \qquad V_S = -J. \tag{24}$$

The direct coupling P interaction is thus a purely relativistic interaction. Since the static terms cancel, combination (Green, 1949b)

$$V_{SV} = V_S + V_V = (1 - \beta_1 \beta_2 - \boldsymbol{\alpha}_1 \cdot \boldsymbol{\alpha}_2)J \tag{25}$$

where $m_S = m_V$ and $g_S{}^2 = g_V{}^2$ is also purely relativistic.

Thus far we have considered only interactions mediated by isoscalar mesons. It is, however, simple to show by using the isospin formalism that, if isovector mesons are involved, we simply obtain the same interaction preceded by $\boldsymbol{\tau}_1 \cdot \boldsymbol{\tau}_2$, where $\boldsymbol{\tau}_1$ and $\boldsymbol{\tau}_2$ are the isospin vectors for the first and second nucleons. In the general case, when both isoscalar and isovector mesons are present, we simply replace the preceding expressions by

$$J = J^0(r) + \boldsymbol{\tau}_1 \cdot \boldsymbol{\tau}_2 J^1(r). \tag{26}$$

The direct coupling Diracian OBEP interactions derived by Kemmer for the corresponding scalar, vector, and pseudoscalar fields are somewhat different, particularly in the relativistic terms. The differences reflect the difference in the use of auxiliary conditions and in the selection of the field Lagrangian.

The Dirac equation for two nucleons interacting via OBEP may be written as

$$[-c\boldsymbol{\alpha}_1 \cdot \mathbf{p}_1 - c\boldsymbol{\alpha}_2 \cdot \mathbf{p}_2 - (\beta_1 + \beta_2)Mc^2 + V^D]\Omega = E\Omega, \tag{27}$$

where $E = W + 2Mc^2$ is the total energy of the system, $M = M_1 = M_2$ is the mass of the nucleons, and $\mathbf{p}_1$ and $\mathbf{p}_2$ their momenta. The wave function Ω is a 16 component, two particle spinor, which is the direct product of two one particle spinors (Breit, 1937)

$$\Omega - \Omega_1 \otimes \Omega_2 = \begin{pmatrix} u_1 \\ w_1 \end{pmatrix} \otimes \begin{pmatrix} u_2 \\ w_2 \end{pmatrix} = \begin{pmatrix} u_1 u_2 & u_1 w_2 \\ w_1 u_2 & w_1 w_2 \end{pmatrix} - \begin{pmatrix} \varphi & \chi_1 \\ \chi_2 & \Psi \end{pmatrix} \tag{28}$$

where u_1 and w_1 are the small and the large components of the spinor Ω_1 for the first nucleon, etc. In Eq. (28) the functions φ, χ_1, χ_2, and Ψ are introduced in place of $u_1 u_2$, $u_1 w_2$, $w_1 u_2$, and $w_1 w_2$, each of which is a 2×2 matrix. The decomposition of Eq. (27) into a set of four coupled equations for φ, χ_1, χ_2, and Ψ is most conveniently accomplished by representing the Dirac matrices in direct product forms (Green 1949c)

$$\boldsymbol{\alpha} = \rho_1 \otimes \boldsymbol{\sigma}, \qquad \beta - \rho_3 \otimes I_\sigma, \qquad \boldsymbol{\sigma} = I_\rho \otimes \boldsymbol{\sigma}, \qquad \gamma_5 = -\rho_1 \otimes I_\sigma. \tag{29}$$

Here $\boldsymbol{\sigma}$ and I_σ are the familiar 2×2 Pauli matrices and ρ_1, ρ_2, ρ_3, and I_ρ are corresponding 2×2 matrices which operate between w and u, taking them as single units. Thus, for example, the effect of operating ρ_1 on Ω_1 is to switch u_1 and w_1. The usual Pauli spin matrices $\boldsymbol{\sigma}$ and I_σ operate within u or w; therefore the ρ's and σ's commute with each other, and a product of two Dirac matrices can be carried out in $\boldsymbol{\sigma}$-matrices and in ρ-matrices, independently. Using the usual rules for 2×2 matrix operators on 1×2 operands and inserting the sum of all the interactions into Eq. (27), we find the coupled equations

$$\begin{aligned}
(E - 2Mc^2 - V_1)\Psi + P_1\chi_1 + P_2\chi_2 - V_2\varphi &= 0, \\
P_1\Psi + (E - V_3)\chi_1 - V_4\chi_2 + P_2\varphi &= 0, \\
P_2\Psi - V_4\chi_1 + (E - V_3)\chi_2 + P_1\varphi &= 0, \\
-V_2\Psi + P_2\chi_1 + P_1\chi_2 + (E + 2Mc^2 - V_1)\varphi &= 0,
\end{aligned} \tag{30}$$

where $P_1 = c(\sigma_1 \cdot \mathbf{p}_1)$, $P_2 = c(\sigma_2 \cdot \mathbf{p}_2)$, and

$$V_1 = -J_S + J_V, \qquad V_2 = J_P, \qquad V_3 = J_S + J_V, \qquad V_4 = -J_P.$$

(31)

Eliminating χ_1 and χ_2 from Eqs. (30), one finds

$$\mathscr{L}_1(\Psi + \varphi) = 0, \qquad \mathscr{L}_2(\Psi - \varphi) = 0 \tag{32}$$

with

$$\mathscr{L}_1 = \frac{(E + h_1)(E + h_2)}{4Mc^2} - Mc^2$$

$$- \frac{1}{4Mc^2}\left\{(E + h_2)P_S \frac{1}{E + h_3} P_S + P_D \frac{1}{E + h_4} P_D(E + h_1)\right\}$$

$$\mathscr{L}_2 = \frac{(E + h_1)(E + h_2)}{4Mc^2} - Mc^2$$

(33)

$$- \frac{1}{4Mc^2}\left\{P_S \frac{1}{E + h_3} P_S(E + h_2) + (E + h_1)P_D \frac{1}{E + h_4} P_D\right\},$$

where $P_S = P_1 + P_2$, $P_D = P_1 - P_2$, $h_1 = -V_1 - V_2$, $h_2 = -V_1 + V_2$, $h_3 = -V_3 - V_4$, and $h_4 = -V_3 + V_4$. Eqs. (32) and (33), which are exact, have been derived by Breit (1958) for the special case of the π-meson field.

The reduction of Eq. (33) to the Schroedinger–Pauli equation is accomplished by assuming that terms like $J_n J_m/M^2 c^4$, $W J_n/M^2 c^4$, and $J_n p^2/M^3 c^4$ are much smaller than unity, where J_n and J_m stand for any of the J in Eq. (31.) Adding the two Eqs. (32) together, expanding the terms like $1/(E + h_i)$ in powers of $1/Mc^2$, and keeping all the terms up to $1/M^2 c^4$, we find a Schroedinger-like equation. However, Ψ itself is not a normalized wave function. Since

$$1 = \Omega^\dagger \Omega \approx \Psi^\dagger [1 + p^2/2M^2 c^2]\Psi, \tag{34}$$

therefore, the approximately normalized wave function

$$\psi = (1 + p^2/4M^2 c^2)\Psi \tag{35}$$

conserves probability to the second order of approximation. Expressing Ψ in terms of ψ, using Eq. (35), we obtain after tedious algebra

$$[p^2/M + V_{\text{tot}}]\psi = (\hbar^2 k^2/M)\psi \tag{36}$$

where

$$V_{\text{tot}} = V_c + V_\sigma(\sigma_1 \cdot \sigma_2) + V_{LS}(\mathbf{L} \cdot \mathbf{S}) + V_T S_{12}$$

$$+ V_\Delta(r)\nabla^2 + V_\nabla(r)(\mathbf{r} \cdot \nabla), \tag{37}$$

where $\mathbf{L}$, $\mathbf{S}$ are the familiar orbital and total spin angular momenta and S_{12} the usual tensor force operator. The contributions to each term in V_{tot} from S, V, and P interactions are given in Table II (Green, 1949b; Green and Sharma, 1965). The last column of Table II gives the additional vector interaction

TABLE II

CONTRIBUTIONS TO $V_{tot}(a = \hbar/Mc)$, $J_1 = r^{-1}(d/dr)J$, $J_2 = r^{-1}(d/dr)J_1$

	P	S	V	V_f
V_c		$-J-\frac{1}{4}a^2\langle\nabla^2 J\rangle$	J	$\dfrac{f}{g}\cdot\frac{1}{2}a^2\langle\nabla^2 J\rangle$
V_σ	$\frac{1}{12}a^2\langle\nabla^2 J\rangle$		$\frac{1}{6}a^2\langle\nabla^2 J\rangle$	$\left(2\dfrac{f}{g}+\dfrac{f^2}{g^2}\right)\frac{1}{6}a^2\langle\nabla^2 J\rangle$
V_{LS}		$\frac{1}{2}a^2 J_1$	$\frac{3}{2}a^2 J_1$	$2\dfrac{f}{g}a^2 J_1$
V_T	$\frac{1}{12}a^2 r^2 J_2$		$-\frac{1}{12}a^2 r^2 J_2$	$-\left(2\dfrac{f}{g}+\dfrac{f^2}{g^2}\right)\frac{1}{12}a^2 r^2 J_2$
V_Δ		$a^2 J$	$-a^2 J$	
V_∇		$-a^2 J_1$	$-a^2 J_1$	

components calculated by Bryan and Scott (1967) when derivative coupling (i.e., f coupling) is permitted. Bryan and Scott in deriving their interactions used Feynman techniques to obtain the nonrelativistic scattering amplitudes. The potential terms, which in the Born approximation, lead to the same scattering amplitudes, were identified. It is gratifying that two such different formalisms led finally to the same results.

It should be emphasized at this point that the velocity dependent terms in Eq. (37), which are obtained from vector and scalar interactions, are inescapably present and associated with the same relativistic effects which lead to spin orbit forces. Terms of similar structure appeared deductively as far back as 1929 in Breit's work on the e–e interaction and later in the N–N interactions which Breit (1937) inferred from approximately relativistic invariance. If cancellation of major static components of the scalar and vector mesons occurs, then of necessity these velocity dependent terms must have a substantial effect (Green, 1949b). The effects are exactly analogous to the current–current interaction in electricity, just as the spin orbit effect can be compared to the interaction between a magnetic dipole and a current element [see Green (1966), and Green and Sawada (1967a, Fig. 6)].

Let us next consider the calculation of the N–N phase shifts associated with a N–N interaction of the form given by Eq. (37). Most of these techniques were developed by workers using phenomenological N–N potentials. However, our discussion will concentrate on the OBEP description.

7.4c   Schroedinger's Equation and the Phase Shifts

We sum the OBEP's due to the several mesons and insert this into the Schroedinger equation (Bryan and Scott, 1967)

$$V = \sum_{v} V^{(v)}, \qquad v = \rho, \omega, \pi, \sigma, \sigma_1, \eta, \phi \tag{38}$$

and

$$-(1/M)\,\nabla^2\psi + V\psi = (k^2/M)\psi. \tag{39}$$

To use established techniques for phenomenological velocity dependent potentials (A. M. Green, 1962), we express the net potential in the form

$$V(r) = V_0(r) - (1/M)[\nabla^2\phi(r) + \phi(r)\,\nabla^2] \tag{40}$$

where V_0 contains all the terms except the momentum dependent term ϕ, which can be determined by comparison with the potentials. For the uncoupled states we let

$$\psi = r^{-1}(1 + 2\phi)^{-1/2}\chi_{lSJ}\,Y^m_{lSJ} \tag{41}$$

where Y^m_{lSJ} are the simultaneous eigenfunctions of the total angular momentum operator $\mathbf{J}$, the orbital angular momentum operator $\mathbf{L}$, and the total spin operator $\mathbf{S}$, belonging to the eigenvalues J, l, and S, respectively. Substituting Eq. (41) into Eq. (40), we find

$$\chi_l'' - l(l+1)r^{-2}\chi_l + k^2\chi_l = MW_l\chi_l \tag{42}$$

where

$$W_l = \frac{V_{0,l}}{1 + 2\phi} - \left(\frac{\phi'}{1 + 2\phi}\right)^2 \frac{1}{M} + \frac{2\phi}{1 + 2\phi}\frac{k^2}{M} \tag{43}$$

and the J and S indices have been suppressed for simplicity. We may now use χ directly to obtain the scattering phase shift, since at some distance well beyond the range of forces ϕ approaches zero asymptotically, and hence, χ goes over to G, the usual wave function.

The tensor force mixes states with the same parity and with $l = J + 1$ and $l = J - 1$ (see Table III). For mixed waves a solution of the Schroedinger

TABLE III

| | Uncoupled states | | | | Coupled states | |
| | $S = 0$ | | $S = 1$ | | $S = 1$ | |
J	$T = 1$	$T = 0$	$T = 1$	$T = 0$	$T = 1$	$T = 0$
0	$^1S_0$		$^3P_0$			
1		$^1P_1$	$^3P_1$			$^3S_1 + {}^3D_1$
2	$^1D_2$			$^3D_2$	$^3P_2 + {}^3F_2$	
3		$^1F_3$	$^3F_3$			$^3D_3 + {}^3G_3$
4	$^1G_4$			$^3G_3$	$^3F_4 + {}^3H_4$	
5		$^1H_5$	$^3H_5$			$^3G_5 + {}^3I_5$

equation for a definite value of J can be written in the form (de Swart and Eberlein, 1960)

$$\psi_{\lambda J}^m = \frac{G_{J-1, J, \lambda}}{r} Y_{J-1, 1, J}^m + \frac{G_{J+1, J, \lambda}}{r} Y_{J+1, 1, J}^m. \qquad (44)$$

The "eigenchannel" label λ ($=\alpha$ and γ) is used to denote that this is the representation in which the scattering matrix is diagonal. When the tensor force is turned off, the $\lambda = \alpha$ denotes the pure $l = J - 1$ wave, and $\lambda = \gamma$ the $l - J + 1$ wave. The $G_{J\lambda}(r)$ are the solutions of the radial wave equation. We may write this solution in the shorthand notation

$$\psi_{\lambda J} = \begin{pmatrix} G_{J-1, J, \lambda} \\ G_{J+1, J, \lambda} \end{pmatrix}. \qquad (45)$$

We assume the net potential given by Eq. (38) has the form

$$V = V_c(r, S, p^2) + V_{LS}(r)\mathbf{L} \cdot \mathbf{S} + V_T(r)S_{12}. \qquad (46)$$

Here $V_c(r, S, p^2)$ is a spin dependent and velocity dependent central potential, $V_1(r)$ denotes the radial dependence of the tensor potential, and $V_{LS}(r)$ the radial dependence of the spin orbit interaction. We now write the Schroedinger equation in the form

$$\frac{d^2}{dr^2} \psi_{\lambda J} = A\psi_{\lambda J} \qquad (47)$$

where $\psi_{\lambda J}$ is given by Eq. (45) and A is the matrix

$$A = U_c + U_T(S_{12}) + U_{LS}(\mathbf{L} \cdot \mathbf{S}) + r^{-2}(L^2) - k^2 \qquad (48)$$

where $U = MV/\hbar^2$ and $k^2 = ME/\hbar^2$, and M is the nucleon mass. The matrices $\mathbf{L}^2$, $\mathbf{L} \cdot \mathbf{S}$, and S_{12} are (Hulthén and Sugawara, 1957)

$$\mathbf{L}^2 = \begin{pmatrix} J(J-1) & 0 \\ 0 & (J+1)(J+2) \end{pmatrix} \tag{49}$$

$$\mathbf{L} \cdot \mathbf{S} = \begin{pmatrix} J-1 & 0 \\ 0 & -(J+2) \end{pmatrix} \tag{50}$$

and

$$S_{12} = \frac{-2}{2J+1} \begin{pmatrix} J-1 & -3[J(J+1)]^{1/2} \\ -3[J(J+1)]^{1/2} & J+2 \end{pmatrix}. \tag{51}$$

The coupled partial differential equations can be handled through a straightforward generalization of the foregoing. Thus for the total angular momentum j, Eqs. (42) and (43) generalize to

$$\frac{1}{M} \begin{pmatrix} \dfrac{d^2}{dr^2} - \dfrac{(J-1)J}{r^2} + k^2 & 0 \\ 0 & \dfrac{d^2}{dr^2} - \dfrac{(J+1)(J+2)}{r^2} + k^2 \end{pmatrix} \begin{pmatrix} \chi_{J-1} \\ \chi_{J+1} \end{pmatrix}$$

$$= \frac{1}{1+2\phi} \begin{pmatrix} V_{0,J-1} & V_{0,T} \\ V_{0,T} & V_{0,J+1} \end{pmatrix} \begin{pmatrix} \chi_{J-1} \\ \chi_{J+1} \end{pmatrix} + \left[\frac{2\phi}{1+2\phi} \frac{k^2}{M} - \left(\frac{\phi'}{1+2\phi} \right)^2 \frac{1}{M} \right]$$

$$\times \begin{pmatrix} \chi_{J-1} \\ \chi_{J+1} \end{pmatrix} \tag{52}$$

where $V_{0,T}$ is entirely given by the S_{12} contributions of the potential. The spin and total angular momentum symbols, s and J, have been suppressed for simplicity.

One now introduces the reaction matrix $\mathcal{M}$ which is a 2×2 matrix defined by

$$\mathcal{L}_{sl}(r) \underset{r \to \infty}{\to} \mathcal{G}_l \delta_{sl} + \mathcal{M}_{sl} \mathcal{F}_l \quad (l, s = J \pm 1) \tag{53}$$

where $\mathcal{G}_l$ and $\mathcal{F}_l$ are the irregular and regular spherical Bessel functions (or Coulomb functions, if charged). Our two independent numerical solutions are denoted by

$$\mathcal{Y}_A \equiv \begin{pmatrix} \mathcal{Y}_{A,J-1} \\ \mathcal{Y}_{A,J+1} \end{pmatrix} \quad \text{and} \quad \mathcal{Y}_B \equiv \begin{pmatrix} \mathcal{Y}_{B,J-1} \\ \mathcal{Y}_{B,J+1} \end{pmatrix} \tag{54}$$

These two may be obtained by solving Eq. (52) numerically, starting with appropriate mutually independent initial conditions. At the matching point r_m, the $\mathcal{Y}$'s are expressed as linear combinations of $\mathcal{L}$, i.e.,

$$\mathcal{Y}_{cl} = \sum_s \alpha_{cs} \mathcal{L}_{sl}, \qquad \mathcal{Y}'_{cl} = \sum_s \alpha_{cs} \mathcal{L}_{sl} \qquad (C = A, B; \text{ at } r = r_m). \tag{55}$$

From these two equations, we obtain α and $\alpha\mathscr{M}$ in terms of $\mathscr{Y}$ and $\mathscr{Y}'$ at r_m. Then, a matrix inversion gives the reaction matrix $\mathscr{M}$ as a function of $\mathscr{Y}$ and $\mathscr{Y}'$ at r_m. The advantage of introducing the $\mathscr{M}$ matrix is that all the quantities so far are real. Since $\mathscr{M}$ must be symmetric, we can check our numerical results by testing to see if $\mathscr{M}_{J-1,J+1} = \mathscr{M}_{J+1,J-1}$.

To connect the $\mathscr{M}$ matrix to the phase shifts we introduce the scattering matrix. The 2×2 scattering matrix $S_{ll'}$ is defined by the outgoing amplitude of the wave

$$\phi_{l'l}(r) \underset{r \to \infty}{\to} \exp[-i(kr - \tfrac{1}{2}l\pi)]\,\delta_{ll'} - S_{ll'}\,\exp[i(kr - \tfrac{1}{2}l\pi)] \tag{56}$$

which has an incoming spherical part only for $l = l'$, where l and l' are either $J + 1$ or $J - 1$, respectively. From conservation of flux and time reversal, it follows that the scattering matrix is unitary and symmetric, can be represented most generally by three real parameters, and, that there exists a unitary transformation U which diagonalizes $S_{ll'}$. Thus, one way of representing the $S_{ll'}$ matrix is

$$S = U e^{2i\Delta} U^{-1} \tag{57}$$

where

$$\Delta = \begin{pmatrix} \delta_\alpha & 0 \\ 0 & \delta_\gamma \end{pmatrix} \tag{58}$$

and

$$U = \begin{pmatrix} \cos \varepsilon & -\sin \varepsilon \\ \sin \varepsilon & \cos \varepsilon \end{pmatrix} \tag{59}$$

This representation, in which $S_{ll'}$ is diagonal, is called the eigenchannel representation, and the three real parameters are in this case δ_α and δ_γ, the eigenphases, and ε, the mixing parameter. Since any solution is a linear combination of $\phi_{l'l}$ we can write in particular, for the eigenchannel wave function.

$$G_{\lambda l} = \sum_{l'} \mathscr{N}_{l'\lambda}\phi_{l'l} \underset{r \to \infty}{\to} \sum_{l'} \{\exp[-i(kr - \tfrac{1}{2}l)]\,\delta_{ll'} - S_{ll'}\,\exp[i(kr - \tfrac{1}{2}l)]\}\mathscr{N}_{l'\lambda} \tag{60}$$

Here, we simply choose $\mathscr{N}$ as the eigenvector of $S_{ll'}$

$$\sum_{l'} S_{ll'}\mathscr{N}_{l'\lambda} = \exp(2i\delta_\lambda)\mathscr{N}_{l\lambda} \qquad (\lambda = \alpha, \gamma; \quad l, l' = J \pm 1) \tag{61}$$

so that the asymptotic form of the eigenchannel wave function is

$$G_{\lambda l} \underset{r \to \infty}{\to} \mathscr{N}_{l\lambda}\{\exp[-i(kr - \tfrac{1}{2}l)] - \exp(2i\,\delta_\lambda)\,\exp[i(kr - \tfrac{1}{2}l\pi)]\}. \tag{62}$$

Defining the eigenvector matrix by

$$\mathscr{N} = \begin{pmatrix} \mathscr{N}_{J-1,\alpha} & \mathscr{N}_{J-1,\gamma} \\ \mathscr{N}_{J+1,\alpha} & \mathscr{N}_{J+1,\gamma} \end{pmatrix} \tag{63}$$

Eq. (61) can be rewritten as

$$S\mathcal{N} = \mathcal{N}e^{2i\Delta}. \tag{64}$$

Comparing Eq. (57) with Eq. (64), we find that $\mathcal{N}$ is a constant multiple of U, that is,

$$\tan\varepsilon = \mathcal{N}_{J+1,\alpha}/\mathcal{N}_{J-1,\alpha} = -\mathcal{N}_{J-1,\gamma}/\mathcal{N}_{J+1,\gamma}. \tag{65}$$

Thus, the asymptotic form of the eigenchannel wave function corresponding to the eigenphase δ_α is

$$G_{\alpha,J-1} \underset{r\to\infty}{\to} -2i\mathcal{N}_{J-1,\alpha}\exp(i\delta_\alpha)\sin[kr - \tfrac{1}{2}(J-1)\pi + \delta_\alpha]$$

$$G_{\alpha,J+1} \underset{r\to\infty}{\to} -2i\mathcal{N}_{J-1,\alpha}\exp(i\delta_\alpha)\tan\varepsilon\sin(kr - \tfrac{1}{2}(J+1)\pi + \delta_\alpha) \tag{66}$$

and similarly, that for the eigenphase δ_γ is

$$G_{\gamma,J-1} \underset{r\to\infty}{\to} 2i\mathcal{N}_{J+1,\lambda}\exp(i\delta_\gamma)\tan\varepsilon\sin(kr - \tfrac{1}{2}(J-1)\pi + \delta_\gamma)$$

$$G_{\gamma,J+1} \underset{r\to\infty}{\to} -2i\mathcal{N}_{J+1,\lambda}\exp(i\delta_\gamma)\sin(kr - \tfrac{1}{2}(J+1)\pi + \delta_\gamma). \tag{67}$$

The relation between the $\mathcal{M}$ matrix and the $S_{ll'}$ matrix is established by comparing the asymptotic form of

$$\phi_{l'l} = \sum_s \xi_{l's}\mathcal{L}_{sl}. \tag{68}$$

Using Eqs. (53) and (56), we find from the coefficients of $\exp[-i(kr - \tfrac{1}{2}l\pi)]$ and $\exp[i(kr - \tfrac{1}{2}l\pi)]$,

$$1 = \tfrac{1}{2}\xi(1 + i\mathcal{M}), \qquad -S = \tfrac{1}{2}\xi(1 - i\mathcal{M}) \tag{69}$$

respectively. The first equation yields $\xi = 2(1 + i\mathcal{M})^{-1}$, and hence from the second equation

$$S = -\frac{1 - i\mathcal{M}}{1 + i\mathcal{M}}. \tag{70}$$

Equation (70) shows that the eigenvector of $\mathcal{M}$ is also the eigenvector of $S_{ll'}$. In fact, if we define the eigenvalues and eigenvectors of $\mathcal{M}$ by

$$\sum_l \mathcal{M}_{sl}u_l^\lambda = m_\lambda u_s^\lambda \tag{71}$$

then we have

$$Su^\lambda = -\frac{1 - im_\lambda}{1 + im_\lambda}u^\lambda \qquad (\lambda = \alpha, \gamma). \tag{72}$$

Comparison with Eqs. (61) and (65) yields

$$\tan\delta_\lambda = 1/m_\lambda \qquad (\lambda = \alpha, \gamma), \qquad \tan\varepsilon = u_{J+1}^\alpha/u_{J-1}^\alpha = -u_{J-1}^\gamma/u_{J+1}^\gamma. \tag{73}$$

In other words, the eigenphases and the mixing parameter are obtained directly by diagonalizing the $\mathcal{M}$ matrix without actually calculating the $S_{ll'}$ matrix. The phase shifts and mixing parameter defined by Eq. (57) are called the Blatt–Biedenharn phases (Blatt and Biedenharn, 1952).

Stapp *et al.* (1957) introduced the so-called nuclear bar phases, by expressing the $S_{ll'}$ matrix in the form

$$S = \begin{pmatrix} \exp(i\bar{\delta}_\alpha) & 0 \\ 0 & \exp(i\bar{\delta}_\gamma) \end{pmatrix} \begin{pmatrix} \cos 2\bar{\varepsilon} & i\sin 2\bar{\varepsilon} \\ i\sin 2\bar{\varepsilon} & \cos 2\bar{\varepsilon} \end{pmatrix} \begin{pmatrix} \exp(i\bar{\delta}_\alpha) & 0 \\ 0 & \exp(i\bar{\delta}_\gamma) \end{pmatrix} \qquad (74)$$

The relations between the Blatt–Biedenharn phase shifts and the nuclear bar phase shifts are

$$\sin(\delta_\alpha - \delta_\gamma) = \sin 2\bar{\varepsilon}/\sin 2\varepsilon$$

$$\sin(\bar{\delta}_\alpha - \bar{\delta}_\gamma) = \tan 2\bar{\varepsilon}/\tan 2\varepsilon \qquad (75)$$

$$\delta_\alpha + \delta_\gamma = \bar{\delta}_\alpha + \bar{\delta}_\gamma.$$

The mixing parameter ρ in the bar phases is given by

$$\rho = \sin 2\bar{\varepsilon}. \qquad (76)$$

Figure 1 shows the theoretical phase shifts for the 2 parameter meson theoretic model of Green and Sawada (1967c) in relationship to the MacGregor *et al.* (1968) phase shifts. This model departs somewhat for the purely relativistic model (Green, 1949b; Green and Sharma, 1965) by incorporating weak additional terms which might be viewed as second order effects. The ρ-meson is included with both direct and derivative coupling constants as established by electromagnetic form factor experiments and Sakurai's (1966) considerations of universal ρ coupling. An $I = 1$, $J = 0$ scalar meson ($\sigma 1$) is also included with $m_{\sigma 1} = m_\rho$ and $g_{\sigma 1}^2 = g_\rho^2$. In addition, a weakly coupled light mass scalar meson (c) with $m_c = 3m_\pi$, is included to represent what might be an $I = 0$, $J = 0$, 2π-continuum effect or possibly enhanced coupling due to the N^* resonance. The two parameters are adjusted to fit the N–N phase shift, i.e., $y_c = 2.35$, and $\Lambda_c = \Lambda_\omega = \Lambda_\rho = \Lambda_{\sigma 1} = 1500$ MeV. Then to preserve the major features of the relativistic model, the extra coupling strength of the ω meson is set to balance the c meson strength, i.e., $g_\omega^2 - g_s^2 = (m_\omega/m_c)^2 g_c^2 = 8.3$ where $g_s^2 = g_\pi^2 = 14.7$, and we set $\Lambda_\pi = m_\omega$. The heavy regulator is arbitrarily set at $U = 20\,M_p$ which has little effect on the actual solutions.

The most recent solutions of Bryan and Scott (1967), using 10 free parameters, do somewhat better on the higher partial waves. However, they do not give the $^3S_1$ and $^1S_0$ phase shifts and ρ_1, and hence, are not very useful for nuclear physics. The 12 parameter solution of Scotti and Wong (1965) also does rather well in fitting the experimental scattering data. The simplification of their model to a 4 parameter model using symmetry considerations (Ball

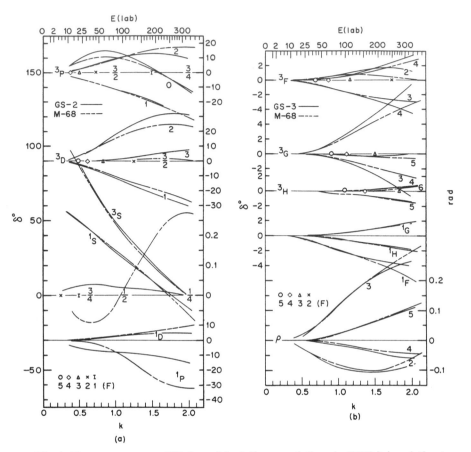

Fig. 1. Two parameter modified model of Green and Sawada (1967c) in relation to phase shifts of MacGregor *et al.* (1968).

(Model includes π-, ω-, ρ-, σ-, σ-$_1$, and c-mesons. Adjusted constants are: $g_c^2 = 2.35$ and $\Lambda = 1500$. Constrainted constants are (see text): $m(\sigma) = m(\omega)$, $m(\sigma_1) = m(\rho)$, $m(c) = 3m_\pi$, $g_\pi^2 = g_s^2 = 14.7$, $g_\omega^2 = 23.0$, $g_\rho^2 = 0.65 = g_{\sigma 1}^2$, $f_\rho/g_\rho = 3.75$.)

et al., 1966) leads to somewhat better P wave phase shifts than the GS 2 parameter model. However, their $^3S_1$ phase shifts are 10 degrees high over a wide energy range. It should be noted that the GS 2 parameter model was adjusted to an earlier set of phase shifts by Arndt *et al.* (1966), in which the rather large error bars were assigned to the $^1P_1$ phase shifts and mixing parameter ρ_1. We can do substantially better by adjusting to the new data using automatic search techniques and by using a few more free parameters. The GS 7 parameter models give substantially better fits to the old phase shifts. The Ueda and Green (1968) 7 parameter model fits the new phase shifts and experimental observables almost quantitatively.

7.4d   Final Summary

It is questionable at this point whether the most meaningful endeavor is to use automatic search techniques to sharpen up the fits with existing OBEP's or to examine fundamental meson theoretic questions. The questions at issue relate to how the N–N interaction is influenced by : (1) the structure of nucleons, (2) auxiliary conditions to the vector meson field (Sharma and Green, 1967), (3) 2BEP, 3BEP, etc. (in particular uncorrelated 2PEP, 3PEP, etc.), (4) the structure of mesons and their resonance widths, (5) recoil effects on virtual meson exchanges, (6) nonlinear effects in reduction to the Breit–Pauli–Schroedinger form, (7) virtual nucleon–antinucleon pair creation processes, (8) the effects of heavier mesons (see Table I), and (9) the possible breakdown of electrodynamics. Indeed the entire gamut of fundamental problems of meson field theory and particle physics might be expected to play a role in the N–N interaction. If, after some of these questions are resolved, the OBEP description improves still further, there is some likelihood that nuclear physics could well feed back understanding on topics which have been thought to be within the domain of elementary particle physics. The nucleus is a container of the meson medium and, hence, might serve as an excellent laboratory to explore the meson field itself.

The question of the existence of the scalar meson needed in the one boson exchange potential approach is still a matter of uncertainty. On the old model of Fermi and Yang (1949), mesons are viewed as composite states of nucleons and antinucleons. Thus the π-meson was viewed as a $^1S_0^-$ state of N–$\bar{\text{N}}$. The The intrinsic negative parity is contributed by the antiparticle. Since N and $\bar{\text{N}}$ have masses of 938.3 MeV each, presumably, if they were bound by 1640 MeV, they would appear as a meson with a mass of 137 MeV. The vector mesons would then represent the $^3S_1^-$ state of the N $\bar{\text{N}}$ system. Then presumably, the $^3P_2^-$, $^3P_1^+$, and $^3P_0^+$ multiplet would correspond to higher masses. The Sakata (1956) model in which the Λ-particle with strangeness one, serves as a third fundamental member, extends the Fermi–Yang idea in a way which accounts nicely for strange mesons such as the K's. It provides a good classification scheme for all the presently known meson octets and singlets. The same set of states is taken over in more recent schemes, which are based upon the picture of mesons as composite particles made of quarks and antiquarks. To date, most of the known boson resonances fall nicely into this scheme of things (Goldhaber, 1967). All two particle states (N $\bar{\text{N}}$ or q $\bar{\text{q}}$) have been identified rather clearly except the $^3P_0^+$. The π_v- and η_v-mesons in the latest listing (Rosenfeld *et al.*, 1968) have the correct quantum numbers. If the coupling constants are appropriate, these mesons can also serve to cancel the major static fields of the ω- and ρ-mesons. Indeed, using these heavy scalar mesons and a form factor regularization technique, Ueda and Green (1968) have developed a 7 parameter realistic OBEP which reproduces all of the N–N data quite precisely. The subject is a topical one and progress on the N–N aspects and the particle physics aspects is proceeding rapidly. It is gratifying that at last, mesons have arrived on the scene which have the quantum numbers of Yukawa's original scalar theory of 1935. Such mesons are needed in current OBEM, to achieve quantitative fits to a vast body of high energy N–N scattering data.

In comparing OBEP's to phenomenological N–N potentials we must be wary of using statistical criteria which are truly not relevant to the comparisons being undertaken. Frugality in the use of adjustable parameters is a part of the heritage of the scientists who developed the optical and shell models, and has always been a basic criterion as to the creditability of a proposed model. From painful experience in low energy N–N studies, we know that thousands of data points have provided information on only four or five intrinsic parameters. A variety of considerations suggest that the 0 to 330 MeV region might be characterized by descriptions requiring no more than 30–50 intrinsic parameters, even though experimental information might have been gathered from about 2000 data points. If now one uses a potential description requiring 30–50 phenomenological parameters, then this is not a theoretical model but simply a parametrization of the phase shifts or the experimental data in the elastic domain. Thus, in assigning an accuracy criterion to this type of description as compared to a meson theoretic model using a limited number of parameters, we must be careful not to use the customary practice of assigning, as the degrees of freedom, the number of data points less the number of adjusted constants. For 2000 data points a 40 parameter model is scarcely penalized with respect to say a 4 parameter model. This violates common sense, since it is well known that one can fit an elephant with enough parameters. A reasonable penalty would be something like dividing by the number of intrinsic parameters less the number of adjustable constants. On this basis, a 40 parameter potential description would be penalized rather heavily as compared to a 4 parameter description, as common sense would suggest that it should be.

These rather elusive considerations are questions of basic importance to the decision as to what types of potentials to employ in the nuclear many body problem. A theoretical model with say 4 parameters, which fits the elastic scattering data moderately well, is probably a natural representation of experiment, and hence, probably furnishes a fairly reliable basis for extrapolation to the untested domains. A 40 parameter model which might fit the free N–N phase shifts more precisely must be a rather artificial representation, and while probably trustworthy in interpolation, is probably not trustworthy in extrapolation. Since the nuclear many body problems involve calculation of " off the energy shell " matrix elements we must really have considerable faith in the assumed N–N interaction. Thus OBEP's which do rather well with only a few parameters will inevitably gain the attention of nuclear structure theorists. A few attempts have already been made to apply OBEP's to the nuclear many body problem, which attempts are probably indicative of future efforts.

Preston *et al.* (1967) have calculated the state-by-state contributions to the t matrix using velocity dependent OBEP's derived by D. Wong (1964) which they have adjusted to be in reasonable agreement with N–N scattering data. They find that these are very similar to those found by Bhargava and Sprung (1967) for phenomenological potentials. Their work thus indicates that reasonable results will be obtained in nuclear matter calculations. Ingber (1967), and Brueckner and Ingber (1967), stimulated by D. Wong's OBEM efforts, report excellent results for nuclear matter using a velocity dependent OBEP associated with π-, ω-, σ-, η-, ρ- mesons and an adaptation of Brueckner, Bethe, and Goldstone techniques in their nuclear matter calculations.

McCarthy and Köhler (1968), using the highly velocity dependent one parameter OBEP of Green and Sawada (1967b), with corrections for ^1P phase shifts, obtain a binding energy of 7.2 MeV per nucleon for O^{16} in close correspondence with the experimental value of 8 MeV. They used the same reaction matrix, Hartree–Fock calculational methods which for various hard core phenomenological interactions yielded only 2–3 MeV/N binding.

These few studies indicate that the availability of good OBEP N–N interactions now permits nuclear theorists to make a major assault on the nuclear many body problem with some confidence as to the physical reasonableness of this basic force law. These many body studies should proceed with all possible variations. Thus the three body problem which provides a rigid test for important techniques can serve as an excellent test of the N–N interaction. The four body He^4 is our simplest closed shell nucleus and it, along with the light s–d nuclei are also tractable testing grounds for OBEP's as well as for Hartree–Fock techniques. Thomas Fermi Dirac models of heavy nuclei and infinite nuclear matter should give an overall survey of the results which could be expected from the many possible variations of OBEP's. Thus, in this effort, we must plan to advance simultaneously our understanding of the N–N interaction as we advance our understanding of the nuclear many body problem.

In concluding this work it would seem that, while we have been groping in darkness since 1912 in our attempts to understand the nature of nuclear forces and the structure of the nucleus, glimmers of light have appeared on the horizon. Figure 2 depicts schematically the many pronged attacks now underway which involve, among others, all the topics which we have dealt with in this work. If free rein is given to all reasonable approaches, and if a spirit of open-minded-ness and cooperative interchange is maintained, then it may be within our grasp to achieve our ultimate goal: an understanding of the fundamental principles governing the physics of the nucleus.

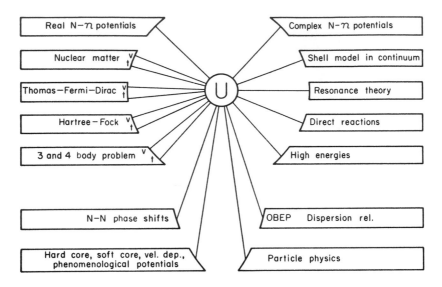

Fig. 2. Theoretical efforts toward a fundamental understanding of nuclear physics.

References

ADAIR, R. K. (1954). *Phys. Rev.* **94**, 737.

AGODI, A., and EBERLI, E. (1960). *Nuovo Cimento* **18**, 718.

AIRY, G. B. (1839). *Proc. Cambridge Phil. Soc.* **6**, 379.

AMALDI, U., Jr., CAMPOS VENUTI, G., CORTELLESSA, G., DESANCTIS, E., FRULLANI, S., LOMBARD, R., and SALVADORI, P. (1966). *Phys. Letters* **22**, 593.

ANDERSON, H. L., JOHNSON, C. S., HINCKS, E. P., RABOY, S., and TRAIL, C. C. (1963). *Phys. Letters* **6**, 261.

ANDERSON, H. L., McKEE, R. J., HARGROVE, C. K., and HINCKS, E. P. (1966). *Phys. Rev. Letters* **16**, 434.

ARNDT, R. A., BRYAN, R. A., and MacGREGOR, M. H. (1966). *Phys. Letters* **21**, 314; *Phys. Rev.* **152**, 1490.

ARONS, M. E., HAN, M. Y., and SUDARSHAN, E. C. G. (1963). *Phys. Rev.* **137**, B1085.

AUERBACH, E. H. (1962). Brookhaven Natl. Lab. Rept., Upton, New York, BNL-6562.

AUERBACH, E. H., DOVER, C. B., KERMAN, A. K., LEMMER, R. H., and SCHWARCZ, E. H. (1966). *Phys. Rev. Letters* **17**, 1184.

AUSTERN, N. (1961). *Ann. Phys. (N.Y.)* **15**, 299.

AUSTERN, N. (1967). *Ann. Phys. (N.Y.)* **45**, 113.

BABIKOV, V. V. (1963). *Progr. Theoret. Phys. (Kyoto)* **29**, 712.

BABIKOV, V. V. (1966). *Nucl. Phys.* **76**, 665.

BAKER, G. A., JR., and BAKER, G. A., SR. (1956). *Can. J. Phys.* **34**, 423.

BALL, J. B., FULMER, C. B., and BASSEL, R. H. (1964). *Phys. Rev.* **135**, B706.

BALL, J. S., SCOTTI, A., and WONG, D. Y. (1966). *Phys. Rev.* **142**, 1000.

BARANGER, M. (1967). *Proc. Intern. Conf. Nucl. Phys., Gatlinburg, Tennessee, 1967* (R. L. Becker, C. D. Goodman, P. H. Stelson, and A. Zucker, eds.), p. 659. Academic Press, New York.

BARRETT, R. C., HILL, A. D., and HODGSON, P. E. (1965). *Nucl. Phys.* **62**, 133.

BARSCHALL, H. H. (1952). *Phys. Rev.* **86**, 431.

BARTLETT, J. H., JR. (1936). *Phys. Rev.* **49**, 102L.

BARTLETT, M. S. (1932). *Phys. Rev.* **41**, 370; **42**, 145.

BASSEL, R. H., DRISKO, R. M., SATCHLER, G. R., LEE, L. L., JR., SCHIFFER, J. P., and ZEIDMAN, B. (1964). *Phys. Rev.* **136**, B960.

BATCHELOR, R., and TOWLE, J. H. (1963). *Nucl. Phys.* **47**, 385.
BATTY, C. J. (1961). *Nucl. Phys.* **23**, 562.
BAUER, R. W., ANDERSON, J. D., LUTZ, H. F., WONG, C., McCLURE, J. W., and POHL, B. A. (1967). *Nucl. Phys.* **A93**, 673.
BAUGH, D. J., GREENLEES, G. W., LILLEY, J. S., and ROMAN, S. (1965). *Nucl. Phys.* **65**, 33.
BAUGH, D. J., GRIFFITH, J. A. R., and ROMAN, S. (1966). *Nucl. Phys.* **83**, 481.
BENVENISTE, J., MITCHELL, A. C., BUCK, B., and FULMER, C. B. (1964). *Phys. Rev.* **133**, B323.
BETHE, H.A. (1940a). *Phys. Rev.* **57**, 260, 390.
BETHE, H. A. (1940b). *Phys. Rev.* **57**, 1125.
BETHE, H. A. (1949). *Phys. Rev.* **76**, 38.
BETHE, H. A. (1953). *Sci. Am.* p. 1 (September 1953).
BETHE, H. A. (1956a). *Phys. Rev.* **103**, 1353.
BETHE, H. A. (1956b). *Physica* **22**, 941.
BETHE, H. A. (1965). *Phys. Rev.* **138**, B804.
BETHE, H. A., (1968). *Phys. Rev.* **167**, 879.
BETHE, H. A., and BACHER, R. F. (1936). *Rev. Mod. Phys.* **8**, 82.
BETHE, H. A., and GOLDSTONE, J. (1957). *Proc. Roy. Soc.* (*London*) **A238**, 551.
BETHE, H. A., BRANDOW, B. H., and PETCHEK, A. G. (1963). *Phys. Rev.* **129**, 225.
BEYSTER, J. R., WALT, M., and SALMI, E. W. (1956). *Phys. Rev.* **104**, 1319.
BHARGAVA, P. C., and SPRUNG, D. W. L. (1967). *Ann. Phys.* (*N.Y.*) **42**, 222.
BINGHAM, C. R., HALBERT, M. L., and BASSEL, R. H. (1966). *Phys. Rev.* **148**, 1174.
BITTERS, F., and FESHBACH, H. (1953). *Phys. Rev.* **92**, 837.
BJORKLUND, F. J. (1959). *Proc. Intern. Conf. Nucl. Optical Model, Tallahassee, Florida, 1959.* Florida State Univ. Studies No. 32, p. 1.
BJORKLUND, F. J., and FERNBACH, S. (1958). *Phys. Rev.* **109**, 1295.
BJORKLUND, F. J., FERNBACH, S., and SHERMAN, N. (1956). *Phys. Rev.* **101**, 1832.
BLAIR, J. S. (1957). *Phys. Rev.* **108**, 827.
BLATT, J. M., and BIEDENHARN, L. C. (1952). *Phys. Rev.* **86**, 399.
BLATT, J. M., and JACKSON, J. D. (1949). *Phys. Rev.* **76**, 18.
BLATT, J. M., and WEISSKOPF, V. F. (1952). "Theoretical Nuclear Physics," p. 139. Wiley, New York.
BLOCH, C. (1957). *Nucl. Phys.* **4**, 503.
BLOCK, B., and FESHBACH, H. (1963). *Ann. Phys.* (*N.Y.*) **23**, 47.
BLUMBERG, L. N., GROSS, E. E., VAN DER WOUDE, A., ZUCKER, A., and BASSEL, R. H. (1966). *Phys. Rev.* **147**, 812.
BOCHIN, V. P., ZHEREBTSOVA, K. I., ZOLOTAREV, V. S., KOMAROV, V. A., KRASNOV, L. V., LITVIN, V. F., MEMILOV, YU. A., NOVATSKY, B. G., and PISKORZH, SH. (1964). *Nucl. Phys.* **51**, 161.
BOCK, R., DAVID, P., DUHM, H. H., HEFELE, H., LYNEN, U., and STOCK, R. (1967). *Nucl. Phys.* **A92**, 539.
BOHM, D., and FORD, K. W. (1950). *Phys. Rev.* **79**, 745.
BOHR, A. (1952). *Kgl. Danske Videnskab, Selskab, Mat.-Fys. Medd.* **26**. No. 14.
BOHR, A., and MOTTELSON, B. R. (1953). *Kgl. Danske Videnskab. Selskab, Mat.-Fys. Medd.* **27**, No. 16.
BOHR, N. (1936). *Nature* **137**, 344.
BOHR, N., and WHEELER, J. A. (1939). *Phys. Rev.* **56**, 426.
BOPP, F. (1942). *Ann. Physik* **42**, 573.
BOSCHITZ, E. T. (1966). *Bull. Am. Phys. Soc.* **11**, 355.
BOSCHITZ, E. T., CHABRE, M., CONZETT, H. E., and SLOBODRIAN, R. J. (1966). *Proc. 2nd Intern. Conf. Polarization Phenomena Nucleons, Karlsruhe, 1965* (P. Huber and H. Schopper, eds.). Birkhäuser, Baset and Stuttgart, 1966.

BRANDOW, B. H. (1967). *Rev. Mod. Phys.* **39**, 771.
BREIT, G. (1929). *Phys. Rev.* **34**, 553.
BREIT, G. (1932). *Phys. Rev.* **39**, 616.
BREIT, G. (1937). *Phys. Rev.* **51**, 248, 778.
BREIT, G. (1958). *Phys. Rev.* **111**, 652.
BREIT, G., and WIGNER, E. P. (1936). *Phys. Rev.* **49**, 519, 642.
BREIT, G., CONDON, E. U., and PRESENT, R. D. (1936). *Phys. Rev.* **50**, 825.
BREIT, G., OFSTROFSKY, M., and JOHNSON, D. P. (1936a). *Phys. Rev.* **49**, 22.
BREIT, G., HULL, M. H., JR., LASSILA, K. E., and PYATT, K. D. (1960). *Phys. Rev.* **120**, 2227.
BREIT, G., HULL, M. H., JR., LASSILA, K. E., and PYATT, K. D. (1962). *Phys. Rev.* **218**, 826.
BREIT, G., SEAMON, R. E., FRIEDMAN, K. A., HARACZ, R. D., HOLT, J. M., and PRAKASH, A. (1968). *Phys. Rev.* **165**, 1579.
BRENIG, W. (1959). *Nucl. Phys.* **13**, 333.
BRIX, P., and KOPFERMANN, H. (1951). *Fetschr. Akad. Wiss. Göttingen Math.-Phys.* **K1**, 17.
BRIX, P., and KOPFERMANN, H. (1958). *Rev. Mod. Phys.* **30**, 517.
BROEK, H. W., YNTEMA, J. L., BUCK, B., and SATCHLER, G. R. (1965). *Nucl. Phys.* **64**, 259.
BROWN, G. E. (1959). *Rev. Mod. Phys.* **31**, 893.
BROWN, G. E. (1967). "Unified Theory of Nuclear Models and Forces." North-Holland Publ., Amsterdam.
BROWN, G. E., GUNN, J. H., and GOULD, P. (1963). *Nucl. Phys.* **46**, 598.
BRUECKNER, K. A. (1954). *Phys. Rev.* **96**, 508.
BRUECKNER, K. A. (1955). *Phys. Rev.* **97**, 1353.
BRUECKNER, K. A., and DABROWSKI, J. (1964). *Phys. Rev.* **131**, B722.
BRUECKNER, K. A., and GAMMEL, J. L. (1958). *Phys. Rev.* **109**, 1023.
BRUECKNER, K. A., and INGBER, L. (1967). *Intern. Conf. Nucl. Struct.*, 1967. Institute for Nuclear Study, Univ. of Tokyo, contribution 3.6.
BRUECKNER, K. A., and MASTERSON, K. S. (1962). *Phys. Rev.* **128**, 2267.
BRUECKNER, K. A., and WATSON, K. M. (1953). *Phys. Rev.* **90**, 699.
BRUECKNER, K. A., LEVINSON, C. A., and MAHMOUD, H. M. (1954). *Phys. Rev.* **95**, 217.
BRUECKNER, K. A., GAMMEL J. L., and WEITZNER, H. (1958). *Phys. Rev.* **110**, 431.
BRUECKNER, K. A., LOCKETT, A. M., and ROTENBERG, M. (1961). *Phys. Rev.* **121**, 255.
BRYAN, R. A., and ARNDT, R. A. (1966). *Phys. Rev.* **150**, 1299.
BRYAN, R. A., and SCOTT, B. L. (1964). *Phys. Rev.* **135**, B434.
BRYAN, R. A., and SCOTT, B. L. (1967). *Phys. Rev.* **164**, 1215.
BRYAN, R. A., DISMUKES, C. R., and RAMSAY, W. (1963). *Nucl. Phys.* **45**, 353.
BRYANT, C., and JARMIE, N. (1967). Los Alamos Sci. Rept., LA-DC-8111.
BUCK, B. (1963). *Phys. Rev.* **130**, 712.
BUCK, B., and PEREY, F. G. (1962). *Phys. Rev. Letters* **8**, 444.
CAMERON, A. G. W. (1957). *Can. J. Phys.* **35**, 1021.
CAMERON, J. M., CARLSON, R. F., ELDRIDGE, H. B., RICHARDSON, J. R., VAN OERS, W. T. H., and VERDA, J. W. (1967). *Intern. Conf. Nucl. Struct.*, 1967. Institute for Nuclear Study, Univ. of Tokyo, contribution 8.53.
CHADWICK, J. (1932). *Nature* **129**, 312; *Proc. Roy. Soc. (London)* **136**, 692.
CHASE, D. M., and ROHRLICH, F. (1954). *Phys. Rev.* **94**, 81.
CHASE, D. M., WILETS, L., and EDMONDS, A. R. (1958). *Phys. Rev.* **110**, 1080.
CHESTON, W. B., and GLASSGOLD, A. E. (1957). *Phys. Rev.* **106**, 1215.
CHEW, G. F. (1950). *Phys. Rev.* **80**, 196.
CHEW, G. F., and GOLDBERGER, M. L. (1952). *Phys. Rev.* **87**, 778.
CHEW, G. F., and WICK, G. C. (1952). *Phys. Rev.* **85**, 636.
CINDRO, N., WALL, N. S., and MELKANOFF, M. A. (1959). Mass. Inst. of Technol., Lab. for Nucl. Sci., Cambridge, Massachusetts. Progr. Rept. No. 54, p. 144 (AECU-425).

CLARK, J. W., and WESTHAUS, P. (1966). *Phys. Rev.* **144**, 833.

CLEMENT, C. F. (1963). *Phys. Rev.* **128**, 2724.

CLEMENTEL, E., and VILLI, C. (1955). *Nuovo Cimento* **2**, 176.

CLINE, D., ALFORD, W. P., and BLAU, L.M. (1965). *Nucl. Phys.* **73**, 33.

COCKROFT, J. D., and WALTON, E. T. (1932). *Nature* **129**, 649; *Proc. Roy. Soc. (London)* **136**, 619; *Proc. Roy. Soc. (London)* **137**, 229.

CONDON, E. U., and GURNEY, R. W. (1928). *Nature* **122**, 439.

COOK, L. J., MACMILLAN, E. M., PETERSON, J. M., and SEWEL, D. C. (1949). *Phys. Rev.* **75**, 7.

COOPER, L. M., and HENLEY, E. M. (1953). *Phys. Rev.* **92**, 801.

CORYELL, C. D., and SUESS, H. E. (1952). *Phys. Rev.* **86**, 609.

CRAIG, R. M., DORE, J. C., GREENLEES, G. W., LILLEY, J. S., LOWE, J., and ROWE, P. C. (1964). *Nucl. Phys.* **58**, 515.

CRAIG, R. M., DORE, J. C., GREENLEES, G. W., LOWE, J., and WATSON, D. L. (1966a). *Nucl. Phys.* **83**, 493.

CRAIG, R. M., DORE, J. C., GREENLEES, G. W., LOWE, J., and WATSON, D. L. (1966b). *Nucl. Phys.* **79**, 177.

DAEHNICK, W. W. (1964). *Phys. Rev.* **135**, B1168.

DANOS, M., and GREINER, W. (1965). *Phys. Rev.* **138**, B93.

DANOS, M., and GREINER, W. (1966). *Phys. Rev.* **146**, 708.

DAREWYCH, G., and GREEN, A. E. S. (1967). *Phys. Rev.* **164**, 1324.

DAVIES, K. T. R., KRIEGER, S. J., and BARANGER, M. (1967). *Nucl. Phys.* **84**, 545.

DAY, B. D. (1967). *Rev. Mod. Phys.* **39**, 745.

DE SHALIT, A. (1964). *Proc. Intern. Conf. Nucl. Phys., Paris, 1964.* Editions de Centre National de la Recherche Scientifique, Paris.

DE SHALIT, A., and TALMI, I. (1963). "Nuclear Shell Theory." Academic Press, New York.

DE SWART, J. J., and EBERLEIN, P. J. (1960). Univ. of Rochester, Rochester, New York. Rept. No. NYO-9030.

DEVONS, S., COHEN, R. C., KANARIS, A. D., and NISSIM-SABAT, C. (1964). *Phys. Letters* **11**, 70.

DEVONS, S. CHASMAN, C., RISLINEN, R. A., COHEN, R. C., and NISSIM-SABAT, C. (1965) *Phys. Rev. Letters* **14**, 181.

DEVONS, S., BARDIN, T. T., BARRETT, R. C., COHEN, R. C., HITLIN, D., MACAGNO, E., NISSIM-SABAT, C., RAINWATER, J., RUNGE, K., and WU, C.S. (1966). *Phys. Rev. Letters* **16**, 718.

DICELLO, J. F., IGO, G., and ROUSH, M. L. (1967). *Phys. Rev.* **157**, 1001.

DICKENS, J. K. (1962). Ph.D. Thesis, Univ. of Southern California, Los Angeles (unpublished).

DICKENS, J. K., and PEREY, F. G. (1965). *Phys. Rev.* **138**, B1080, B1083.

DICKENS, J. K., HANER, D. A., and WADDEL, C. N. (1962). *Bull. Am. Phys. Soc.* **7**, 285.

DICKENS, J. K., HANER, D. A., and WADDEL, C. N. (1963). *Phys. Rev.* **132**, 2159.

DIRAC, P. A. M. (1932). *Proc. Roy. Soc. (London)* **136**, 453.

DIRAC, P. A. M., FOCK, V. A., and PODOLSKY, B. (1932). *Z. Physik Sowjetunion* **2**, 473.

DIVADEENAM, M. (1967). Ph.D. thesis, Duke Univ., Durham, North Carolina (unpublished).

DRELL, S. (1955). *Phys. Rev.* **100**, 97.

DRISKO, R. M., and RYBICKI, F. (1966). *Phys. Rev. Letters* **16**, 275.

DRISKO, R. M., SATCHLER, G. R., and BASSEL, R. H. (1963). *Phys. Letters* **5**, 347.

DUERR, H. (1956). *Phys. Rev.* **103**, 469.

DUERR, H. (1958). *Phys. Rev.* **109**, 117.

DUKAREVICH, YU. V., DYUMIN, A. N., and KAMINKER, D. M. (1967). *Nucl. Phys.* **A92**, 433.

DUKE, C. B. (1963). *Phys. Rev.* **129**, 681.

DURISCH, J. E., and GOULD, P. (1965). *Phys. Rev.* **137**, B906.

DUTTA, S. K., WILSON, W. A., and GREEN, A. E. S. (1968). *J. Math. Phys.* (to be published).
EARWAKER, L. G. (1967). *Nucl. Phys.* **A90**, 56.
EISBERG, R. M., YENNIE, D. R., and WILKINSON, D. H. (1960). *Nucl. Phys.* **18**, 338.
ELSASSER, W. (1933). *J. Phys. Radium* **4**, 549.
ELSASSER, W. (1934). *J. Phys. Radium* **5**, 389, 635; *Compt. Rend.* **199**, 46, 1213.
ELTON, L. R. B. (1961). *Nucl. Phys.* **23**, 681.
ELTON, L. R. B. (1966). *Nucl. Phys.* **89**, 69.
EMMERICH, W. S. (1955). *Phys. Rev.* **98**, 148 (A).
ENDT, P. M., and VAN DER LEUN, C. (1962). *Nucl. Phys.* **34**, 1.
ERWIN, A. R., MARCH, R., WALKER, W. D., and WEST, E. (1961). *Phys. Rev. Letters* **6**, 628.
FANNON, J. A., BURGE, E. J., SMITH, D. A., and GANGULY, N. K. (1967). *Nucl. Phys.* **A97**, 263.
FANO, U. (1961). *Phys. Rev.* **124**, 1866.
FAY, C. H. (1936). *Phys. Rev.* **50**, 560.
FEENBERG, E. (1947). *Rev. Mod. Phys.* **19**, 239.
FEENBERG, E. (1950). *Phys. Rev.* **77**, 6.
FEENBERG, E. (1955). "Shell Theory of the Nucleus." Princeton Univ. Press, Princeton, New Jersey.
FEENBERG, E., and KNIPP, J. K. (1935). *Phys. Rev.* **48**, 906.
FERMI, E. (1932). *Rev. Mod. Phys.* **4**, 487.
FERMI, E. (1949). "Nuclear Physics." Univ. of Chicago Press, Chicago, Illinois.
FERMI, E., and YANG, C. N. (1949). *Phys. Rev.* **76**, 1739.
FERNBACH, S. (1958). *Rev. Mod. Phys.* **30**, 414.
FERNBACH, S., SERBER, R., and TAYLOR, T. B. (1949). *Phys. Rev.* **75**, 1352.
FESHBACH, H. (1958a). *Ann. Phys. (N.Y.)* **5**, 357.
FESHBACH, H. (1958b). *Ann. Rev. Nucl. Sci.* **8**, 49.
FESHBACH, H. (1960). *In* "Nuclear Spectroscopy" (F. Ajzenberg-Selove, ed.), Part B, p. 1046. Academic Press, New York.
FESHBACH, H. (1962). *Ann. Phys. (N.Y.)* **19**, 287.
FESHBACH, H. (1964). *Rev. Mod. Phys.* **36**, 1076.
FESHBACH, H., and LOMMON, E. (1956). *Phys. Rev.* **102**, 891.
FESHBACH, H., and WEISSKOPF, V. F. (1949). *Phys. Rev.* **76**, 1550.
FESHBACH, H., PEASLEE, D. C., and WEISSKOPF, V. F. (1947). *Phys. Rev.* **71**, 145.
FESHBACH, H., PORTER, C. E., and WEISSKOPF, V. F. (1953). *Phys. Rev.* **90**, 166.
FESHBACH, H., PORTER, C. E., and WEISSKOPF, V. F. (1954). *Phys. Rev.* **96**, 448.
FESHBACH, H., KERMAN, A. K., and LEMMER, R. H. (1964). *Proc. Intern. Conf. Nucl. Phys., Paris, 1964.* Editions du Centre Nationale de la Recherche Scientifigue, Paris, contribution C141.
FESHBACH, H., KERMAN, A. K., and LEMMER, R. H. (1967). *Ann. Phys. (N.Y.)* **41**, 230.
FEYNMAN, R. P. (1949). *Phys. Rev.* **76**, 769.
FIEDELDEY, H. (1967). *Nucl. Phys.* **A96**, 463.
FIEDELDEY, H., and FRAHN, W. E. (1961). *Ann. Phys. (N.Y.)* **16**, 387.
FISHER, T. R., SHELLEY, E. G., SAFRATA, R. S., MCCARTHY, J., and BARRETT, R. C. (1966). *Phys. Rev. Letters*, **17**, 36.
FISHER, T. R., SAFRATA, R. S., SHELLEY, E. G., MCCARTHY, J., AUSTIN, S. M., and BARRETT, R. C. (1967). *Phys. Rev.* **157**, 1149.
FITCH, V. L., and RAINWATER, J. (1953). *Phys. Rev.* **92**, 789.
FLORIDA (1959). *Proc. Intern. Conf. Nucl. Optical Model, Tallahassee, Florida*, 1959. Florida State Univ. Srudies, No. 32.
FLORIDA (1967). *Rev. Mod. Phys.* **39**, No. 3. (*Proc. Intern. Conf. N-N Interaction, Univ. of Florida, Gainesville, Florida 1967*).
FLYNN, E. R., and BASSEL, R. H. (1965). *Phys. Rev. Letters* **15**, 168.

FOCK, V. A. (1934). *Z. Physik Sowjetunion* **6**, 449.

FOCK, V. A., and PODOLSKY, B. (1932). *Z. Physik Sowjetunion* **1**, 801.

FORD. K. W., and BOHM, D. (1950). *Phys. Rev.* **79**, 745.

FORD, K. W., and WHEELER, J. A. (1959a). *Ann. Phys.* (*N.Y.*) **7**, 259.

FORD, K. W., and WHEELER, J. A. (1959b). *Ann. Phys* (*N.Y.*) **7**, 287.

FRAHN, W. E., and LEMMER, R. H. (1957). *Nuovo Cimento* **5**, 1564.

FRANCIS, N. C., and WATSON, K. M. (1953). *Phys. Rev.* **92**, 291.

FRANCO, V. (1965). *Phys. Rev.* **140**, B1501.

FRAUTSCHI, S. C. (1963). "Regge Poles and *S*-Matrix Theory," p. 131. Benjamin, New York.

FRENCH, J. B., and GOLDBERGER, M. L. (1952). *Phys. Rev.* **87**, 899.

FRICKE, M. P., and SATCHLER, G. R. (1965). *Phys. Rev.* **139**, B567.

FRICKE, M. P., GROSS, E. E., MORTON, B. J., and ZUCKER, A. (1967). *Phys. Rev.* **156**, 1207.

FRIEDMAN, F. L., and WEISSKOPF, V. F. (1955). *In* "Niels Bohr and the Development of Physics" (W. Pauli, ed.). Pergamon Press, Oxford.

FULMER, C. B., BALL, J. B., SCOTT, A., and WHITEN, M. L. (1967). *Phys. Letters* **24B**, 505.

FURUICHI, S. (1967). *Progr. Theoret. Phys.* (*Kyoto*), *Suppl.* **39**, 190.

GAMMEL, J. L., and THALER, R. M. (1957). *Phys. Rev.* **107**, 291.

GAMMEL, J. L., CHRISTIAN, R. S., and THALER, R. M. (1957). *Phys. Rev.* **105**, 311.

GAMOW, G. (1928). *Z. Physik* **51**, 204; **52**, 510.

GERJUOY, E., and SAXON, D. S. (1954). *Phys. Rev.* **94**, 1445.

GERSTEN, A. (1967). *Nucl. Phys.* **A96**, 288.

GERSTEN, A., and GREEN, A. E. S. (1968). *Bull. Am. Phys. Soc.* **13**, 627.

GIBSON, E. F., RIDLEY, B. W., KRANSHAAR, J. J., RICKEY, M. E., and BASSEL, R. H. (1967). *Phys. Rev.* **155**, 1194, 1208.

GLASSGOLD, A. E., CHESTON, W. B., STEIN, M. L., SCHULDT, S. B., and ERICKSON, G. W. (1957). *Phys. Rev.* **106**, 1207.

GLAUBER, R. J. (1955). *Phys. Rev.* **100**, 242.

GOLDBERGER, M. L. (1960). *Proc. Midwestern Conf. Theoret. Phys., Purdue Univ., Lafayette, Indiana, April 1960*, p. 50.

GOLDFARB, L. J. B., GREENLEES, G. W., and HOOPER, M.B. (1966). *Phys. Rev.* **144**, 829.

GOLDHABER, G. (1967). Quantum Numbers of Boson Resonances, *Cern School Phys. September, 1967*. CERN 67–24, Vol. 3.

GOLDSTEIN, H. (1950). "Classical Mechanics." Addison-Wesley, Reading, Massachusetts.

GOLDSTONE, J. (1957). *Proc. Roy. Soc.* (*London*) **A239**, 267.

GOMES, L. C. (1959). *Phys. Rev.* **116**, 1226.

GOMES, L. C., WALECKA, J. D., and WEISSKOPF, V. F. (1958). *Ann. Phys.* (*N.Y.*) **3**, 241.

GOOD, W. M., PAYA, D., WAGNER, R., and TAMURA, T. (1966). *Phys. Rev.* **151**, 912.

GOTTFRIED, K. (1956). *Phys. Rev.* **103**, 1017.

GREEN, A. E. S. (1948). *Phys. Rev.* **73**, 26, 519L.

GREEN, A. E. S. (1949a). *Phys. Rev.* **75**, 1926.

GREEN, A. E. S. (1949b). *Phys. Rev.* **76**, 460A, 870L.

GREEN, A. E. S. (1949c). Unpublished notes.

GREEN, A. E. S. (1951). *Phys. Rev.* **83**, 1248.

GREEN, A. E. S. (1954). *Phys. Rev.* **95**, 1006.

GREEN, A. E. S. (1955). *Phys. Rev.* **99**, 1410.

GREEN, A. E. S. (1956a). *Phys. Rev.* **102**, 325.

GREEN, A. E. S. (1956b). *Phys. Rev.* **104**, 1617.

GREEN, A. E. S. (1956c). *Bull. Am. Phys. Soc.* **1**, 269 (see also Progr. Rept, No. II, A.E.C. Contract AT-(40–1)-1755, February 1956).

GREEN, A. E. S. (1957). *Bull. Am. Phys. Soc.* **2**, 25 (see also Progr. Rept. No. III, A.E.C. Contract AT-(30–1)-1755, February 1956).

GREEN, A. E. S. (1958a). *Rev. Mod. Phys.* **30**, 580.

GREEN, A. E. S. (1958b). *Proc. U.N. Intern. Conf. Peaceful Uses At. Energy, 2nd, Geneva, 1958,* **2**, 50.

GREEN, A. E. S. (1958c). *Proc. Conf. Reactions Complex Nuclei, 1st, Gatlinburg, Tennessee, 1958.* Invited paper, ORNL-2606, p. 306.

GREEN, A. E. S. (1959). *Proc. Intern. Conf. Nucl. Optical Model, Tallahassee, Florida, 1959.* Florida State Univ. Studies, No. 32.

GREEN, A. E. S. (1966). *Am. J. Phys.* **34**, 723A.

GREEN, A. E. S., and EDWARDS, D. (1953). *Phys. Rev.* **91**, 46.

GREEN, A. E. S., and ENGLER, N. (1953). *Phys. Rev.* **91**, 40.

GREEN, A. E. S., and LEE, K. (1955). *Phys. Rev.* **99**, 772.

GREEN, A. E. S., and MILLER, D. (1968). *Bull. Am. Phys. Soc.* **13**, 628.

GREEN, A. E. S., and SAWADA, T. (1967a). *Nucl. Phys.* **B2**, 267.

GREEN, A. E. S., and SAWADA, T. (1967b). *Rev. Mod. Phys.* **39**, 594.

GREEN, A. E. S., and SAWADA, T. (1967c). *Intern. Conf. Nucl. Struct., Tokyo, 1967.* Institute for Nuclear Study, Univ. of Tokyo, contribution 3.5.

GREEN, A. E. S., and SHARMA, R. D. (1965). *Phys. Rev. Letters* **14**, 380.

GREEN, A. E. S., and SOOD, P. C. (1958). *Phys. Rev.* **111**, 1147.

GREEN, A. E. S., MINOGUE, R. B., OPPENHIEM, R., MARUCCI, N. J., and ENGLER, N. (1952). *Phys. Rev.* **86**, 654A.

GREEN, A. E. S., LEE, K., and BERKLEY, R. J. (1956). *Phys. Rev.* **107**, 1625.

GREEN, A. E. S., PORTER, C. E., and SAXON, D. S. (1959). *Proc. Conf. Nucl. Optical Model, Tallahassee, Florida, 1959.* Florida State Univ. Studies, No. 32.

GREEN, A. E. S., SAWADA, T., and SHARMA, R. D. (1966). *In* "Isobaric Spin in Nuclear Physics" (J. D. Fox and D. Robson, eds.), p. 113. Academic Press, New York.

GREEN, A. E. S., DAREWYCH, G., and BEREZDIVIN, R. (1967a). *Phys. Rev.* **157**, 929.

GREEN, A. E. S., MACGREGOR, M. H., and WILSON, R. (eds.) (1967b). (*Proc. Intern. Conf. N-N Interaction, Gainsville, Florida, 1967*) *Rev. Mod. Phys.* **39**, 495.

GREEN, A. M. (1962). *Nucl. Phys.* **33**, 218.

GREENLEES, G. W., and PYLE, G. J. (1966). *Phys. Rev.* **149**, 836.

GRIFFITH, J. A. R., and ROMAN, S. (1965). *Phys. Letters* **19**, 410.

GRIFFITH, T. C., and POWER, E. A. (eds.) (1960). "Nuclear Forces and the Few Nucleon Problem." Pergamon Press, Oxford.

GUGGENHEIMER, K. (1934). *J. Phys. Radium* **5**, 253, 475.

HAFELE, J. C., FLYNN, E. R., and BLAIR, A. G. (1967). *Phys. Rev.* **155**, 1238.

HAHN, O., and STRASSMAN, F. (1939). *Naturwiss,* **27**, 11.

HALBERT, E. C. (1964). *Nucl. Phys.* **50**, 353.

HARDIE, G., DANGLE, R. L., and OPPLIGER, L. D. (1963). *Phys. Rev.* **129**, 353.

HAXEL, O., JENSEN, J. H. D., and SUESS, H. E. (1949). *Phys. Rev.* **75**, 1766L.

HAXEL, O., JENSEN, J. H. D., and SUESS, H. E. (1950). *Z. Physik.* **128**, 295.

HEISENBERG, W. (1932). *Z. Physik* **77**, 1.

HEISENBERG, W. (1934). Rapport du VIIme Congrès Solvay, Paris.

HEISENBERG, W. (1935). *Z. Physik* **96**, 473.

HEISENBERG, W. (1957). *Nucl. Phys.* **4**, 532.

HEISENBERG, W., and PAULI, W. (1929). *Z. Physik* **56**, 1

HERNDON, R. C., SCHMID, E. W., and TANG, Y. C. (1963). *Nucl. Phys.* **42**, 113.

HIEBERT, J. C., NEWMAN, E., and BASSEL, R. H. (1967). *Phys. Rev.* **154**, 898.

HILL, D. L., and WHEELER, J. A. (1953). *Phys. Rev.* **89**, 1102.

HILLMAN, P., JOHANSSON, A., and TIBELL, G. (1958). *Phys. Rev.* **110**, 1218.

HODGSON, P. E. (1960a). *Nucl. Phys.* **21**, 21.

HODGSON, P. E. (1960b). *Nucl. Phys.* **21**, 28.

HOGDSON, P. E. (1961). *Nucl. Phys.* **23**, 499.

HODGSON, P. E. (1963a). *Phys. Letters* **3**, 352.

HODGSON, P. E. (1963b). "The Optical Model of Elastic Scattering." Oxford Univ. Press, London and New York.

HODGSON, P. E. (1964). *Proc. Intern. Conf. Nucl. Phys., Paris, 1964*, p. 257. Editions du Centre National de la Recherche Scientifique, Paris.

HOFSTADTER, R. (1958). *Rev. Mod. Phys.* **30**, 412.

HOFSTADTER, R. (1965). *Phys. Rev. Letters* **15**, 758.

HOFSTADTER, R. (1966). *Phys. Rev. Letters* **16**, 528.

HOFSTADTER, R., and CHAMBERS, E. E. (1956). *Phys. Rev.* **103**, 1454.

HOFSTADTER, R., FECHTER, H. R., and MCINTYRE, J. A. (1953). *Phys. Rev.* **92**, 978.

HOFSTADTER, R., CROISSIAUX, M., WALKER, A. E., YEARIAN, M. R., RAVENHALE, D. G., CLARK, B. C., and HERMAN, R. (1965). *Phys. Rev.*. **137**, B865.

HOSHIZAKI, N., OTSUKI, S., WATARI, W., and YONEZAWA, M. (1962). *Progr. Theoret. Phys. (Kyoto)* **27**, 1199.

HUANG, K., and YANG, C. N. (1957). *Phys. Rev.* **105**, 1119.

HÜFNER, J., MAHAUX, D., and WEIDENMÜLLER, H. A. (1967). *Nucl. Phys.* **A105**, 489.

HUGHES, D. J., SPRUNG, D. W. L., and VOLKOV, A. B. (1967). *Proc. Intern. Conf. Nucl. Phys., Gatlinburg, Tennessee, 1967* (R. L. Becker, C. D. Goodman, P. H. Stelson, and A. Zucker, eds.), p. 710. Academic Press, New York.

HULL, M. H., JR., LASSILA, K. E., RUPPEL, H. M., MCDONALD, F. A., and BREIT, G. (1961). *Phys. Rev.* **122**, 1606.

HULL, M. H., JR., LASSILA, K. E., RUPPEL, H. M., MCDONALD, F.A., and BREIT, G. (1962). *Phys. Rev.* **128**, 830.

HULTHÉN, L., and SUGAWARA, M. (1957). *In* "Handbuch der Physik" (S. Flügge ed)., Springer, Berlin.

HUMBLET, J., and ROSENFELD, L. (1961). *Nucl. Phys.* **26**, 529.

IGO, G. (1958). *Phys. Rev. Letters* **1**, 72.

IGO, G. (1959a). *Phys. Rev. Letters* **3**, 308.

IGO, G. (1959b). *Phys. Rev.* **115**, 1665.

IGO, G. (1960). *Phys. Rev.* **117**, 1079.

IGO, G., and THALER, R. M. (1957). *Phys. Rev.* **106**, 126.

INGBER, L. (1967). *Rev. Mod. Phys.* **39**, 648 (*Proc. Intern. Conf. N–N Interaction, Gainesville, Florida, 1967*).

INGLIS, D. R. (1936). *Phys. Rev.* **50**, 783.

JAIN, A. P. (1963). *Nucl. Phys.* **50**, 157.

JAIN, S. C., and SRIVASTAVA, B. K. (1967). *Phys. Rev.* **164**, 1223.

JASTROW, R. (1950). *Phys. Rev.* **79**, 389.

JASTROW, R. (1951). *Phys. Rev.* **81**, 165.

JOHNSON, M. H., and TELLER, E. (1955). *Phys. Rev.* **98**, 783.

JOHANSSON, A., TIBELL, G., PARKER, K., and HODGSON, P. E. (1960). *Nucl. Phys.* **21**, 383.

JOHANSSON, A., SVANBERG, U., and HODGSON, P. E. (1961). *Ark. Fysik* **19**, 541.

JOHANSSON, B. (1965). *Nucl. Phys.* **67**, 289.

KAPUR, P. L., and PEIERLS, R. E. (1938). *Proc. Roy. Soc. (London)* **A166**, 277.

KEMMER, N. (1938). *Proc. Roy. Soc. (London)* **A166**, 127.

KERMAN, A. K., and PAL, M. K. (1967). *Phys. Rev.* **162**, 970.

KERMAN, A. K., MCMANUS, H., and THALER, R. M. (1959). *Ann. Phys. (N.Y.)* **8**, 551.

KERMAN, A. K., RODBERG, L., and YOUNG, J. (1963). *Phys. Rev. Letters* **11**, 422.

KIM, C. C., BUNCH, S. M., DEVINS, D. W., and FORSTER, H. H. (1964). *Nucl. Phys.* **58**, 32.

KLEIN, A. (1955). *Phys. Rev.* **99**, 998.

KLINKENBERG, P. F. A. (1952). *Rev. Mod. Phys.* **24**, 63.

KÖHLER, H. S. (1956). *Nucl. Phys.* **1**, 433.

KÖHLER, H. S. (1958). *Nucl. Phys.* **6**, 161.

KÖHLER, H. S., and McCARTHY, R. J. (1967). *Nucl. Phys.* **A106**, 313.

KÖPP, G. (1967). *Rev. Mod. Phys.* **39**, 640.

KÖPP, G., and KRAMER, G. (1965). *Phys. Letters* **19**, 593.

KOOPMANS, T. (1933). *Physica* **1**, 104.

KOSSANYI-DEMAY, P., DE SWINIARSKI, R., and GLASHAUSER, C. (1967). *Nucl. Phys.* **A94**, 513.

KRIEGER, S. J., BARANGER, M., and DAVIES, K. T. R. (1966). *Phys. Letters* **22**, 607.

KRIEGER, S. J., BARANGER, M., and DAVIES, K. T. R. (1967). Private communication.

KRUEGER, T. K., and MARGOLIS, B. (1961). *Bull. Am. Phys. Soc.* **6**, 94; *Nucl. Phys.* **28**, 578.

KÜMMEL, H., MATTAUCH, J., THIELE, W., and WAPSTRA, A. II. (1966). *Nucl. Phys.* **81**, 129.

KUO, T. T. S., and BROWN, G. E. (1965). *Phys. Letters* **18**, 54.

LANDAU, L. D., and LIFSHITZ, E. M. (1956). "Course of Theoretical Physics," Vol. 3 (Quantum Mechanics, Nonrelativistic Theory). Pergamon Press, Oxford.

LANDAU, L. D., and SMORODINSKY, J. (1944). *Zh. Eksperim. i Teor. Fiz.* **8**, 154.

LANDE, A., and BLOCK, B. (1964). *Phys. Rev. Letters* **12**, 334.

LANE, A. M. (1957). *Rev. Mod. Phys.* **29**, 191.

LANE, A. M. (1962). *Nucl. Phys.* **35**, 676.

LANE, A. M., and ROBSON, D. (1966). *Phys. Rev.* **151**, 774.

LANE, A. M., and THOMAS, R. G. (1958). *Rev. Mod. Phys.* **30**, 257.

LANE, A. M., and WANDEL, C. F. (1955). *Phys. Rev.* **98**, 1524.

LANE, A. M., THOMAS, R. G., and WIGNER, E. P. (1955). *Phys. Rev.* **98**, 693.

LANE, A. M., LYNN, J. E., MELKONIAN, E., and RAE, E. R. (1959). *Phys. Rev. Letters* **2**, 424.

LAWSON, J. D. (1953). *Phil. Mag.* **44**, 102.

LEE, H. K., and McMANUS, H. (1968). *Phys. Rev. Letters* **20**, 337.

LEE, K., and GREEN, A. E. S. (1956a). *Proc. Intern. Conf. Peaceful Uses At. Anergy, Geneva, 1955* **2**, 113.

LEE, K., and GREEN, A. E. S. (1956b). *Bull. Am. Phys. Soc.* **1**, 16 [see also Progr. Rept. No. 11, A.E.C. Contract AT-(40–1)-1755 (February, 1956)].

LEE, L. L., JR., SCHIFFER, J. P., ZEIDMAN, B., SATCHLER, G. R., DRISKO, R. M., and BASSEL, R. H. (1964). *Phys. Rev.* **136**, B971.

LEE, L. L., JR., SCHIFFER, J. P., ZEIDMAN, B., SATCHLER, G. R., DRISKO, R. M., and BASSEL, R. H. (1965). *Phys. Rev.* **138**, B6A.

LEE, T. D. (1954). *Phys. Rev.* **95**, 1329.

LE LEVIER, R. E., and SAXON, D. S. (1952). *Phys. Rev.* **87**, 40.

LEMMER, R. H. (1960). Single Particle States in Strongly Deformed Nuclei. Ph.D. Thesis, Florida State Univ., Tallahassee, Florida, February 1960.

LEMMER, R. II., and GREEN, A. E. S. (1960). *Phys. Rev.* **119**, 1043.

LEMMER, R. H., MARIS, T. A. T., und TANG, Y. C. (1959). *Nucl. Phys.* **12**, 619.

LEPORE, J. V. (1950). *Phys. Rev.* **79**, 137.

LEVY, II. B. (1957). *Phys. Rev.* **106**, 1265.

LEVY, M. M. (1954). *Phys. Rev.* **94**, 460.

LICHTENBERG, D. B. (1962). *Nuovo Cimento* **25**, 1106.

LIPPERHEIDE, R. (1966). *Nucl. Phys.* **89**, 97.

LIPPERHEIDE, R. (1967). *Nucl. Phys.* **A105**, 545.

LIPPMAN, B. A., and SCHWINGER, J. (1950). *Phys. Rev.* **79**, 469.

LOMMON, E., and FESHBACH, H. (1967). *Rev. Mod. Phys.* **39**, 611.

LOWE, J., and WATSON, D. L. (1966). *Phys. Letters* **23**, 261.

LOWE, J., and WATSON, D. L. (1967). *Phys. Letters* **B24**, 174.

LUTZ, H. F., MASON, J. B., and KARVELIS, M. D. (1963). *Nucl. Phys.* **47**, 521.

McCARTHY, R. J., and KÖHLER, H. S. (1968). *Phys. Rev. Letters* **20**, 671.

MacDONALD, F. A., and HULL, M. H., JR. (1966). *Phys. Rev.* **143**, 838.

MacDONALD, W. M., (1964). *Nucl. Phys.* **54**, 393.
McFadden, L., and Satchler, G. R. (1966). *Nucl. Phys.* **84**, 177.
MacGregor, M. H., Arndt, R. A., and Wright, R. M. (1968). *Phys. Rev.* **169**, 1128.
McKean, R. S., Jr. (1962). *Phys. Rev.* **125**, 1399.
McManigal, P. G., Eandi, R. D., Kaplan, S. M., and Mayer, B. J. (1965). *Phys. Rev.* **137**, B620.
McVoy, K. W. (1965). *Phys. Letters* **17**, 46.
McVoy, K. W. (1967). *Ann. Phys.* (*N.Y.*) **43**, 91.
Maglic, B. C., Alvarez, L. W., Rosenfeld, A. H., and Stevenson, M. L. (1961). *Phys. Rev. Letters* **7**, 178.
Majorana, E. (1933). *Z. Physik* **82**, 137.
Makino, M. Q., Waddel, C. N., and Eisberg, R. M. (1964). *Nucl. Phys.* **50**, 145.
Malenka, B. J. (1952). *Phys. Rev.* **86**, 68.
Malenka, B. J., Kruse, U. E., and Ramsey, N. F. (1953). *Phys. Rev.* **91**, 1165.
Margenau, H. (1934). *Phys. Rev.* **46**, 613.
Margolis, B., and Troubetskoy, E. S. (1957). *Phys. Rev.* **106**, 105.
Marinov, A., Lee, L. L., Jr., and Schiffer, J. P. (1966). *Phys. Rev.* **145**, 852.
Marshak, R. E. (1960). *Sci. Am.* **202**, 98.
Martin, P., and de Dominicis, C. (1957). *Phys. Rev.* **105**, 1417.
Mattauch, J., and Flügge, S. (1946). "Introduction to Nuclear Physics." Wiley (Interscience), New York.
Mayer, M. G. (1948). *Phys. Rev.* **74**, 235.
Mayer, M. G. (1950). *Phys. Rev.* **78**, 1622.
Mayer, M. G., and Jensen, J. H. D. (1955). "Elementary Theory of Nuclear Shell Structure," Wiley, New York.
Melkanoff, M. A. (1959). *Proc. Intern. Conf. Nucl. Optical Model, Tallahassee, Florida, 1959.* Florida State Univ. Studies, No. 32, p. 204.
Melkanoff, M. A., and Nodvik, J. S. (1962). Unpublished.
Melkanoff, M. A., Moszkowski, S. A., Nodvik, J. S., and Saxon, D. S. (1956). *Phys. Rev.* **101**, 507.
Melkanoff, M. A., Nodvik, J. S., Saxon, D. S., and Woods, R. D. (1957). *Phys. Rev.* **106**, 793.
Melkanoff, M. A., Sawada, T., and Raynal, J. (1966). *Methods Computational Phys.* **6**, 2.
Messiah, A. (1958). "Quantum Mechanics." Wiley, New York.
Meyerhof, W. E., and Tombrello, T. A. (1968). *Nucl. Phys.* **A109**, 1.
Miller, D. W., Adair, R. K., Bockelman, C. K., and Darden, S. E. (1952). *Phys. Rev.* **88**, 83.
Mittelstaedt, P. (1965). *Acta Phys. Acad. Sci. Hung.* **19**, 303.
Mittlestaedt, P., and Ristig, M. (1966). *Z. Physik* **193**, 349.
Møller, C. (1931). *Z. Physik* **70**, 786.
Møller, C., and Rosenfeld, L. (1940). *Kgl. Danske Videnskab Selskab Mat.-Fys. Medd.* **17**, No. 8.
Mohling, F. (1962). *Phys. Rev.* **128**, 1365.
Moldauer, P. A. (1962). *Phys. Rev. Letters* **9**, 17.
Moldauer, P. A. (1963). *Nucl. Phys.* **47**, 65.
Moravcsik, M. J. (1963). "The Two-Nucleon Interaction." Oxford Univ. Press (Clarendon), London and New York.
Moshinsky, M. (1954). *J. Phys. Radium* **15**, 264.
Moshinsky, M. (1957). *Phys. Rev.* **106**, 117.
Moshinsky, M. (1959). *Nucl. Phys.* **13**, 104.
Moszkowski, S. A., (1953). *Phys. Rev.* **89**, 474.

MOSZKOWSKI, S. A. (1967). *Rev. Mod. Phys.* **39**, 657.

MOSZKOWSKI, S. A., and SCOTT, B. L. (1960). *Ann. Phys. (N.Y.)* **11**, 65.

MOTT, N. F., and MASSEY, H. S. W. (1933). "Theory of Atomic Collison," 1st ed. Oxford Univ. Press, London and New York.

MOTT, N. F., and MASSEY, H. S. W. (1965). "Theory of Atomic Collision," 3rd ed. Oxford Univ. Press, London and New York.

MOTTELSON, B. R., and NILSSON, S. G. (1959). *Kgl. Danske Videnskab Selskab, Mat.-Fys. Skrifter* **1**, No. 8.

MOZER, F. S. (1959). *Phys. Rev.* **116**, 970.

MYERS, W. D., and SWIATECKI, W. J. (1966). *Nucl. Phys.* **81**, 1.

NEMIROVSKY, P. E. (1959). *Soviet Phys. JETP* (English transl.) **9**, 408.

NEWMAN, E., BECKER, L. C., PREEDOM, B. M., and HIEBERT, J. C. (1967). *Nucl. Phys.* **A100**, 225.

NEWTON, R. G. (1958). *Ann. Phys. (N.Y.)* **4**, 29.

NEWTON, R. G., and FONDA, L. (1960). *Ann. Phys. (N.Y.)* **10**, 490.

NILSSON, S. G. (1955). *Kgl. Danske Videnskab Selskab, Mat.-Fys. Medd.* **29**, No. 16.

NISHIDA, Y. (1957). *Progr. Theoret. Phys. (Kyoto)* **17**, 506.

NISHIDA, Y. (1958). *Progr. Theoret. Phys. (Kyoto)* **19**, 389.

NISIMURA, K. (1967). *Progr. Theoret. Phys. (Kyoto), Suppl.* **39**, 286.

NODVIK, J. S., DUKE, C. B., and MELKANOFF, M. A. (1962). *Phys. Rev.* **125**, 975.

NORDHEIM, L. W. (1951). *Rev. Mod. Phys.* **23**, 322.

NOYES, H. P. (1961a). *Proc. Rutherford Jubilee Intern. Conf., Manchester, 1961*, p. 65. Heywood, London.

NOYES, H. P. (1961b). Univ. of California Radiation Lab. Rept. UCRL-6402.

OGAWA, S., SAWADA, S., UEDA, T., WATARI, W., and YONEZAWA, M., (1967). *Progr. Theoret. Phys. (Kyoto), Suppl.* **39**, 140.

OLKOWSKY, J., and RAYNAL, J. (1961). *Nucl. Phys.* **24**, 269.

OXLEY, C. L., and SCHAMBERGER, R. D. (1952). *Phys. Rev.* **85**, 416.

OXLEY, C. L., CARTWRIGHT, W., ROUVINA, J., BASKIER, E., KLEIN, D., RING, J., and SKILLMAN, W. (1953). *Phys. Rev.* **91**, 419.

PAIS, A., and UHLENBECK, G. E. (1950). *Phys. Rev.* **79**, 146.

PAL, M. K., and STAMP, A. P. (1967). *Phys. Rev.* **158**, 924; *Nucl. Phys.* **A99**, 228.

PASTERNACK, S., and SNYDER, H. S. (1950). *Phys. Rev.* **80**, 921.

PAULI, W. (1933). *In* "Handbuch der Physik" (S. Flugge, ed.), 2nd ed., Vol. 24, p. 1. Springer, Berlin.

PAULI, W., and VILLARS, F. (1949). *Rev. Mod. Phys.* **21**, 434.

PEIERLS, R. E. (1959). *Proc. Intern. Conf. Nucl. Optical Model, Tallahassee, Florida, 1959.* Florida State Univ. Studies, No. 32, p. 262.

PEIERLS, R. E. (1960). *Proc. Intern. Conf. Nucl. Struct., Kingston, Ont., 1960* (D. A. Bromley and E. W. Vogt, eds.), p. 7. Univ. of Toronto Press, Toronto.

PEKERIS, C. L. (1934). *Phys. Rev.* **41**, 98

PEREY, C. M., and PEREY, F. G. (1963). *Phys. Rev.* **132**, 755.

PEREY, C. M., and PEREY, F. G. (1964). *Phys. Rev.* **134**, 353.

PEREY, C. M., and PEREY, F. G. (1966). *Phys. Rev.* **152**, 923.

PEREY, F. G. (1963). *Phys. Rev.* **131**, 745.

PEREY, F. G., and BUCK, B. (1962). *Nucl. Phys.* **32**, 353.

PEREY, F. G., and SATCHLER, G. R. (1967). *Nucl. Phys.* **A97**, 515.

PEREY, F. G., and SAXON, D. S. (1964). *Phys. Letters* **10**, 107.

PEREY, F. G., and SCHIFFER, J. P. (1966). *Phys. Rev. Letters* **17**, 324.

PETERSON, J. M. (1962). *Phys. Rev.* **125**, 955.

PICARD, J. (1965). *Nucl. Phys.* **68**, 153.

PODOLSKY, B. (1942). *Phys. Rev.* **62**, 68.

PORTER, C. E. (1958). *Phys. Rev.* **112**, 1722.

PRESTON, M. A., KIANG, D., and YIP, P. (1967). *Proc. Intern. Conf. Nucl. Phys., Gatlinburg, Tennessee, 1966* (R. L. Becker, C. D. Goodman, P. H. Stelson, and A. Zucker, eds.), p. 654. Academic Press, New York.

PROCA, A. (1936). *J. Phys. Radium* **7**, 347.

PTP (1967). *Progr. Theoret. Phys. (Kyoto), Supply.* **39**, (H. Yukawa, ed.).

PUFF, R. D. (1961). *Ann. Phys. (N.Y.)* **13**, 317.

PUZIKOV, L., RYNDIN, R., and SMORODINSKY, J. (1957). *Nucl. Phys.* **3**, 436.

RAINWATER, J. (1950). *Phys. Rev.* **79**, 432.

RAJARAMAN, R., and BETHE, H. A. (1967). *Rev. Mod. Phys.* **39**, 745.

RARITA, W., and SCHWINGER, J. (1941). *Phys. Rev.* **59**, 436.

RATCLIFF, K. F., and AUSTERN, N. (1967). *Ann. Phys. (N.Y.)* **42**, 185.

RAYNAL, J. (1963). *Phys. Letters* **3**, 331; **7**, 281.

RAZAVY, M. (1963). *Phys. Rev.* **130**, 1091.

RAZAVY, M., FIELD, G., and LEVINGER, J. S. (1962). *Phys. Rev.* **125**, 269.

RIDLEY, B. W., and TURNER, J. F. (1964). *Nucl. Phys.* **58**, 497.

RIESENFELD, W. B., and WATSON, K. M. (1956). *Phys. Rev.* **102**, 1157.

ROBINSON, C. P., JOHN, J., ALDRIDGE, J. P., and DAVIS, R. H. (1967). *Bull. Am. Phys. Soc.* **12**, 1184.

ROBSON, D., and LANE, A. M. (1967). *Phys. Rev.* **161**, 982.

RODBERG, L. (1961). *Phys. Rev.* **124**, 210.

ROJO, O., and SIMMONS, L. M. (1962). *Phys. Rev.* **125**, 273.

ROLLAND, C., GEOFFRION, B., MARTY, N., MORLET, M., TATISCHEFF, F., and WILLIS, A. (1966). *Nucl. Phys.* **80**, 625.

ROOK, J. R. (1965). *Nucl. Phys.* **61**, 219.

ROOS, P. G., and WALL, N. S. (1965). *Phys. Rev.* **140**, B1237.

ROSE, M. E. (1957). "Elementary Theory of Angular Momentum." Wiley, New York.

ROSEN, L. (1960). *Proc. Intern. Conf. Nucl. Struct., Kingston, Ont., 1960* (D. A. Bromley and E. W. Vogt, eds.), p. 185. Univ. of Toronto Press, Toronto.

ROSEN, L., and LELAND, W. T. (1962). *Phys. Rev. Letters* **8**, 379.

ROSEN, L., BROLLEY, J. E., and STEWARD, L. (1961). *Phys. Rev.* **121**, 1423.

ROSEN, L., DARRIULAT, P., FARAGGI, H., and GARIN, A. (1962). *Nucl. Phys.* **33**, 458.

ROSEN, L., PEERY, J. G., GOLDHABER, A. S., and AUERBACH, E. H. (1965). *Ann. Phys (N.Y.)* **34**, 96.

ROSENFELD, A. H., BARASH-SCHMIDT, N., BARBARO-GALTIERI, A., PRICE, L. R., SÖDING, P., WOHL, C. G., ROOS, M., and WILLIS, W. J. (1968). *Rev. Mod. Phys.* **40**, 77.

ROSENFELD, L. (1932). *Z. Physik* **76**, 729.

ROSENFELD, L. (1949). "Nuclear Forces," p. 22. North-Holland Publ., Amsterdam.

ROSS, A. A., MARK, H., and LAWSON, R. D. (1956a). *Phys. Rev.* **102**, 1613.

ROSS, A. A., LAWSON, R. D., and MARK, H. (1956b). *Phys. Rev.* **104**, 401.

ROTHE, E. W., ROL, P. K., and BERNSTEIN, R. B. (1962). *Phys. Rev.* **128**, 659.

RUSTGI, M. L. (1964). *Nucl. Phys.* **59**, 460.

RUSTGI, M. L. (1967). *Phys. Letters*, **B24**, 229.

SAKATA, S. (1956). *Progr. Theoret. Phys. (Kyoto)* **16**, 686.

SAKURAI, J. J. (1966). *Phys. Rev. Letters* **17**, 1021.

SAPLAKOGLU, A., BOLLINGER, L. M., and COTÉ, R. E. (1958). *Phys. Rev.* **109**, 1258.

SATCHLER, G. R. (1958). *Phys. Rev.* **109**, 429.

SATCHLER, G. R. (1966). *Nucl. Phys.* **85**, 273.

SATCHLER, G. R. (1967a). *Nucl. Phys.* **A91**, 75.

SATCHLER, G. R. (1967b). *Nucl. Phys.* **A92**, 273.

SATCHLER, G. R., and HAYBRON, R. M. (1964). *Phys. Letters* **11**, 313.

SATCHLER, G. R., DRISKO, R. M., and BASSEL, R. H. (1964). *Phys. Rev.* **136**, B637.

SAWADA, S., UEDA, T., WATARI, W., and YONEZAWA, M. (1962). *Progr. Theoret. Phys.* (*Kyoto*) **28**, 991.

SAWADA, S., UEDA, T., WATARI, W., and YONEZAWA, M. (1964). *Progr. Theoret. Phys.* (*Kyoto*) **32**, 380.

SAWADA, T. (1965). *Nucl. Phys.* **74**, 289.

SAWICKI, J. (1954). *Acta Phys. Polon.* **13**, 225.

SAXON, D. S. (1957). *Phys. Rev.* **107**, 871.

SCHIFF, L. I. (1955). "Quantum Mechanics," 2nd ed. McGraw-Hill, New York.

SCHIFF, L. I. (1956). *Phys. Rev.* **103**, 443.

SCHNITZER, H. J., and SUDARSHAN, E. C. G. (1961). *Phys. Rev.* **123**, 2193.

SCHWINGER, J. (1942). *Phys. Rev.* **61**, 387.

SCHWINGER, J. (1950). *Phys. Rev.* **78**, 136.

SCOTT, B. L., and MOSZKOWSKI, S. A., (1961). *Ann. Phys.* (*N.Y.*) **14**, 107.

SCOTT, D. K., FISHER, P. S., and CHANT, N. S. (1967). *Nucl. Phys.* **A99**, 177.

SCOTTI, A., and WONG, D. Y. (1963). *Phys. Rev. Letters* **10**, 142.

SCOTTI, A., and WONG, D. Y. (1965). *Phys. Rev.* **B128**, 145.

SEEGER, P. A. (1961). *Nucl. Phys.* **25**, 1.

SERBER, R. (1947). *Phys. Rev.* **72**, 1114.

SHAKIN, C. M. (1963). *Ann. Phys.* (*N.Y.*) **22**, 373.

SHAKIN, C. M., WAGHMARE, Y. R., TOMASELLI, M., and HULL, M. H., JR. (1967a). *Phys. Rev.* **161**, 1015.

SHAKIN, C. M., WAGHMARE, Y. R., and HULL, M. H., JR. (1967b). *Phys. Rev.* **161**, 1006.

SHARMA, R. D. (1964). Unpublished notes.

SHARMA, R D., and GREEN, A.E.S. (1967). *Nucl. Phys.* **B3**, 33.

SIEGERT, A. J. F. (1939). *Phys. Rev.* **56**, 750.

SIGNELL, P., and DURSO, J. (1967). *Rev. Mod. Phys.* **39**, 635.

SLAUS, I., and ALFORD, W. P. (1959). *Phys. Rev.* **114**, 1054.

SLIV, L. A., and KHARITONOV, YU. I. (1965). *Phys. Letters* **16**, 176.

SNOWDEN, S. C., and WHITEHEAD, N. D. (1954). *Phys. Rev.* **94**, 1267.

SOOD, P. C. (1965). *Phys. Letters* **19**, 52.

SOOD, P. C. (1966). *Nucl. Phys.* **89**, 553.

SOOD, P. C., and GREEN, A. E. S. (1958). *Nucl. Phys.* **5**, 574.

SOPER, J. M. (1966). *In* "Isobaric Spin in Nuclear Physics" (J. D. Fox and D. Robson, eds.), p. 565. Academic Press, New York.

STAMP, A. P. (1967). *Nucl. Phys.* **A105**, 627.

STANFORD (1958). *Rev. Mod. Phys.* **30**, 412 (*Proc. Intern. Congr. Nucl. Size and Density Distribution, Stanford, December 1957*).

STAPP, H. P., YPSILANTIS, T. J., and METROPOLIS, N. (1957). *Phys. Rev.* **105**, 302.

STOCKER, W. (1966). *Z. Physik* **193**, 310.

SUDARSHAN, E. C. G. (1961). *Phys. Rev.* **123**, 2183.

SWAMY, N. V. V. J. (1961). *Indian J. Phys.* **35**, 170.

SWAMY, N. V. V. J., and GREEN, A. E. S. (1957). *Bull. Am. Phys. Soc.* **2**, 287.

SWIATECKI, W. J. (1951). *Proc. Phys. Soc.* (*London*) **A64**, 226.

SWIFT, A., and ELTON, L. R. B. (1966). *Phys. Rev. Letters* **17**, 484.

TABAKIN, F. (1964). *Ann. Phys.* (*N.Y.*) **30**, 51.

TABAKIN, F., and DAVIES, K. T. R. (1966). *Phys. Rev.* **150**, 793.

TAKEDA, G., and WATSON, K. M. (1955). *Phys. Rev.* **97**, 1336.

TAKETANI, M., NAKAMURA, S., and SASAKI, M. (1951). *Progr. Theor. Phys.* (*Kyoto*) **6**, 578.

TAKETANI, M., MACHIDA, S., and OHNUMA, S. (1952). *Progr. Theoret. Phys.* (*Kyoto*) **7**, 45.

TALMAN, J. D. (1956). *Phys. Rev.* **102**, 455.

TALMI, I. (1952). *Helv. Phys. Acta* **25**, 185.

TAMAGAKI, R. (1967). *Rev. Mod. Phys.* **39**, 629.

TAMAGAKI, R., and WATARI, W. (1967). *Progr. Theoret. Phys. (Kyoto), Suppl.* **39**, 23.

TAMURA, T. (1965). *Rev. Mod. Phys.* **37**, 679.

TAMURA, T., and TERASAWA, T. (1964). *Phys. Letters* **8**, 41.

TANG, Y. C., and HERNDON, R. C. (1967). *Nucl. Phys.* **A93**, 692.

TANG, Y. C., LEMMER, R. H., WYATT, P. J., and GREEN, A. E. S. (1959). *Phys. Rev.* **116**, 402.

TEICHMANN, T., and WIGNER, E. P. (1952). *Phys. Rev.* **87**, 123.

THOMAS, R. N., BURGE, E. J., and HODGSON, P. E. (1964). *Nucl. Phys.* **52**, 93.

TJIN A DJIE, H. R. E., and BROCKMAN, K. W. (1965). *Nucl. Phys.* **74**, 417.

TURNER, J. F., RIDLEY, B. W., CAVANAGH, P. F., GARD, G. A., and HARDACRE, A. G. (1964). *Nucl. Phys.* **58**, 509.

TYREN, H., KULLANDER, S., SUNDBERG, O., RAMACHANDRAN, R., and ISACSSON, P. (1966). *Nucl. Phys.* **79**, 321.

UEDA, T., and GREEN, A. E. S. (1968). *Phys. Rev.* (to be published).

URETSKY, J. L. (1957). Ph.D. dissertation, Mass. Inst. Technol., Cambridge, Massachusetts (unpublished).

VALENTIN, L. (1965). *Nucl. Phys.* **62**, 81.

VAN VLECK, J. H. (1935). *Phys. Rev.* **48**, 367.

VENTER, R. H., and FRAHN, W. E., (1964). *Ann. Phys. (N.Y.)* **27**, 385.

WAGNER, R., MILLER, P. D., TAMURA, T., and MARSHAK, H. (1965). *Phys. Rev.* **139**, B29.

WALT, M., and BARSCHALL, H. H. (1954). *Phys. Rev.* **93**, 1062.

WAPSTRA, A. H. (1952). *Physica* **18**, 2.

WATANABE, S. (1958). *Nucl. Phys.* **8**, 484.

WATSON, K. M. (1953). *Phys. Rev.* **89**, 575.

WAY, K., and WHEELER, J. A. (1936). *Phys. Rev.* **50**, 675.

WEIDENMÜLLER, H. A. (1966). *Nucl. Phys.* **75**, 189.

WEISSKOPF, V. F. (1956). *Proc. Intern. Conf. Peaceful Uses At. Energy, Geneva, 1955* **2**, 23.

WEIZSÄCKER, C. F. (1935). *Z. Physik* **96**, 431.

WELLER, H. R., and ROBERSON, N. R. (1968). Private communication.

WHEELER, J. A. (1936). *Phys. Rev.* **50**, 643.

WICK, G. C. (1934). *Nuovo Cimento* **11**, 227.

WIGNER, E. P. (1933). *Phys. Rev.* **43**, 252; *Z. Physik.* **83**, 253.

WIGNER, E. P. (1936). Private communication to Bethe and Bacher [see Bethe and Bacher (1936, p. 117)].

WIGNER, E. P., and EISENBUD, L. (1947). *Phys. Rev.* **72**, 29.

WILMORE, D., and HODGSON, P. E. (1964). *Nucl. Phys.* **55**, 673.

WILSON, R. (1963). "The Nucleon–Nucleon Interaction." Wiley (Interscience), New York.

WING, J., and FONG, P. (1964). *Phys. Rev.* **136**, B923.

WINNER, D. R., and DRISKO, R. M. (1965). Dept. of Physics and Sarah Mellon Scaife Radiation Lab., Univ. of Pittsburgh, Pittsburgh, Pennsylvania, Technical report.

WITTERN, H. W. (1965). *Nucl. Phys.* **62**, 628.

WOLFENSTEIN, L., and ASHKIN, J. (1952). *Phys. Rev.* **85**, 947.

WONG, C. W. (1967). *Nucl. Phys.* **A104**, 417.

WONG, D. Y. (1964). *Nucl. Phys.* **55**, 212.

WONG, D. Y. (1967). *Rev. Mod. Phys.* **39**, 622.

WOODS, R. D., and SAXON, D. S. (1954). *Phys. Rev.* **95**, 577.

WYATT, P. J., WILLS, J. G., and GREEN, A. E. S. (1960). *Phys. Rev.* **119**, 1031.

YUKAWA, H. (1935). *Proc. Phys. Math. Soc. Japan* **17**, 48.

ZAFIRATOS, C. D., OLIPHANT, T. A., LEVIN, J. S., and CRANBERG, L. (1965). *Phys. Rev. Letters* **14**, 193.

ZAMICK, L. (1963). *Ann. Phys. (N.Y.)* **21**, 550.

ZELDES, H. A. (1965). *Nucl. Phys.* **63**, 1.

Author Index

A

Adair, R. K., 6, 39 *337*, *346*
Agodi, A., 308, *337*
Airy, G. B., 156, *337*
Aldridge, J. P., 261, *348*
Alford, W. P., 246, 256, *349*, *340*
Alvarez, L. W., 314, *346*
Amaldi, U., Jr., 186, *337*
Anderson, H. L., 90, *337*
Anderson, J. D., 244, *338*
Arndt, R. A., 281, 315, 331, 332, *337*, *339*, *346*
Arons, M. E., 319, *337*
Ashkin, J., 280, *350*
Auerbach, E. H., 90, 204, 205, 206, 207, 208, 213, 216, 219, 224, 226, 227, 229, 246, *337*, *348*
Austern, N., 158, 160, 163, 248, 310, 313, *337*, *348*
Austin, S. M., 229, 230, 231, *341*

B

Babikov, V. V., 315, *337*
Bacher, R. F., 1, 2, 48, 52, 286, 322, *338*
Baker, G. A., Jr., 53, *337*
Baker, G. A., Sr., 53, *337*

Ball, J. B., 204, 223, 226, 228, *342*
Ball, J. S., 226, 228, 315, 331, *337*
Baranger, M., 186, 298, 300, *337*, *340*, *345*
Barash-Schmidt, N., 315, 333, *348*
Bararo Galtieri, A., 315, 333, *348*
Bardin, T. T., 90, *340*
Barrett, R. C., 90, 207, 213, 217, 226, 229, 230, 231, 243, 244, *337*, *340*, *341*
Barschall, H. H., 6, 7, 130, 161, *337*, *350*
Bartlett, J. H., Jr., 267, *337*
Bartlett, M. S., 1, *337*
Baskier, E., 280, *347*
Bassel, R. H., 161, 213, 221, 226, 227, 228, 243, 248, 249, 250, 256, 257, 258, 259, 260, *337*, *338*, *340*, *341*, *342*, *343*, *345*, *348*
Batchelor, R., 246, *338*
Batty, C. J., 233, 235, *338*
Bauer, R. W., 244, *338*
Baugh, D. J., 217, 226, 228, *338*
Becker, L. C., 254, *347*
Benveniste, J., 227, 228, *338*
Berezdivin, R., 182, 185, 186, *343*
Berkley, R. J., 75, 79, 80, 81, *343*
Bernstein, R. B., 164, *348*
Bethe, H. A., 1, 2, 3, 48, 52, 88, 89, 167, 262, 270, 286, 289, 291, 295, 296, 297, 316, 322, *338*, *348*
Beyster, J. R., 118, 167, 212, *338*

351

Subject Index